WORD GAMES

New Edition

SANDY BROWNJOHN

Hodder & Stoughton

A MEMBER OF THE HODDER HEADLINE GROUP

ACKNOWLEDGEMENTS

The author and publishers would like to thank the following:

p86 *Sea Shell* © Enid Madoc-Jones; p86 *The Main-Deep* © James Stephens; p108 *Foolish Questions* © William Cole; p118 *A London Sparrow's 'If'* © J.A. Lindon; p122 *Leaves* © Ted Hughes, from *Season Songs* by Ted Hughes, Faber and Faber Ltd.

Please note that the following are copyright Sandy Brownjohn:
p34 *On the Move*; p95 'One witless wildebeest...'; p99 *Birds of Britain and Europe*; p100 *Place Names*; p103 *How to make a Monster*; p105 *How to make a Giraffe*; p106 *How to make March*; p113 Riddle: 'I am in the earth...'; p117 Last parody of *Mary Had a Little Lamb*; p120 'On Monday the weather was clear and bright...'; and all other made up examples.

Every effort has been made to trace copyright holders of material reproduced in this book. Any rights not acknowledged here will be acknowledged in subsequent printings if notice is given to the publisher.

Orders: please contact Bookpoint Ltd, 130 Milton Park, Abingdon, Oxon OX14 4SB.
Telephone: (44) 01235 827720; Fax: (44) 01235 400454. Lines are open from 9.00am–6.00pm, Monday to Saturday, with a 24 hour message answering service. Email address: orders@bookpoint.co.uk

British Library Cataloguing in Publication Data
A catalogue record for this title is available from The British Library

ISBN 0 340 78115 7

First published 2001
Impression number   10 9 8 7 6 5 4 3 2
Year   2005 2004 2003 2002 2001

Copyright © 2001 Sandy Brownjohn

Typeset by Multiplex Techniques Ltd, Brook Industrial Park, Mill Brook Road, St. Mary Cray, Kent BR5 3SR.
Printed in Great Britain by Hodder & Stoughton Educational, a division of Hodder Headline Plc, 338 Euston Road, London NW1 3BH by Hobbs the Printers, Totton, Hampshire.

CONTENTS

INTRODUCTION: HOW TO USE THIS BOOK

Once, when children did not have access to televisions, computers, Gameboys or the Internet, word games were one of the ways they used to entertain themselves. In more recent years these seemed to have been forgotten by all but the most inveterate games players, and were certainly not utilised enough in schools. Virtually the only game that really survived was Hangman – which does not actually appear in this book. However, children do still enjoy playing word games if someone shows them how to do it, and this book attempts to set out for today's teachers a number of games which will be helpful in their teaching.

If play is considered important as a way of learning – and it is acknowledged as such for young children – there is no reason why it should not go on being so for the rest of our lives. Word games are one of the best ways of encouraging children to play with the language, and it is through such play that we can discover its possibilities and develop a lifelong love of words. We all remember things much better if we have enjoyed an experience, and with the advent of the National Literacy Strategy there is even more need to find ways of varying lessons and reinjecting some of the fun that used to be in teaching.

I hope that *Word Games* will go some way towards doing this. At the very least, it should offer teachers some alternative ideas for approaching the teaching of English.

The games are loosely divided into three broad categories: spelling and letter-based games; simple grammar and alphabet-based games; and writing and poetry-based games and exercises. Each section contains photocopiable pages for use directly with pupils. There are also teachers' pages explaining the games and suggesting ways of approaching them with classes, as well as follow-up work. At the foot of each of these pages are summarised points showing what aspects of the curriculum are covered. The chart at the front is intended as a handy reference to the different areas covered in the whole book. Many of the 'games' are creative in make-up and link learning about specific language techniques with pupils' own writing.

It is recommended that teachers always work on a class example first before giving pupils the photocopied sheets. In a number of cases it is also advised that pupils work with others, most often in pairs, rather than on their own. This gives them more confidence to be adventurous, challenges their individual modes of thinking, and, above all, means they are likely to have more fun. These are not called games for nothing! Sometimes there are winners, sometimes not. But, there should always be enjoyment.

Sandy Brownjohn

REFERENCE CHART RELATING TO THE ENGLISH CURRICULUM

TEACHER'S PAGES IN THIS BOOK	Alliteration	Acronyms	Acrostics	Adjectives	Adverbs	Alphabets	Clichés	Compound words	Comprehension	Dictionary work	Grammar	Homophones	Idioms	Inventing words	Kennings	Metaphors	Nouns	Onomatopoeia	Palindromes	Parody	Planning stories	Prepositions	Puns	Rhyme
SECTION ONE																								
Page 12		■				■					■						■							
Page 18										■														
Page 22																								
Page 25										■									■				■	
Page 29								■		■														
Page 32										■		■											■	
Page 36																								
Page 40																								
SECTION TWO																								
Page 46								■			■						■							
Page 49						■					■						■							■
Page 51							■				■				■		■							
Page 52											■						■							
Page 55			■								■													
Page 57											■													
Page 60				■							■												■	
Page 63																								
SECTION THREE																								
Page 69													■											■
Page 72			■																■					
Page 75																								■
Page 77								■	■	■														■
Page 79																								■
Page 82																		■					
Page 87						■				■										■				
Page 90			■												■									
Page 93	■									■														
Page 98	■																		■					■
Page 101																								
Page 104							■																	
Page 107														■		■								
Page 111																								
Page 116																			■				■	
Page 119																								

NATIONAL CURRICULUM REQUIREMENTS

Rhythm	Riddles	Sentences	Similes	Slang	Spelling	Syllables	Synonyms	Thesaurus	Tongue twisters	Verbs	Vocabulary	Vowels	Wordplay	Writing list poems	Writing pattern poems	Writing poetry	Collaboration	Listening skills	Literary terms	Making books	Memory skills	Planning writing	Speaking skills	Use of reference books

SECTION 1

SPELLING AND LETTER-BASED WORD GAMES

WORD GAMES (1, 2, 3 & 4) – TEACHER'S PAGE

The following four pages contain games which mostly concentrate on finding words beginning with specific letters of the alphabet.

Word Chains is about finding words on a theme. Each new word must begin with the last letter of the previous word. The object is to make the chain as long as possible and not to complete it by ending with the same letter that began the first word. It can be played orally by the whole class, or as a written game for one person.

Alphabet Themes can be played by one person or several. The idea is to find a noun for each letter of the alphabet based on a theme. After a set time the number of answers is counted and a score is given out of 26. Encourage pupils to enter those they can find easily and to go back to ones that demand more thought.

Anagrams is a game which can help spelling. Playing with the individual letters of a word to create another word is good practice for seeing how words are made up. The anagram puzzles at the end are on the theme of British towns/cities. You might also want to suggest a theme for the pupils' own anagrams. For example, *lemon* is clearly an anagram of *melon*, *grape* makes *pager*, and *pear* can be *reap*.

Telegrams is a game from the time when there still were telegrams. The essence of a real telegram was to communicate the message in as few words as possible to keep the cost down because you paid by the word. Nowadays it should perhaps be renamed e-mails or pagers! The best known and most used of such things is not actually a word: SWALK – Sealed With A Loving Kiss.

Acronyms is a similar game in that players must find words that begin with predetermined letters. Here they have to provide sensible definitions, of a kind that might appear in a dictionary, for each word.

For most of the above games the fun is in the playing and in seeing what other people do with the same problem. You pit your wits against others or just against yourself. Scoring is not really necessary but can be incorporated into the game if required. The value is in manipulating letters and words, and in taxing your ingenuity.

> ● Spelling ● Nouns on a theme ● Order of alphabet ● Thinking of words beginning with specific letters ● Understanding of literary terms – anagrams and acronyms

• WORD CHAINS •

This is a game to play orally with any number of people. The object of the game is to make the longest possible chain of words on a theme. Each new word must begin with the last letter of the previous word. Below are some examples.

Theme: animals   ca**t** – **t**ige**r** – **r**hinocero**s** – **s**nak**e** – **e**lephan**t** – **t**errapi**n** – **n** (etc.)

Theme: food   nut**s** – **s**andwic**h** – **h**a**m** – **m**ouss**e** – **e**g**g** – **g**rapefrui**t** – **t** (etc.)

Theme: British towns/cities   Londo**n** – **N**orwic**h** – **H**arlo**w** – **W**idne**s** – **S**wanse**a** – **A**berdee**n** – **N**ewr**y** – **Y**or**k** – **K**ings Lyn**n** – **N** (etc.)

People are out if they cannot think of a next word, or if they complete the chain by saying a word which ends with the same letter as the beginning of the very first word. If this happens, the next player can go back to the previous word and try to continue the chain.

OTHER THEMES TO TRY

> **birds**   **people's first names**   **countries**
>
> **makes of cars**   **colours**   **famous characters in literature**
>
> **famous writers**   **football teams**   **world towns/cities**

TRY WRITING a word chain down. This time you work on your own.

COMPLETE A FEW OF THE EXAMPLES ABOVE. See how long you can make them.

_____

_____

_____

_____

_____

_____

_____

_____

_____

_____

• ALPHABET THEMES •

CHOOSE A THEME – For example:

famous writers	creatures in literature and cinema	British towns
wild flowers	boys' names	girls' names countries of the world
makes of cars	food	birds colours real animals

This game is played orally by two or more people. It can be played by whole classes.

The object is to find a word on the chosen theme for each letter of the alphabet.

You take it in turns to think of the next one. Anyone who cannot find one in about 20 seconds is out of the game. The winner is the person who stays in the longest.

You can also play ALPHABET THEMES on paper with two or more people.

Choose a theme and give yourselves a time limit, perhaps 20–30 minutes.

When the time is up, the winner is the one who has found the most words out of 26.

A_____   B_____   C_____   D_____   E_____

F_____   G_____   H_____   I_____   J_____

K_____   L_____   M_____   N_____   O_____

P_____   Q_____   R_____   S_____   T_____

U_____   V_____   W_____   X_____   Y_____

Z_____   SCORE (number out of 26) _____

CAN YOU COMPLETE the following Alphabet theme? Do you know where they all come from?

Theme: creatures in literature and cinema

Aslan   **B**lack Beauty   **C**hanticleer   **D**onald Duck   **E**eyore   **F**lipper

Greymalkin   **H**ector   **I**ncey Wincey Spider   **J**umble   **K**ing Kong

Lassie   **M**ole   **N**apoleon   **O** (etc.)

• ANAGRAMS •

An ANAGRAM is a word made from <u>all</u> the letters of another word.

For example: write the letters of the word LIVE inside a circle, or put them on separate small squares of paper.

We can make all these words from the four letters: LIVE   EVIL   VEIL   VILE   LEVI. How many words can you make from the following?

(2 words)   (3 words)   (4 words)   (5 words)

With 4 letters there are actually 24 possible word combinations but not all will exist. Can you find all 24 of the 4 letters **O P S T**? The first few have been done for you.

O P T S	P T S O	S O P T	T S O P
O _ _ _	P _ _ _	S _ _ _	T _ _ _
O _ _ _	P _ _ _	S _ _ _	T _ _ _
O _ _ _	P _ _ _	S _ _ _	T _ _ _
O _ _ _	P _ _ _	S _ _ _	T _ _ _
O _ _ _	P _ _ _	S _ _ _	T _ _ _

Six of these exist. Put a circle round each of them. Use a dictionary to help you decide. Some of the other 18 might make new words. Underline the ones you can actually say (some combinations of letters are not possible in English words, such as PSTO).

What do you think they might mean? Make up definitions for them.

FIND words (and their anagrams) of your own. REMEMBER to use <u>all</u> the letters, and the new words <u>must</u> exist. Swap anagrams with a friend and try to solve them.

SOLVE the following anagram puzzles. They are names of British towns or cities.

Can you find them in the atlas?

BLOT SIR • ELF BATS • CHIN ROW • WET CLEANS • NEVER SINS • BRAG ON • FORE HERD • DOT WASP • NOMAD SITE • RAN CASTLE • ELF FISHED • TORC ENVY • GATE SEVEN • WAS SANE • EASY LIP • OGHAM • SURLY BIAS • LOUD GAS • GEM DIBBER • ALL CRIES

· TELEGRAMS ·

The idea of the game TELEGRAMS, which is a game for two or more people, is to imagine that you have to get a message to somebody in only a few words. The number of words you can use is determined by the number of letters in a town (or country) of your choice. Each letter begins the next word in the message. For example:

| HARWICH: | **H**elp! **A**tlantic **R**ough, **W**ith **I**cebergs. **C**rossing – **H**orrendous |

| HAMBURG: | **H**ave **A M**arvellous **B**irthday, **U**ncle **R**oger – **G**emma |

| HOLLAND: | **H**ope **O**ur **L**ove **L**asts **A**nd **N**ever **D**ies |

| EGYPT: | **E**njoyed **G**etting **Y**our **P**resent **T**oday |

TO PLAY

1   Choose a town or country.
2   Everyone now has ten minutes to make up as many messages as they can using the letters of the word. (Make sure they sound as if they are real messages.)

If you are stuck for a word, the dictionary might help to give you ideas.

TOWN or COUNTRY

_____   _____

_____   _____

_____   _____

_____   _____

_____   _____

_____   _____

_____   _____

_____   _____

_____   _____

_____   _____

● ACRONYMS ●

This game is for one or more players. ACRONYMS are commonly words made from the first letters of an organisation, invention or activity. For example:

NASA: **N**ational **A**eronautics and **S**pace **A**dministration

UNICEF: **U**nited **N**ations **I**nternational **C**hildren's **E**mergency **F**und

FIDO: **F**og **I**nvestigation and **D**ispersal **O**peration

TO PLAY

1   Choose a word (probably a noun, adjective or verb).
2   Then write a definition for it. Each word of your definition must begin with the letters of your original choice IN ORDER. (Dictionaries can help you find appropriate words for your definitions.) Play against a friend to see who can make up the best definitions.

Examples:

Noun – CANDLE – **C**an **A**lleviate **N**ight's **D**arkness; **L**ight **E**mitting

Adjective – SLOW– **S**luggish, **L**umbering **O**r **W**itless

Verb – LAUGH – **L**et **A**n **U**nexpected **G**uffaw **H**appen

Now you try:

Noun		
Adjective		
Verb		
Noun		
Adjective		
Verb		
Noun		
Adjective		
Verb		
Noun		
Adjective		
Verb		

WORD GAMES (5, 6 & 7) – TEACHER'S PAGE

The next three word games are ways of looking at words or letter patterns hidden within other words. They can be very helpful in getting pupils to see spelling patterns and to play with letters in ways that will help them remember how words are spelt.

The game element, as always, makes everything more fun, and pupils are more likely to remember something they have enjoyed doing.

Words Within Words. This is a well-known and well tried game which usually never fails to engage pupils. One of the beauties of this game is that, in common with most other games in this book, there is no need to worry about differentiation. All pupils can attempt it and all will find some words. Those who need stretching will rise to the challenge of trying to find all 100 possible words – some will even try to beat that total. Pupils will achieve at their own level, but <u>all</u> will achieve something. Since the majority of the possible words are three or four letters in length they are not difficult to find and will reinforce spelling patterns, (e.g. cat, cot, cut).

It is always a good idea to try something out as a whole class first, so that pupils know what to do. Put your own word on the board and spend about ten minutes or so seeing how many words you can find together. Even quite short words can yield a crop of others. So as not to spend too long on this, a five-letter word might be best. Encourage the use of the dictionary to check whether words exist.

Mischmasch. This is a slightly harder game and you might consider letting some pupils work together so that poorer spellers are not excluded. The object is to find words containing the given three-letter combinations. Clearly the dictionary will be of help here and there is usually more than one possible answer. Again, do some as a class first. You will need to choose your own combinations, but the following may help to start things off: **atc** (as in *latch, batch, catch* etc. and *catcall, oatcake*); **adi** (as in *radio, trading, ladies,* etc.); **ngl** (as in *jungle, angle,* etc. and *singleton, wingless*).

Buried Words. You can introduce this game by playing a similar but easier game – that of finding words of two or more letters within a word. For example, **cobra** contains *cob* and *bra*; **alphabet** contains *alp, abet* and *bet*; **simile** contains *mile*; **onomatopoiea** contains *on, no, ma, mat, to, atop* and *top*; and **literacy** contains *lit, it, era* and *racy*.

Spend a reasonable time playing this way as a class before you give pupils the photocopied game. This will ensure that their minds are practised in looking for hidden words. You can ask pupils to volunteer to write a word on the board and see if their fellow pupils can find what is hidden in it. They can use dictionaries to find words to use. You can even challenge them to see who can find the word which contains the most other words – this will not always be the longest.

> • Spelling patterns • Breaking down and building up words • Use of dictionary
> • Consolidation of phonic work • Looking at words from different angles

• WORDS WITHIN WORDS •

The object of this game is to find as many words (of two or more letters) as possible, in a given time, from the letters of another word. The letters cannot be repeated unless, of course, they occur more than once in the original word. Proper names are not allowed.

For example, how many words can you find from the letters of the word **'CREATE'**? Here are 25 – there are probably more.

acre act arc are art at ate car care cart cat cater crate

ear eat eater erect rat rate react tare tea tear trace tree

How many words can you find from the letters of the word **'EDUCATION'**.

There are at least 100 different words that can be made. Play against a friend and see who can find the most in 20 minutes.

GRAND TOTAL _____

· MISCHMASCH ·

This game was invented by Lewis Carroll in 1880. Players present each other with groups of, say, three letters. The idea is to find words with these letters within them, in the same order. Proper names are not allowed.

For example, which words contain the letters -**iti**-? Answers could be: c**iti**zen, p**iti**ful, m**iti**gate, l**iti**gate, prim**iti**ve.

Can you find words which contain the following letters?

wkw	ldr	rke	chn	rcl	xtu	ndw
mbl	ngu	zzl	ffi	usa	rsl	pti

How many did you find? Give yourself a point for each correct word.

The game is even more interesting if you give letters which link a word of two parts. For example, which words contain the letters -**ndc**-? Answers could be: sa**ndc**astle, ha**ndc**uff, wi**ndc**heater, gra**ndc**hild.

Can you find compound words containing the following?

ndb	ckg	ilw	olb	mew	htm	yes

Now, find a partner to play against. Each of you write eight groups of three letters in the first column of the grid below. Now swap papers and see how many words you can find for each group of letters. 1 point for each ordinary word; 2 points for each compound word. The winner will be the person who scores the most points.

LETTER GROUPS	WORDS
1	
2	
3	
4	
5	
6	
7	
8	

• BURIED WORDS •

BURIED WORDS is a game where words on a theme are hidden within a sentence. You have to find them. For Example (theme = flowers):

A rhinoce**ros e**xhibits a large horn on its nose.
The greengrocer had some **sweet pea**rs for sale.
The rain had frozen into hailstone**s now drop**ping on the lawn.

Find the following buried words (theme = birds):

SENTENCE		ANSWER
1	A fish's fin churns up the water.	_____
2	The fishermen began netting as many fish as they could.	_____
3	We allow long-standing members to bring guests to meetings.	_____
4	Let us wander wherever we want.	_____
5	I'm fed up with rushing about all the time.	_____
6	We climbed over the stile and went into the field.	_____
7	He made a terrific row when he practised the drums.	_____
8	We were together only for a short time on that occasion.	_____
9	We went to Mexico this year and had a fortnight in Galeana.	_____
10	When I am ill I crave nothing more than peace and quiet.	_____

Make up your own sentences with buried words. Make a list of some animals and then try to hide them in sentences like those above. When you have finished, swap with a friend and try to solve each other's (theme = animals).

SENTENCE	ANSWER
_____	_____
_____	_____
_____	_____
_____	_____
_____	_____
_____	_____
_____	_____
_____	_____
_____	_____

WORDSEARCH – TEACHER'S PAGE

Pupils will probably already be familiar with wordsearches and how to operate them. In case some are not it is advisable to go through what one should do. They need to be aware that you can look for words both downwards and upwards vertically, both backwards and forwards horizontally, and both up and down diagonally from left to right and from right to left.

In the wordsearch on the next page it will probably be helpful if they use a coloured pencil to outline the words they find – this will make them clearer against a black and white background.

Since all the words hidden in the wordsearch are terms used in this book of games, you may wish to leave this activity until the very end so that pupils are already familiar with the terms. Alternatively, this can offer an opportunity to familiarise pupils with terms they will encounter but do not necessarily know yet.

Remind them to tick off each word as they find it, so as not to miss any out. You might find it helpful to put a small wordsearch of your own on the board so that you can work first as a class to find your hidden words. Do not make it too large a square as this will take up too much class time to solve, not to mention your own time in preparation!

CREATING A WORDSEARCH

When pupils create their own wordsearch on the grid provided overleaf, they should first find all the words they will conceal. These are to be on a theme. All the words they find should be written initially in the space below, and checked for correct spelling using a dictionary or appropriate book, so they do not forget to put them in the grid. This list will also be used by the friend who later tries to find them.

This is a chance for pupils to use other reference books from the library to find their words on a theme. They will find lists in indexes of natural history and other relevant books. Be aware that this means pupils will need access to these books, so you would be advised to make sure they are available. Either have a number in the classroom already, or go with them all to the library and give them only a short time to find a book so that you can return all together to start work. Do not make the mistake of letting pupils go to find books on their own, or they may never appear again! I say this from bitter experience.

The number of words they will need for this size of grid will be somewhere between 12 and 20. Too many words, especially if they are long, will be difficult, if not impossible, to fit into it. Too few will be too easy to find.

Show them how words can cross through each other on the grid – they should be able to see this from having done the previous activity. The best way to approach entering their words is to put the longest ones in first. All their words must be put on the grid before they fill in the remaining squares with any letters they wish to complete it. When it is finished they swap with a friend and try to solve each other's wordsearch.

> • Finding words on a theme • Enlarging vocabulary • Familiarising with indexes in reference books • Matching words and patterns in reading and searching for words • Creating a puzzle for someone else to solve

• WORDSEARCH •

V	P	I	L	M	S	I	R	E	N	O	O	P	S	Y	N	M	R
O	N	O	U	N	O	D	N	I	L	V	A	P	P	O	S	Y	N
C	K	E	N	E	V	I	T	C	E	J	D	A	O	V	I	N	U
A	I	K	I	R	H	O	O	R	A	P	S	B	P	C	U	O	N
C	N	E	V	N	O	M	B	O	D	E	L	L	A	C	L	N	O
I	N	N	O	T	I	M	A	R	G	O	P	I	L	N	U	Y	S
T	E	A	C	R	O	S	P	A	R	D	R	O	I	O	R	S	A
S	K	L	A	L	E	K	P	E	A	N	W	K	N	I	H	L	L
O	U	A	L	L	I	T	N	R	G	S	G	O	D	O	P	I	L
R	N	O	I	B	C	O	A	K	E	R	R	S	R	H	S	A	I
C	I	M	C	O	H	I	N	R	A	P	A	R	O	D	Y	R	T
A	I	E	O	P	O	T	A	M	O	N	O	N	M	H	T	R	E
S	N	S	O	M	B	R	G	A	D	Y	R	S	E	K	H	V	R
T	G	M	U	Y	R	V	R	R	A	O	E	H	I	Y	R	P	A
Y	O	P	A	M	E	T	A	P	H	O	R	G	T	T	I	N	T
H	T	T	L	R	V	U	M	P	L	Y	S	H	L	L	I	D	I
R	E	E	L	D	D	I	R	P	E	C	M	D	A	M	T	O	O
M	O	B	I	M	A	R	G	N	I	N	N	E	K	M	T	D	N

Find the following words which are all literary terms. Look up, down, sideways, back-to-front and diagonally. Ring the words in the grid and tick them off below when you have found them.

ACROSTIC	KENNING	PREPOSITION	SYNONYM
ADJECTIVE	LIPOGRAM	PRONOUN	UNIVOCALIC
ADVERB	METAPHOR	RHYME	VERB
ALLITERATION	NOUN ✓	RHYTHM	
ANAGRAM	ONOMATOPOEIA	RIDDLE	
HOMOPHONE	PALINDROME	SIMILE	
IDIOM	PARODY	SPOONERISM	

• CREATE YOUR OWN WORDSEARCH •

Use the grid below to create your own WORDSEARCH on a theme.

Choose a theme for the words you will hide in the grid and list them underneath. For example, choose one of these or find your own theme:

> **football teams   countries   animals   makes of cars   book characters   trees**
>
> **flowers   vegetables   birds   historical heroes   gods in classical mythology**

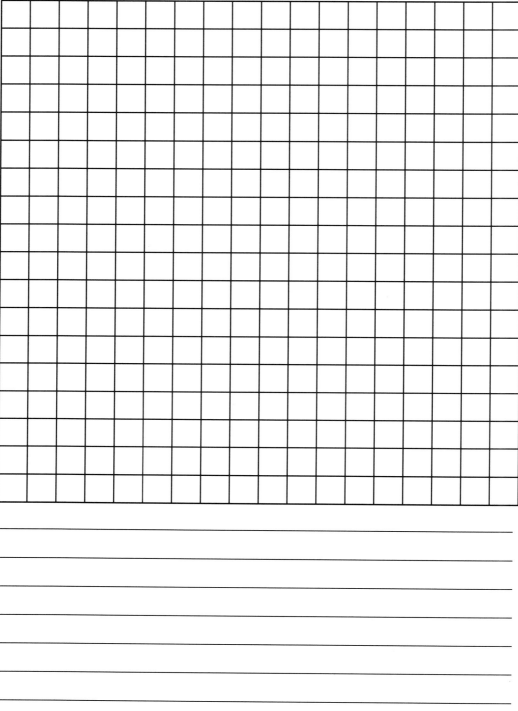

_____

_____

_____

_____

_____

_____

Swap wordsearches with a friend and try to find each other's words.

WORD GAMES (8, 9, & 10) – TEACHER'S PAGE

Spoonerisms are named after the Reverend William Archibald Spooner, one-time dean, later warden of New College Oxford. We are all fairly familiar with what they are as we all at some time, often when tired, mix up our words by transposing initial letters. Two of the examples – *chish 'n' fips* and *one swell foop* – quoted on the pupil's page are not strictly spoonerisms although they are common slips in the same manner.

A proper spoonerism should make sense by creating actual words when letters are transposed. They are usually fun the first time you come across them and pupils will enjoy this use of language. This is one of the language techniques often used in jokes (along with homophones, homonyms and other punning wordplay).

It is worth asking pupils to bring in their joke books. You can then find jokes that work by using different language techniques. It is a good idea to make a class joke book with examples of these, plus any that pupils can make up themselves. This can be illustrated and will add to the class library – it is likely to be a popular reading book! It will help pupils to understand the effects of these different techniques and encourage them to play with language.

Palindromes. Like spoonerisms, palindromes are fun when you first hear about them – it has to be said that they can pall over a longer period. However, making up palindromic phrases or sentences is more interesting, if a little difficult to accomplish well.

The variation (word palindromes) mentioned on the pupil's page, offers more scope. There are also a few palindromic jokes which could be added to the class joke book. The main benefit of finding single palindromes lies in the excitement of the hunt through the dictionary and the consequent flexibility of mind when approaching words. Instead of just reading words from left to right, pupils realise that you can see them from different angles. This is a spin-off from most of the word games in this section. It gets them in among the letters, almost touching and savouring each word, instead of seeing them from a distance, as it were.

Punny Book Titles. This well-known game has amused children for years and to some grown-ups may appear old hat or just produce a groan at the thought of it. But this is adult thinking of a certain kind and not how children think. The English language is full of possibilities for puns and the child in all of us can respond to wordplay. I would go as far as to say that all teachers of English <u>should</u> enjoy word games as they are an important element in our knowledge and handling of language. Make sure that your pupils say the names out loud because this is the way to hear what they are actually seeming to say. Looking at words on the page is not enough. The book titles pupils devise must obviously be appropriate to the names.

● Finding words in the dictionary ● Analysing jokes according to language techniques ● Looking at words in different ways ● Fun and confidence with language

• SPOONERISMS •

A SPOONERISM is a phrase where the initial letters of some words have swapped places, thus changing the sense and usually making it funny. They are always spoken, and are usually said by accident, often when someone is tired, or thinking too fast. For example:

Sally wanted to *bake the bread* **would become Sally wanted to** *break the bed*

Sometimes not just initial letters but whole words change places. Here are two sayings:

To leave no tern unstoned (original = To leave no stone unturned)

Time wounds all heels   (original = Time heals all wounds)

Spoonerisms are named after the Reverend William Archibald Spooner (1844–1930), dean, and later warden, of New College Oxford. He is said to have made such mistakes frequently and the following are some examples which are supposed to be from him, although some may have been made up by others.

SPOONERISM	WHAT SHOULD HE HAVE SAID?
The Lord is a shoving leopard	_____
He's a boiled sprat	_____
A well-boiled icicle	_____
Let us drink to the queer old dean	_____
A half-warmed fish	_____
'Sir, you have deliberately *tasted two whole worms*;	_____
you have *hissed all my mystery lectures*	_____
and been caught *fighting a liar* in the quad;	_____
you will leave Oxford by the next *town drain*.'	_____

MAKE UP SOME SPOONERISMS OF YOUR OWN

Spoonerisms must make sense. *Chish 'n' fips* and *one swell foop* are well-known but are not proper spoonerisms as the words created do not exist.

_____   _____

_____   _____

_____   _____

_____   _____

Many jokes are based on spoonerisms. For example:

What's the difference between a gunslinger and a boat's siren? One shoots from the hip and the other hoots from the ship.

Collect other examples of spoonerisms from joke books.

● PALINDROMES ●

PALINDROMES are words, phrases, or even whole sentences that can be read exactly the same backwards as forwards. For example:

> bib   mum   dad   level   rotor   madam
>
> draw onward   Dennis and Edna sinned   live not on evil

THREE FAMOUS PALINDROMES

- A man, a plan, a canal – Panama
- Supposed to have been said by Napoleon: Able was I ere I saw Elba
- What the first man said to the first woman: Madam, I'm Adam

FIND AS MANY PALINDROMIC WORDS AS YOU CAN. Many of them are three-letter words. The longest are eleven letters long! For example:

> **kinnikinnik**   = a kind of tobacco used by American Indians
>
> **Ooloopooloo** = a language dialect spoken in Queensland, Australia

Use the dictionary to help you and work with a partner.

_____	_____	_____	_____
_____	_____	_____	_____
_____	_____	_____	_____
_____	_____	_____	_____
_____	_____	_____	_____
_____	_____	_____	_____
_____	_____	_____	_____
_____	_____	_____	_____
_____	_____	_____	_____
_____	_____	_____	_____
_____	_____	_____	_____
_____	_____	_____	_____

Can you make up some palindromic phrases or sentences of your own? It is quite difficult to do and to ensure that they make sense. You can try **word palindromes** – where you read *whole sentences* in reverse. For example:

Women understand men; few men understand women.

• PUNNY BOOK TITLES •

This is a game that you can play on your own, although it can be more fun to work with a partner.

The idea is to make up book titles that could have been written by people whose names are puns of a sort. The following examples will give you the idea. Say the names out loud to hear what they are <u>really</u> saying!

The Haunted House, by Hugo Furst

Keeping Secrets, by June O'Watt

Winter Snacks, by Sue Playdell

The Home Baker, by Roland Butter

MAKE UP BOOK TITLES for the following authors:

_____ by   I. C. Hands

_____ by   Holly Daze

_____ by   Hans Orff

_____ by   Ivor Bunyan

_____ by   Eva Brick

_____ by   Rocky Shaw

_____ by   Lettice Prey

_____ by   Wanamaker Prophet

_____ by   Frank N. Styne

_____ by   Mike Arbust

_____ by   Eileen Dover

_____ by   Cherie Pye

_____ by   Moses Lawn

_____ by   Dinah Might

_____ by   Dai Llarffin

Now make up some of your own, both titles and authors:

_____ by

_____ by

_____ by

_____ by

WORD GAMES (11 & 12) – TEACHER'S PAGE

Univocalics are words, phrases, whole sentences, or even paragraphs, poems and stories, which contain only one of the vowels. The best way to introduce this is to work as a whole class and find some single-word univocalics; e.g. *minim, refer, level* (also palindromes!), *letter, murmur, abracadabra, potshot, element, severe, catamaran, suburb, instinct, remember* etc. Of course, there are many two-, three- and four-letter words containing only one vowel and, according to the age and experience of your pupils, you may wish to begin with these simpler words. Pupils will need to find some of these anyway when they play the game. Remember, words containing the letter Y are not allowed as Y is a surrogate vowel and does the same job.

To help them remember the word *univocalic*, show them how it breaks down for meaning into *uni* (one) and *vocalic* (vowel sound, originally from Latin *vox*, *vocis* = the voice). You might look for other words using the same roots to show the meaning, e.g. **unit** (one thing), **uni**on (joined as one), **uni**cycle (one-wheeled cycle), **voc**al (sounded by the voice), **voc**abulary (words in a language), and **voice** itself.

Try to make up some simple sentences or phrases with the class so that they know exactly what to do when it is their turn, such as: *cats catch rats*; *keep the secret*; *sit in this light*; *lost dogs howl*; *Mum jumps up*.

The game demands that pupils use dictionaries to collect a number of univocalic words and then select those they can put together into a sensible sentence. This can be as simple or complicated as they wish and should ensure that all pupils, regardless of ability, can come up with something. Those who need stretching have the opportunity to show what they can do.

Lipograms could be said to be almost the opposite of the previous game. Lipograms are phrases, sentences or whole stories and poems, which leave out one letter of the alphabet completely. As with all these games, it is a good idea to work as a class first so that everyone knows what to do. Try making up simple phrases leaving out one letter of the alphabet. Obviously it is harder to leave out more frequently used letters such as E, S and T, than it is to leave out letters such as J, X and Q. It is, however, not too difficult and should be possible for all pupils to accomplish.

You can have some fun with lipograms by rewriting well-known nursery rhymes leaving out one letter of the alphabet. Every word containing that letter must be replaced with another word or phrase as near as possible in meaning to the original. This encourages pupils to use thesauruses and is really an exercise in comprehension as well as being particularly good practice for writing poetry, where it is advisable not to use the same words all the time but to find other ways of saying the same thing – but in this case still not using the missing letter! Here is 'Three Blind Mice' without the letter 'i':

Three small rodents who could not see/ See how they run/They all ran after Mrs Farmer/ Who used a sharp steel blade to cut off the long appendages attached to the creatures' bottoms/ Surely, you never saw such an event throughout all your born days/ As these three small rodents who could not see.

> - Use of dictionary to find words • Consolidation of spelling patterns
> - Fun with the language • Use of thesauruses to find alternative words
> - Simple comprehension for accuracy of meaning

• UNIVOCALICS •

UNIVOCALICS are pieces of writing which use only one of the vowels –
A E I O or U. They can be sentences or whole paragraphs. For example:

A	Adam's cat can't play cards at all – and that's a fact!
E	Help ferrets get better press! They're decent, clever pets.
I	I sight pink pigs with impish wings in flight.
O	John's worn odd socks to school for God knows how long.
U	Sun's up – bugs buzz, bulls stump up dust, ducks slurp mud plus grub up crumbs.

In English, the most used letter of the whole alphabet is E and one of the most
famous univocalics is said to be in a church. It rhymes and goes as follows:

> **P R S V R Y P R F C T M N**
>
> **V R K P T H S P R C P T S T N**

Can you solve the puzzle by putting the letter E in wherever it helps to make
sense?

Beware! There is an old word which we do not use any more, though you will
probably have heard of it.

MAKE UP some univocalics of your own. The best way to start is to look through
the dictionary and make a list of words containing only your chosen vowel. (U is
definitely the most difficult vowel to choose!)

Remember small words like *so*, *the*, *and*, *in*, *with*, *on*, etc. Words which use the
letter Y as a syllable are not allowed (e.g. *wor**y*** or *on**y***).

List your words below.

_____ _____ _____ _____

_____ _____ _____ _____

_____ _____ _____ _____

_____ _____ _____ _____

_____ _____ _____ _____

_____ _____ _____ _____

_____ _____ _____ _____

_____ _____ _____ _____

_____ _____ _____ _____

_____ _____ _____ _____

_____ _____ _____ _____

Now use your words to make up your own univocalics. Your sentences must make
sense. Can you write one for each of the five vowels? U is hard! Which did you find
easiest? Read what you have written to your friends and hear what they have done.

• LIPOGRAMS •

LIPOGRAMS are pieces of writing which leave out one letter of the alphabet.

They have been popular with some writers since the time of the ancient Greeks.

Many people throughout history have attempted whole stories or plays which have left out a letter, usually a vowel (A or E) as this is more challenging than leaving out a consonant like F or J. The longest piece ever written in this way was a 50,000 word novel called *Gadsby*, published by an American, Ernest Vincent Wright, in 1939. He left out the letter E, the letter of the alphabet most used in English!

TRY WRITING LIPOGRAM SENTENCES firstly without E, then without these letters: A, T, R, S, O. For example:

No E: I want to go to Timbuktu for my holidays but will probably go to Blackpool.

No A: How do dogs decide where to bury their bones?

No T: Some people have never sampled samphire, known as 'poor man's asparagus'.

No R: A cat is an animal of infinite wisdom and elegant poise.

No S: A bull in a china department could be a bit of a problem.

No O: What if the three bears had stayed in that day because it was raining?

No E: _____

_____

No A: _____

_____

No T: _____

_____

No R: _____

_____

No S: _____

_____

No O: _____

_____

Share your lipogram sentences with your friends. Which did you each find easiest?

TRY WRITING a lipogram short story. You can work with a friend on this.

Which letter will you leave out? You could even start your story with one of your sentences above, and then see where it leads you.

OR

WRITE 26 lipogram sentences leaving out each letter of the alphabet in turn.

You could make these into an illustrated ABC book, but with a difference.

Each page would be headed No A, No B, No C, etc.

WORD GAMES (13 &14) – TEACHER'S PAGE

Synonyms are words that have similar meanings and are found in thesauruses.

It is important for pupils' writing that they have practice in finding synonyms. In both poetry and prose, but particularly in poetry, it is advisable not to repeat words, unless repetition is part of the intention. If a main word (usually a noun, verb or adjective) is to have any impact on a reader or listener it should only be used once; otherwise its effect is negated. The first activity asks pupils to find synonyms for such words. Doing this will also widen their vocabulary.

The second activity asks them to find as many different words for 'moving' as possible. This includes small movements, such as *twitch* and *blink*, as well as words such as *slither, sidle, tiptoe, stampede, promenade, rampage and stumble*.

The poem, '*On the Move*', offers a pattern for pupils to use some of the words they have found. All this will help to improve their writing and replace the ubiquitous 'went' with rather more interesting and varied words.

The other verb which crops up with regular monotony in pupils' writing is 'said', so spend time as a class seeing how many different verbs they can find for the ways people and animals communicate. There are over 100 of these, including such examples as *mumble, grumble, bark, roar, declare, demand, whisper, murmur*.

You might do this first before they embark on the photocopied activity.

Ideally all the words found will be displayed around the classroom, either on a wall or window display, or as mobiles from the ceiling. This ensures that over the next weeks your pupils will be encouraged to use the words in their writing, especially if you remind them. They are more likely to use words they have found themselves, and when they take time to gaze around looking for inspiration, their eyes will inevitably light upon the words – there will be no escape! Not only will this widen both their spoken and written vocabulary, but it will make their writing far more interesting for you to read – fewer *went*s and *said*s.

Homophones are words that sound the same when pronounced, but have different spellings and different derivations. They are the very stuff of puns.

For this activity pupils are encouraged to use dictionaries to find their homophones and the second activity asks them to find the correct homophone for each wrong one. This can help many children with their spelling. However, be aware that it can also confuse others who already have problems. You may want to consider whether this activity is appropriate for all pupils. Trying to remember the difference between *their, there* and *they're* can put some pupils back.

Perhaps one of the best ways of introducing homophones is to ask pupils to bring in their joke books. So many jokes rely on the good old English pun, usually utilising homophones, and collecting these can be great fun. It also serves to alert pupils to homophones and they are more likely to remember the spelling differences as they have seen the words in context as well. Lessons are often learnt best where laughter is involved – or in this case probably groans, which are a common reaction to puns!

You can add these homophone jokes to the class joke book which you started with Word Games 8, 9 and 10.

- Widening spoken and written vocabulary • Use of dictionaries and thesauruses
- Spelling • Finding different ways of saying the same thing • Wordplay

• SYNONYMS •

SYNONYMS are words that are similar in meaning. For example: *sad, unhappy, blue, miserable, depressed, dejected, joyless.* You can find synonyms in a THESAURUS.

How many synonyms can you find for the following words?

happy (adj.) _____

large (adj.) _____

small (adj.) _____

charming (adj.) _____

a thought (noun) _____

a copy (noun) _____

a beginning (noun) _____

a friend (noun) _____

to answer (verb) _____

to shout (verb) _____

to eat (verb) _____

to ask (verb) _____

DID YOU KNOW that there are over 300 different ways 'to move'? How many can you find? Use dictionaries and thesauruses, and work with a friend.

_____ _____ _____ _____ _____
_____ _____ _____ _____ _____
_____ _____ _____ _____ _____
_____ _____ _____ _____ _____
_____ _____ _____ _____ _____
_____ _____ _____ _____ _____
_____ _____ _____ _____ _____
_____ _____ _____ _____ _____
_____ _____ _____ _____ _____
_____ _____ _____ _____ _____
_____ _____ _____ _____ _____
_____ _____ _____ _____ _____
_____ _____ _____ _____ _____

Use the words you have found to write a poem on the same pattern as '*On the Move*'.

Your teacher will read the poem to you. Think how different animals move.

On the Move

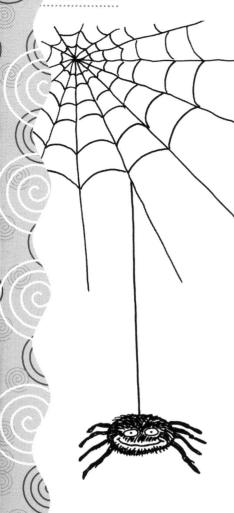

When lions have had enough of your talk,
They *stalk*.

When mice realise they have to *hurry*,
They *scurry*.

When camels have really got the hump
They *slump*.

When kestrels on hover are ready to *swo*
They *stoop*.

When bulls in a china shop are at large,
They *charge*.

When foxes sit in the shadows and sulk,
They *skulk*.

When snakes feel they're all of a dither,
They *slither*.

When hens are *grubbing* around on spec,
They *peck*.

When spiders don't want to do any work,
They *lurk*.

When wasps decide to have a fling,
They *sting*.

When cows wake from post-prandial slumber,
They *lumber*.

When sheep are in their quiet phase,
They *graze*.

When kangaroos *go* off in a flounce,
They *bounce*.

But when we are in for a long walk,
We *baulk*.

We *shamble* and *shuffle*,
And *scramble* and *scuffle*,
And *kick* up a rumpus and dust –
For we'll only *move* if we must!

Sandy Brownjohn

The words in italics are all verbs of movement.

34

• HOMOPHONES •

Whether the weather be fine
Or whether the weather be not,
Whether the weather be cold
Or whether the weather be hot,
We'll weather the weather,
Whatever the weather,
Whether we like it or not.

HOMOPHONES are words that sound the same but are spelt differently. There are many homophones in English. For example, *whether* and *weather*, *bear* and *bare*, *queue, cue* and *Kew*.

HOW MANY HOMOPHONES can you find? You might find the dictionary very helpful.

	&			&	
_____	&	_____	_____	&	_____
_____	&	_____	_____	&	_____
_____	&	_____	_____	&	_____
_____	&	_____	_____	&	_____
_____	&	_____	_____	&	_____
_____	&	_____	_____	&	_____
_____	&	_____	_____	&	_____
_____	&	_____	_____	&	_____
_____	&	_____	_____	&	_____
_____	&	_____	_____	&	_____

WRITE a short story in one paragraph using as many homophones as you can.

Put in the wrong words and then ask a friend to see if they can rewrite it with the correct words which will all be homophones. For example:

> *Eye eight* a *peace* of *meet* and it *maid* me *brake* a tooth. *Ewe* could *here* me *grown* along the *hole rode*. *Aye* went *strait two* the dentist because of the *pane* and asked *hymn* if he *wood* fix it *four* me. He said he *mite bee* able *too*, *butt* next *thyme two grille* my *stake* properly.

There are 26 homophones in the above piece. How should each of the words have been spelt?

WORD GAMES (15, 16 & 17) – TEACHER'S PAGE

Word Ladders or **Doublets** was invented by Lewis Carroll who enjoyed word games of all sorts. It is a game which can be very helpful for spelling as pupils have to move one step at a time from one word to another, related, word by changing only one letter each time. There are usually a number of different ways to do this and the game element allows for points to be won. Anyone who completes the ladder gains one point, and whoever does it in the fewest steps gains an extra point.

Dictionaries can be very useful in playing this game and the younger and more inexperienced the pupils, the more you would encourage them to use the dictionary. This will ensure that the words they use actually exist and in that spelling. They will also find new words this way and thus enlarge their vocabulary. With older pupils you might wish them to play without the dictionary.

When they do the activity put them in groups of two or three to play against each other and the clock. The time allowed will depend on the age and ability of the pupils. Try the game yourself as preparation and base your timing on your own experience with the puzzles.

Back to Front is another scoring game based on two related equal-length words. The first is written vertically from top to bottom, the second vertically from bottom to top. A gap is left between them. The object of the game is to fill in the gaps with words that begin with the given first letter and end with the given last letter. The longer the word, the greater the point score. The examples on the pupil's page show how this is done.

All pupils can take part in this game, and you would expect more able ones to find the longest words. Less able pupils will still be able to find words, and so play the game. It might be sensible to put the pupils in groups according to ability so that they play against others who are nearer their level of attainment. This will ensure that all pupils have a chance of winning and that no pupil will demoralise the less able ones. If necessary let some pupils play in pairs to give them confidence. They can use dictionaries, too, to make sure that words are spelt correctly so they do not lose points. Work as a class first on the board, starting with examples of three-letter words. A simpler variation of this is to choose only one word, writing it first down the page and then in reverse. For example:

P a N	P ai N	P ermissio N
E y E	E as E	E xistenc E
N i P	N ea P	N ightca P

The Queen's English is a game of finding words. The commercial game, Boggle, comes from this. Although the game set out on the pupils' page stipulates words of three letters or more, you can vary this according to the ability of your pupils. Words of two letters would be acceptable for less able or less experienced players. This is another game which can help with spellings and pupils are actively encouraged to use the dictionary to check for correct spelling. You can make up a word square very easily to practise as a class on the board first, and pupils can make their own to pass over to friends or to solve themselves. Just fill in the squares randomly with any letters.

- Use of dictionary
- Spelling practice
- Wordplay
- Using and extending vocabulary

• WORD LADDERS OR DOUBLETS •

DOUBLETS is a game invented by Lewis Carroll. It is more commonly known as WORD LADDERS.

The object of the game is to get from one word to another (related) word, one step at a time, changing one letter each step. The player who does it in the fewest steps is the winner. For example:

How would you get from HEAD to FEET?

PLAYER 1	PLAYER 2	PLAYER 3
HEAD	HEAD	HEAD
DEAD – 1st move	HEA**T** – 1st move	HEL**D** – 1st move
DE**E**D – 2nd move	**F**EAT – 2nd move	**W**ELD – 2nd move
FEED – 3rd move	FE**E**T – 3rd move	WEL**T** – 3rd move
FE**E**T – 4th move		**F**ELT – 4th move
		FE**E**T – 5th move
Player 2 wins this game.		

PLAY against one or two friends to see who can solve the following word ladders in the fewest steps. Give yourselves a time limit and do one ladder at a time.

After each ladder, everyone who has managed to move from one word to the other earns 1 point. The player who has done it in the fewest steps gains an extra point.

Add all your points up at the end to see who is the overall winner.

WILD	SOCK	NOSE	GIVE	DAWN	SLEEP	HOME
TAME	SHOE	FACE	TAKE	DUSK	DREAM	AWAY

FIND your own pairs of words for word ladders. Remember, both words must have the same number of letters. Swap your puzzles with a friend and solve each other's.

• BACK TO FRONT •

BACK TO FRONT is a game for two or more people. To play you need two words containing the same number of letters. For example:

great **and** *small*

Each player writes the first word vertically down the page (from top to bottom) and the second opposite (from bottom to top), as below. Leave space between the two.

The object of the game is to place letters between each opposite pair to make a word. As with most word games, proper names are not allowed.

Points are scored for each letter of each word. So, the longer the word you can find, the higher your score. The winner is the player with the highest score. For example:

1ST PLAYER	SCORE	2ND PLAYER	SCORE	3RD PLAYER	SCORE
G o a L	4	G r a d u a L	7	G i r L	5
R o y a L	5	R e s p e c t f u L	10	R i g h t f u L	8
E r A	3	E u p h o r i A	8	E x t r A	5
A l a r M	5	A p h o r i s M	8	A f f i r M	6
T i m e S	5	T o r t o i s e S	9	T e m p e r S	7
TOTAL	22	**TOTAL**	42	**TOTAL**	31

The 2nd PLAYER has the most points and is, therefore, the winner.

PLAY back to front against a friend, or a group of friends. Try the words below:

```
                  Score                           Score
C           T |    |        M            R |    |
L           E |    |        A            O |    |
E           E |    |        J            N |    |
A           H |    |        O            I |    |
N           S |    |        R            M |    |
            ____                         ____

                  Score                           Score
C           S |    |        F            D |    |
H           W |    |        O            N |    |
E           A |    |        R            I |    |
E           R |    |        G            M |    |
S           T |    |        E            E |    |
E           S |    |        T            R |    |
            ____                         ____
```

TRY the same words again, but this time use a dictionary. You should be able to find some very long words to fill the gaps. Give yourself a time limit and play against a friend. Now find you own pairs of words and play against your friends with these.

• THE QUEEN'S ENGLISH •

THE QUEEN'S ENGLISH is a game for two or more players. The object of the game is to make as many words, of three letters or more, as possible from a given grid of letters.

Players take it in turns to have a try, and if someone cannot go they are out. Each player can start on any square and then moves one square at a time – up, down, sideways or diagonally – to make a word. Use a pencil to point out the moves.

During a game no words can be used twice, and proper names are not allowed.

No letter can be used twice within the same word. For example:

The moves to get the word 'potash' are shown on the square below. HOW MANY MORE WORDS CAN YOU FIND?

F	M	R	E	Q
H	E	G	W	U
I	S	D	O	T
C	A	T	P	E
U	B	N	O	G

_____

_____

_____

_____

_____

PLAY the Queen's English against a friend. There are three different squares below for you to play on. Make a note of the words you both find underneath the squares. You can check any spellings in the dictionary.

P	A	S	I	T
O	G	A	H	U
F	R	E	M	E
E	T	E	D	L
L	E	N	B	O

S	O	C	F	E
S	E	H	U	A
O	T	Q	R	P
E	U	M	A	D
I	R	I	N	G

T	L	U	K	S
E	I	C	E	N
T	F	O	Y	I
A	M	E	L	E
D	A	R	P	H

WORD GAMES (18 & 19)
– TEACHER'S PAGE

Gridlock is probably most suitable for 10-year olds and over. It requires players to enter letters wherever they wish onto a 5 x 5 grid. Players take it in turns to say a letter and everyone must put that letter into the grid before the next letter is given. Once a letter is in the grid it cannot be moved. The object is to make as many words as possible (vertically or horizontally) of two letters or more. When scoring, letters cannot be counted twice in one direction, and one-letter words, such as 'I' and 'a', are not admissible. I have actually played this with a whole class of Year 6 children, each of us taking it in turns to say a letter, and everyone having their own grid to enter them in.

This is not a game that can easily be played as a class on the board, because as people can see the grid they will be tempted to say letters to complete words. The only way you can do this – and it would, of course, help pupils to see how it is played before they try – is to ask pupils for 25 letters in advance which you then have to enter in the order they have been given. Better still, use a pack of alphabet cards, or similar, and choose letters at random from these. This will simulate a real game more effectively. Ideally the game is played by only two people, but groups of up to five can work well. As with many games there is a high degree of luck involved – in the letters you are given, and in where you choose to put them, as they cannot be moved once entered.

Socrates is a game of logic. It requires players to concentrate hard and to apply logic in order to think ahead and plan their next move. It is wonderful to play, but is not for the faint-hearted. From the answers given you must deduce which letters are in the word, and which are not. An answer of 'nothing' is very useful as it means you can eliminate all four of those letters from the problem. However, those four letters will help you to establish other elements of the word. With an answer of 'one O', you can use three of the deleted letters to help establish which of the others is the correct letter. There are several other strategies which can be employed and these will become apparent after playing the game for a while. As with some other games, it can be harder to explain all the intricacies than it is actually to play it. So, try it out and it will become clearer.

As an introduction to the game you can play with the whole class on the board. One person chooses a word which they write on a piece of paper so that they can refer to it when giving answers. Class members take it in turns to ask a four-letter word, each of which is written on the board. The answers (how many Xs or Os) are written down underneath. Pupils gradually work out what the original word is by using their powers of deduction. It can help to have the alphabet written out so that eliminated letters can be crossed off as they occur.

As a pencil and paper game Socrates can be played anywhere, at any time. Some words, such as *lynx, onyx, hymn* and *cyst*, are often the equivalent of the ace serve in tennis. Remember, that no double or repeated letters are allowed: also no proper names or plurals.

> • Wordplay   • Development of logical thinking   • Spelling

•GRIDLOCK•

GRIDLOCK is a game for two people, although it can be played by a small group. Find a friend to play against in a round of Gridlock.

1   Each player draws a grid, five squares by five squares.
2   The first player calls out a letter of the alphabet, and each of you must enter it in one of the squares **immediately**. It is up to you where you write it.
3   Then, the second player calls out a letter of the alphabet. You each enter this letter into the grid, too. Do not look at each other's grids.
4   This continues, with players taking it in turns to call out letters. Letters must be entered immediately and cannot be changed.
5   The object of the game is to make as many words of two or more letters when read either across (from left to right) or down. Diagonals do not count.
6   When it is your turn, you obviously say letters which help you with words you have in mind. Your opponent's choice of letters will not always help you, so you must enter them where you think they *might* do some good!
7   When all 25 squares are full, you count up your scores (points out of 50).

A five-letter word = 5 points;   a four-letter word = 4 Points; a three-letter word = 3 points; a two-letter word = 2 points. For example (Player 1):

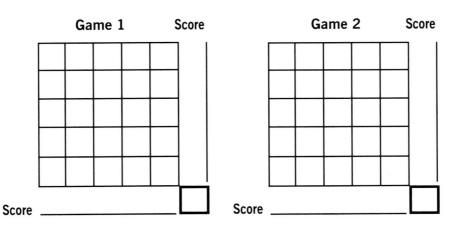

YOUR TURN TO PLAY GRIDLOCK

• SOCRATES •

SOCRATES is a game of logic for two people. Each player thinks of a four-letter word and the aim is to be the first to work out your opponent's word through a process of elimination.

1   Each choose a four-letter word (no repeated letters, plurals, or proper names).
    For example: 1st Player, SEAL;   2nd Player, HURT.

2   Take it in turns to suggest four-letter words to each other. The person being asked matches the suggestion against their chosen word and answers with an **X for a correct letter in the right place**, and an **O for a correct letter in the wrong place**. For example:

1st Player's word = SEAL		**2nd Player's word = HURT**	
2nd Player asks	BAIT	1st Player asks	MADE
1st Player answers	'one O'	2nd Player answers	'nothing'
2nd Players asks	DARE	1st Player asks	RIOT
1st Player answers	'two Os'	2nd Player answers	'one X, one O'
2nd Player asks	REAL	1st Player asks	SORT
1st Player answers	'three Xs'	2nd Player answers	'two Xs'
2nd Player asks	READ	1st Player asks	BORN
1st Player answers	'two Xs'	2nd Player answers	'one X'
2nd Player asks	MEAL	1st Player asks	HOST
1st Player answers	'three Xs'	2nd Player answers	'two Xs'
2nd Player asks	HEAL	1st Player asks	MOST
1st Player answers	'three Xs'	2nd Player answers	'one X'
2nd Player asks	PEAL	1st Player asks	HURT
1st Player answers	'three Xs'	2nd Player answers	'Yes!'

The 1st Player wins this game.

PLAY SOCRATES AGAINST A FRIEND.

YOUR WORD

_____

(FRIEND'S GUESSES AND YOUR ANSWERS)   YOUR GUESSES AND ANSWERS

_____ _____	_____ _____
_____ _____	_____ _____
_____ _____	_____ _____
_____ _____	_____ _____
_____ _____	_____ _____
_____ _____	_____ _____
_____ _____	_____ _____
_____ _____	_____ _____

SECTION 2

SIMPLE GRAMMAR AND ALPHABET-BASED GAMES

The Nine Parts of Speech

Three little words you often see

Are ARTICLES *a, an* and *the*.

A NOUN is the name of anything

As *school* or *garden, hoop* or *swing.*

ADJECTIVES tell the kind of noun,

As *great, small, pretty, white* or *brown*.

Instead of nouns the PRONOUNS stand;

She and *he* are two I've found.

VERBS tell of something to be done;

To *read, count, sing, laugh, jump* or *run*.

How things are done the ADVERBS tell;

As *slowly, quickly, ill* or *well*.

CONJUNCTIONS join the words together;

As men *and* women, wind *and* weather.

The PREPOSITION stands before

A noun, as *in* or *through* the door.

The INTERJECTION shows surprise,

As *Oh!* How pretty! *Ah!* How wise!

The whole are called nine parts of speech,

Which reading, writing and speaking teach.

Old rhyme

NOUNS (1) – TEACHER'S PAGE

Nouns are the names of things, people or places.

There are four main categories of nouns:

1 **Common nouns**: e.g. *table, chair, dog, butter, tree, country, finger, priest, girl*

2 **Proper nouns**: (names) e.g. *Westminster Abbey, Philip, Josie, America, Ireland Top Shop* (these always have capital letters)

3 **Collective nouns**: e.g. a *herd* of cattle, an *exultation* of larks, a *skulk* of foxes

4 **Abstract nouns**: e.g. *happiness, jealousy, anger, love, laziness, devotion*

The first category breaks down into further groups according to whether the words are masculine, feminine, common or neuter (i.e. their gender).

● *boy, priest, man, tom-cat, bull* are all masculine

● *girl, deaconess, woman, queen, cow* are all feminine

● *child, cat, dog, person, animal* are all common

● *table, chair, butter, tree, finger* are all neuter

Nouns are magical. Knowing the name of something gives us a power. The very utterance of a name conjures up a picture of it. Not knowing the name of something can put us at a disadvantage. Nouns are the first words we tend to learn.

There are many games and activities involving nouns. Some of these are set out on the next pages. The following oral memory game can be played with a group or a whole class.

The Picnic Game might go like this:

Teacher: I'm going on a picnic, and I am going to take *some oranges*.

1st pupil: I'm going on a picnic and I am going to take *some oranges and sausages*.

2nd pupil: I'm going on a picnic and I am going to take *some oranges, sausages and fresh bread*.

3rd pupil: I'm going on a picnic and I am going to take *some oranges, sausages, fresh bread and ripe peaches*.

This continues round the class with each person repeating the list and then adding something of their own to it. You can make it more interesting by asking children to think of an adjective to go with each noun, as in *fresh* bread and *ripe* peaches.

The game can also be played by adding items alphabetically. So, the teacher's choice might have been **a**pples, to which the first pupil might add **b**eefburgers, the second **C**oca-Cola, the third **d**oughnuts, the fourth **e**ggs, etc. The letter 'x' can be difficult, so you can leave it out if necessary.

The same basic game can be played by inventing a different situation, such as 'We're going to the zoo and we shall see an *alligator*, a *baboon*, a *camel*, a *deer*, etc.'

> ● Introduction to nouns ● Listening skills ● Memory skills
> ● Reinforcing order of the alphabet ● Using words on a theme

BLANK FOR USE WITH
• A–Z WRITING GAMES •

A _____

B _____

C _____

D _____

E _____

F _____

G _____

H _____

I _____

J _____

K _____

L _____

M _____

N _____

O _____

P _____

Q _____

R _____

S _____

T _____

U _____

V _____

W _____

X _____

Y _____

Z _____

• COMMON NOUNS •

There are four types of COMMON NOUNS:

1 **Masculine** (male)
2 **Feminine** (female)
3 **Common** (can be either male or female)
4 **Neuter** (objects, neither male nor female)

These four categories tell us what *gender* a word is.

Sort the nouns below into groups according to their type.

MASCULINE	FEMININE	COMMON	NEUTER
e.g. *boy*	*girl*	*child*	*table*

kitten   paper   telephone   king   elephant   sister   aunt   book

policeman   sandwich   brother   widow   pencil   gardener   hen

stallion   bird   sausages   fox   a prime minister   countess   lawyer

vixen   earl   wellington boots   ewe   town   rabbit

Can you add some more of your own to each list?

NOUNS (2) – TEACHER'S PAGE

A was an Archer who shot at a frog,
B was a Butcher who kept a bull-dog;
C was a Captain all covered with lace,
D was a Drummer who played with much grace;
E was an Esquire with pride on his brow,
F was a Farmer who followed the plough;
G was a Gamester who had but ill-luck,
H was a Hunter and hunted a buck;
I was an Italian who had a white mouse,
J was a Joiner and built up a house;
K was a King so mighty and grand,
L was a Lady who had a white hand;
M was a Miser who hoarded up gold,

N was a Nobleman gallant and bold;
O was an Organ boy who played about town,
P was a Parson who wore a black gown;
Q was a Queen who was fond of her people,
R was a Robin who perched on a steeple;
S was a Sailor who spent all he got,
T was a Tinker who mended a pot;
U was an Usher who loved little boys,
V was a Veteran who sold pretty toys;
W was a Watchman who guarded the door,
X was eXpensive and so became poor;
Y was a Youth who did not love school,
Z was a Zany who looked a great fool.

This is one of the most famous ABC rhymes and was very popular among illustrators of early reading books in the nineteenth century. Many a Victorian child learnt the alphabet this way, and probably learnt to read, too.

As a rhyme it provides a pattern for some creative writing at the same time as giving pupils the chance to consolidate their knowledge of the order of the alphabet and to practise finding nouns.

Pupils write their own rhymes, based on the same rhythm and length of line as the original above. They may or may not actually rhyme it – this is up to them, or according to their ability. Without rhyming, it will still be effective as the strong rhythm will hold it together. Encourage them to say their lines out loud to hear if the rhythm is right. It can help to choose a theme such as: people's jobs (as in the original); animals; the parts of, and items in, a house; people on the beach or at a picnic; food; the ghost train at the fair (see next page); or any other theme you want. For example:

Rhyming

A was an Aardvark who lived in the zoo,
B was a Bear who had little to do;
C was a Cat who was stalking a mouse,
D was a Dog who defended the house;
E was an Elephant, massive and grey,
F was a Ferret who hunted his prey ...

Non-rhyming

A is an Aga for cooking the food,
B is a Bed where I sleep and have dreams;
C is a Chair where my grandmother sits,
D is a Door which leads into the house;
E are the Eaves which are under the roof,
F is the Fanlight that lets in the sun ...

When they have finished their ABCs pupils can make them into alphabet books and illustrate them. If you can arrange this with teachers of younger classes, your pupils might take their books and read them with the younger children. This will give an added purpose and audience for their writing.

- Consolidating knowledge of the order of the alphabet   • Creative writing
- Writing to a pattern   • Learning to hear and use rhythm   • Making a book
- Finding nouns on a theme   • Using rhyme if appropriate

· ABC RHYMES ·

A B C D E F G H I J K L M N O P Q R S T U V W X Y Z

Imagine you are on a ghost train at the fair! The following is the beginning of an alphabet rhyme about just that.

A is an **A**rm that just floats in the air,
B is a **B**at that flies into your hair;
C is a **C**ry like a scream in the night,
D is for **D**racula taking a bite;
E is an **E**cho that haunts in the mind,
F is a **F**ace that floats up from behind;
G is a **G**host glowing luminous white ...

You can write your own ABC rhyme using NOUNS that begin with each letter of the alphabet. A dictionary can help you find suitable nouns. You might like to go on and finish the rhyme above, or you can start a new one about something different.

You can choose one of the following themes or decide on your own setting:

> **people's jobs   food   animals   people on a picnic   people at the beach**
>
> **inside and outside a house   a garden scene   a party   a football match**

Before you start, say the ghost train lines out loud so that you can hear the rhythm of each line. When you write your own rhyme you must use the same rhythm.

You do not need to rhyme, but you can if you want. But remember that your rhymes must help your poem make sense. Do not use any old word just because it rhymes. It is sometimes better to concentrate on getting the rhythm right without worrying about trying to rhyme. You can work on your own, or with a friend if you like.

Here are some examples:

Rhyming

A was an **A**ardvark who lived in the zoo,
B was a **B**ear who had little to do;
C was a **C**at who was stalking a mouse,
D was a **D**og who defended the house;
E was an **E**lephant, massive and grey,
F was a **F**erret who hunted his prey ...

Non-rhyming

A is an **A**ga for cooking the food,
B is a **B**ed where I sleep and have dreams;
C is a **C**hair where my grandmother sits,
D is a **D**oor which leads into the house;
E are the **E**aves which are under the roof,
F is the **F**anlight that lets in the sun ...

When you have finished you could make an ABC book and draw pictures to illustrate each line of your rhyme. You might want to show this to other classes in the school.

NOUNS (3) – TEACHER'S PAGE

Collective nouns is the name for groups of animals, people or things.

There are four main kinds of collective noun.

1   Ancient phrases: e.g. a **skulk** of foxes; a **murder** of crows; a **knot** of toads; a **skein** of geese; a **parliament** of owls; a **boast** of soldiers
2   General terms: e.g. a **herd** of cows; a **flock** of sheep; a **school** of whales; a **bunch** of grapes; a **pack** of cards; a **shoal** of fish
3   Single words denoting a collection (by adding *-age* or *-ery*): e.g. **greenery** (green plants); **cutlery** (knives, forks and spoons); **pottery** (a number of pots); **plumage** (feathers); **foliage** (leaves)
4   Modern puns: e.g. a **gloat** of examiners; a **wince** of dentists

It is worth collecting as many collective nouns as your pupils know or can research from home and library books. You can find books in libraries completely devoted to collective nouns. Many of the ancient ones come from *The Boke of St Albans* (1486) by Dame Juliana Berners. This was a book about the countryside and hunting and contained beautiful phrases most of which have unfortunately slipped from current use. A list of some of these is on page 52. You may also be interested to know that the same book lists the kind of hunting birds each echelon of society was allowed to fly. It is almost a poem in itself, and its last line has provided the title of a modern classic.

> An Eagle for an Emperor,
> a Gyrfalcon for a King;
> a Peregrine for a Prince,
> a Saker for a Knight;
> a Merlin for a Lady,
> a Goshawk for a Yeoman;
> a Sparrowhawk for a Priest,
> a Musket for a Holy-water Clerk;
> a Kestrel for a Knave.

When pupils are engaged in creative writing they should be aware of what a *cliché* is so that they can try to avoid using them. Creative writing should be fresh and new in its language and should combine words in ways that excite. Clearly, using known collective nouns will not do this, so here is an opportunity to talk about *clichés* and encourage your pupils to practise making up new phrases. They should work in small groups of, say, threes. They choose what they want to make a collection of and then talk about these things – what they look like, do, sound like, what you do with them, etc. Sooner or later someone will say a word which seems appropriate for a new collective noun. Each group should try to make up a number of these which can then be put into a class book, perhaps with illustrations.

> ● **Understanding of collective nouns** ● **Creative work – making new collective nouns** ● **Speaking and listening** ● **Collaborative work** ● **Understanding of cliché**

LIST OF SOME COLLECTIVE NOUNS – TEACHER'S PAGE

The following is a selection of existing but lesser-known collective nouns.

A **shrewdness** of apes
A **pace** of asses
A **lodge** of beavers
A **college** of bees
A **fighting** of beggars
A **psalter** of bishops
A **sedge** of bitterns
A **blush** of boys
An **obstinacy** of buffaloes
A **lurch** of buses
A **goring** of butchers
A **sneer** of butlers
A **clowder** of cats
A **glaring** of cats
A **peep** of chicks
A **pie** of coals
A **fawning** of courtiers
A **shrivel** of critics
A **murder** of crows
A **charge** of curates
A **cowardice** of curs
A **decanter** of deans
A **wince** of dentists
A **rash** of dermatologists
A **dole** of doves
A **paddling** of ducks
A **gang** of elk
A **gloat** of examiners
A **fesnyng** of ferrets
A **roost** of fowls
A **skulk** of foxes
A **skein** of geese
A **tower** of giraffes
A **giggle** of girls
A **charm (chirm)** of goldfinches
A **covey** of grouse
A **screech** of gulls
A **down** of hares
A **leash** of hawks
A **warp** of herring

A **blast** of hunters
A **fluther** of jellyfish
A **ring** of jewellers
A **purl** of lace
A **desert** of lapwings
An **exultation** of larks
A **leap** of leopards
A **tissue** of lies
A **sawt** of lions
A **tiding** of magpies
A **faith** of merchants
A **diligence** of messengers
A **fraunch** of milliners
A **labour** of moles
An **abomination** of monks
A **watch** of nightingales
A **flap** of nuns
A **parliament** of owls
A **hive** of oysters
An **ostentation** of peacocks
An **odium** of politicians
A **bevy** of quail
A **flick** of rabbits
An **unkindness** of ravens
A **hurtle** of sheep
A **boast** of soldiers
A **murmuration** of starlings
A **wedge** of swans
A **skulk** of thieves
A **knot** of toads
A **sea** of troubles
A **hover** of trout
A **turn** of turtles
A **prudence** of vicars
A **huddle** of walruses
A **dout** of wildcats
A **non-patience** of wives
A **descent** of woodpeckers
A **zeal** of zebras

• COLLECTIVE NOUNS •

A COLLECTIVE NOUN is a name for a group of animals, people or things. You will already know some of these, such as

> a **gaggle** of geese   a **pride** of lions   a **flock** of sheep   a **swarm** of bees

How many more can you find?
Here are some very old collective nouns which you may not know.

> a **skulk** of foxes   a **clowder** of cats   a **parliament** of owls
> an **exultation** of larks   a **labour** of moles   a **murder** of crows
> a **skein** of geese   a **boast** of soldiers   a **fawning** of courtiers

Can you work out why the words in bold became collective nouns?
You may need to look the words up in a dictionary to see what they mean.
What do you think they tell us about the animals or people?

You can make up your own new collective nouns. In fact, when you write stories or poems you need to make up new phrases. If you use ones that everybody already knows your writing will not be so interesting. Practise making some up now.
You can work with a couple of friends.

- **Decide** what you want to make a collection of – creatures, people, or objects?
- **Then talk together** about them – what do they look like? Where do you find them? What do they do? What can you do with them? What particular characteristics do they have? And so on.
- **Listen** to what each other is saying because sooner or later one of you will say a word which will be ideal for your new collective noun.

See how many you can make up. You might want to illustrate them. Here are some ideas to start you off:

a _____ of toffees   a _____ of crocodiles

a _____ of teachers   a _____ of teeth

a _____ of branches   a _____ of dreams

Here are some examples of made-up collective nouns:

> a **purr** of cats   a **slouch** of snails   a **comfort** of beds   a **crawl** of ants
> a **rainbow** of puddles   a **Mexican wave** of football fans   a **crunch** of biscuits

• CATEGORIES •

This is a game you can play against one or two friends. You will both/all need copies of the CATEGORIES as listed below. There is room for two games on this grid.

	NOUN	SCORE	NOUN	SCORE
Boy's name				
Girl's name				
A bird				
A flower				
A fruit				
A tree				
A fish				
A vegetable				
An animal				
A colour				
A town				
A country				
An author				
A book character				

TO PLAY

1   Choose one letter of the alphabet.
2   Each player must fill in a noun, beginning with that letter, for each category.
3   Set a time limit between 10 and 15 minutes.

SCORING is as follows: 2 points for a correct noun, but only 1 point if someone else has the same noun. Clearly it is good to try to put down unusual nouns which you think no one else will have. That way you score more points!

ADJECTIVES – TEACHER'S PAGE

One of the best ways of introducing **adjectives** to a class is to play a game called the Minister's Cat. There are several ways of doing this – the following is one that works well. Play it orally first with no mention of the word 'adjective' or a definition of its role. This will come later.

The game is based on the ABC and requires each pupil in turn to supply a word, beginning with the next letter of the alphabet, to describe the cat. The object is to see who can stay in the longest. Once you have been through the alphabet, you begin again but no adjective may be repeated (so, if it was *adorable* in the first round, it might be *angry* in the second, *asphyxiated* in the third, etc). You are allowed to cheat with the letter *x* (not many adjectives begin with *x*!) by using words that sound as if they begin with *x*, such as *excited*, *expendable* or *extinct*.

Pupils will be *out* if they (a) repeat an adjective, (b) cannot think of one, or (c) give one beginning with the wrong letter (they often count ahead and forget to listen!). Whoever is last in is the winner. If you wish, the cat can also be given a name.

The game might go something like this:

1st pupil: The Minister's Cat is an *articulated* cat (and his name is Andrew)

2nd pupil: The Minister's Cat is a *boastful* cat (and her name is Bryony)

3rd pupil: The Minister's Cat is a *curmudgeonly* cat (and his name is Curtis) etc.

When the game has been played orally (perhaps a few times), pupils can be encouraged to write their own A–Z. This may be The Minister's Cat, or it might be something else, such as, Our school is a _____ school, The schoolkeeper's dog is _____, Wendy's gerbil is _____, or My bike is _____, etc.

Before they write their own, give them the correct terminology. Write the word **adjective** on the board and ask them to tell you what kind of word it is, based on their experience of using them in the game. If, in future, someone seems to have forgotten what an adjective is, mention of the game will jog their memory: 'You remember. Those were the words we used to describe the Minister's Cat.'

Show them how to find adjectives in the dictionary and encourage them to use words they like the sound or look of and which they did not know before.

When they write on their own they can be shown how to use ditto marks – there is no point in their continually writing out the repeated parts, and *you* do not want to spend time preparing a sheet with blank spaces for the adjectives.

These A–Zs lend themselves to illustration and can make very good wall displays.

> ● **Reinforcing the order of the alphabet** ● Use of dictionary ● Speaking and listening ● **Expansion of vocabulary** ● Memory training ● **Role of ditto marks** ● **Knowledge and understanding of adjectives** ● **Creative writing to a pattern**

• THE MINISTER'S CAT •

A B C D E F G H I J K L M N O P Q R S T U V W X Y Z

Play THE MINISTER'S CAT orally with your teacher and the whole class.

NOW WRITE YOUR OWN ALPHABET MINISTER'S CAT.

The words used to describe the Minister's Cat are called ADJECTIVES. Use a dictionary to find adjectives that you did not know before. If you like the look or sound of them, and the dictionary says they are adjectives, you can use them.

Don't forget you can cheat with the letter X if necessary! Find words that sound as if they begin with X, such as eXcitable, eXpert, eXtinct, eXecrable.

The Minister's Cat is an a_____ cat and its name is A_____
" " " " a b_____ cat " " " " B_____
" " " " " c_____ cat " " " " C_____
" " " " " d_____ " " " " " D_____
" " " " an e_____ " " " " " E_____
" " " " a f_____ " " " " " F_____
" " " " " g_____ " " " " " G_____
" " " " " h_____ " " " " " H_____
" " " " an i_____ " " " " " I_____
" " " " a j_____ " " " " " J_____
" " " " " k_____ " " " " " K_____
" " " " " l_____ " " " " " L_____
" " " " " m_____ " " " " " M_____
" " " " " n_____ " " " " " N_____
" " " " an o_____ " " " " " O_____
" " " " a p_____ " " " " " P_____
" " " " " q_____ " " " " " Q_____
" " " " " r_____ " " " " " R_____
" " " " " s_____ " " " " " S_____
" " " " " t_____ " " " " " T_____
" " " " an u_____ " " " " " U_____
" " " " a v_____ " " " " " V_____
" " " " " w_____ " " " " " W_____
" " " " an(e)x_____ " " " " " X_____
" " " " a y_____ " " " " " Y_____
" " " " " z_____ " " " " " Z_____

You can change what you are writing about, if you wish.
Instead of the Minister's Cat, you might write about one of the following:

> **the neighbour's dog   our school   my house   the headteacher's car**
> **my grandfather/grandmother/mother/father/sister/brother**

What job do you think adjectives do? Write a definition of an adjective.

VERBS (1 & 2) – TEACHER'S PAGE

A Was An Apple Pie is an old rhyme, reproduced on the pupils' page, which uses the alphabet as a framework to concentrate on verbs. Ideally you would play this as a whole class first, perhaps taking one of the suggested beginnings from lower down the pupils' page. People would take it in turns to say what happened to the subject, finding verbs starting with the next letter of the alphabet, as in the examples. You can write it all down on the board as you go. It is best not to give a definition of what verbs are at this point but to wait until after you have played the game. Then you can tell pupils that the words they have been finding are called *verbs* and ask them to say what *they* think a verb is. This way the definition arises out of experience and they are far more likely to remember it. You also have a point of reference when discussing verbs at a later date. If someone cannot remember a few weeks afterwards, you can say: 'You remember! Those were the words we used when we played A Was an Apple Pie.' This will help to fix it in their minds.

When they come to write their own verbal rhymes they can be encouraged to use the dictionary. Show them how dictionary entries also give the part of speech – in this case, verbs. They are then given the confidence to find verbs and use them in their writing.

Alphabetical Actions is an activity which results in more sustained writing using verbs and is, again, based on the alphabet. The idea is to choose a setting – some suggestions are offered on the pupils' page – in which there are at least 26 people. Each one is doing something different. Pupils imagine what might be happening, and having a setting gives them a focus and unity to the piece. They must write a sentence for each letter of the alphabet where the name of the person, and the verb showing what they are doing, are the only words that *have* to begin with the appropriate letter. By now they probably know the word 'verb' and can find entries in the dictionary. Often finding a verb there will give rise to an idea of how to use it, which means that they realise that the dictionary can also be a source of inspiration. The rest of the sentence serves to paint a more detailed picture and pupils should be encouraged to expand on the basic framework to make their writing more interesting.

Be aware that going right through the alphabet can take time – this activity may not be accomplished in one lesson. You can divide the class into two, so that one half tackles A to M, and the other half does N to Z. Then you can combine different halves to create complete A–Zs. The letter X is always a problem and is best dealt with by choosing words that sound as if they begin with X, such as *expelled, exercised, or extracted*. The completed pieces can be put into an alphabet book and illustrated if you wish. This might make a good mini-project – to create a book which can then be taken and read to/with younger children.

> • Consolidation of order of alphabet • Learning about and using verbs
> • Use of dictionary for finding words and inspiration • Writing sentences
> • Collaborative work • Creative writing on a theme

· A WAS AN APPLE PIE ·

VERBS are words that make things happen. They make things move, speak, think and dream. They bring nouns to life and tell you what they are doing.

A *was* an apple pie, N *nodded* at it,
B *bit* it, O *opened* it,
C *cut* it, P *peeped* in it,
D *dealt* it, Q *quartered* it,
E *eat* it, R *ran* for it,
F *fought* for it, S *stole* it,
G *got* it, T *took* it,
H *had* it, U *upset* it,
I *inspected* it, V *viewed* it,
J *jumped* for it, W *wanted* it,
K *kept* it, X, Y, Z and ampersand (&)
L *longed* for it, All *wished* for a piece in hand.
M *mourned* for it,

Old rhyme, probably seventeenth
century

A WAS AN APPLE PIE: an oral game for two or more people

Players take it in turns to say a verb beginning with the next letter of the alphabet to show what was done to the apple pie. If someone cannot think of a verb in time, that person is out. You will probably need to cheat with X! Say words that sound as if they begin with X, such as *exterminated* or *explored*. For example:

1st player: A was an apple pie, A *asked* for it
2nd player: B *bought* it
3rd player: C *cooked* it
4th player: D *divided* it up

And so on. Play the game with a group of friends.

WRITE YOUR OWN VERBAL RHYME

Choose a subject from the suggestions below or find your own idea. Write a verb, and any other words you need, to describe what each letter of the alphabet does to your subject – the dictionary will be very useful in helping you to find appropriate verbs.

A was ... an alphabet book, an alien spaceship, an animal zoo, an athletics match, an ash tree, an Abyssinian cat, an acting school, an ambulance, an anorak.

A _____ B _____
C _____ D _____
E _____ F _____
G _____ H _____
I _____ J _____
K _____ L _____
M _____ N _____
O _____ P _____
Q _____ R _____
S _____ T _____
U _____ V _____
W _____ X _____
Y _____ Z _____

You can also use the above subjects to play the game orally.

· ALPHABETICAL ACTIONS ·

Have fun making up pictures of how people behave in different situations.

1   Imagine a place where there might be lots of people – at least 26.
     You can choose from the list below, or think of your own:

> **a day at the seaside   a class discussion   a visit to the market   a party
> a football match   the playground   the cinema   on the train/bus**

2   Write an interesting one-line sentence to describe what people are doing.
     The main verb in each line must begin with the next letter of the alphabet, but
     you can also give people names beginning with the same letter.
3   Work with a partner and write A to M on your paper and N to Z on your
     friend's.
     You can use the dictionary to help you find suitable verbs.

EXAMPLE: 'On the Ferry'

Anadil *acted* as though she had been at sea all her life,
Boris *believed* they were all going to drown,
Chris *chanced* leaning over the side just that bit too far,
Denzil *decided* to eat all his sandwiches before they were out of the harbour,
Ellen *entertained* everyone by pretending to be sick … etc.

Now you have a go.

(Title) _____

_____
_____
_____
_____
_____
_____
_____
_____
_____
_____
_____
_____
_____
_____
_____
_____

ADVERBS AND PREPOSITIONS

The Adverb Game is a well-known drama game for loosening up at the beginning of a session. How it is played is set out on the pupils' page and should be clear. It is fun to play and helps pupils to realise the job an adverb does. Depending on the adverb used, the tone and mode of behaviour can differ. So, adverbs can be said to be descriptive – it is not only adjectives that describe, both verbs and adverbs do as well! This game will also help pupils gain confidence in doing things in front of other people, as well as encouraging improvisation in drama.

Tom Swifties are also known as **Apt Adverbs**. Again, these are described on the pupil's page and should be easy to understand. They obviously belong to the area of jokes and wordplay, as do other activities in this book, namely homophones (see page 35), spoonerisms (see page 26), palindromes (see page 27) and punny book titles (see page 28). Any good examples made up by pupils should be added to the class joke book which will be a record of language being used in different ways. The enjoyment pupils have in doing this is important in forming their perception of English. We all like to have a laugh and are more likely to remember what we have learnt if it has been fun to do. This is one reason why word games are so important as an approach to understanding language.

Prepositions. The simplest use of prepositions is dealt with here – i.e. those prepositions that tell us where something is physically in relation to something else. (It does not deal with the problems that arise with other prepositions, such as *to, for, by, with* and *from* – some of the shortest words in English which cause pedants to become very hot under the collar! For example, purists would say that it is '*different from*', but you are more likely to hear '*different to*' or even '*different than*' these days. Likewise, it should be '*He gave it to you and me*', but we increasingly hear '*He gave it to you and I*'. The language changes constantly and common usage dictates what will survive. Even though the second example is based on a misunderstanding added to lack of knowledge about the dative case, it is gradually gaining ground.)

Enough of that! The activity on the pupils' page is really a writing exercise which serves to highlight the job of the simple prepositions. Depending on the prepositions you use, you are forced to look at something from a different angle. By writing about a subject in this way, pupils are given a framework for writing a detailed description. The result is a sustained description which forces them to dwell on their subject instead of skirting over it as they too often do. It makes them look hard and mine the subject for all possibilities. Anything that can give them practice in doing this will be useful for their future writing. And because it is written two lines at a time they do not lose the thread of what they are trying to say. Interruptions, or even breaks from one lesson to the next, will not affect the continuity of the piece.

- Understanding and use of adverbs ● Wordplay ● Drama activity
- Understanding and use of prepositions of place ● Creative writing ● Seeing a subject from different angles ● Another approach to writing descriptions

• THE ADVERB GAME •

ADVERBS tell us HOW something is done. They always go with verbs. For example: You did that *well*; He laughed *uproariously* at all my jokes; *Luckily* I was rescued; The cat was *spectacularly* sick after eating a whole carton of cream!

THE ADVERB GAME: a group game

1 One or two people leave the room. The rest of the group agree on an adverb.
2 Those outside are called back and have to guess what the adverb is. They do this by asking members of the group to act out a task **in the manner of the adverb**; for example, sing baa baa black sheep **in the manner of the adverb**, or, eat your dinner **in the manner of the adverb**, or walk round the room with a man-eating tiger **in the manner of the adverb**.
3 People can guess as soon as they think they know. Some adverbs which might be useful are:

> **grumpily stupidly reluctantly hilariously wildly silently sleepily slowly**

• TOM SWIFTIES •

Also known as Apt Adverbs, the aim of this game is to make up sentences in which the adverb, used to describe how someone said something, is an amusing and witty pun. For example:

'I'd better take you to Casualty,' said Mary *hospitably*.
'A fortnight's too long,' she moaned *weakly*.
'Shouldn't we camp here for the night?' she asked *intently*.
'I've always wanted a dog,' he said *impetuously*.
'It's about time I had my hair cut,' he said *gruesomely*.
'A visit to the dentist will do you good,' Mum insisted *bracingly*.
'Star Wars was a great film,' he said *forcefully*.

Try writing your own Tom Swifties. Make up sentences to go with the adverbs below, and then find some of your own.

_____ she said *hoarsely*.
_____ he asked *gravely*.
_____ said John *woodenly*.
_____ she murmured *saucily*.
_____ he answered *doggedly*.

_____
_____
_____
_____
_____

• PREPOSITIONS •

A PREPOSITION is a word placed before a noun (or pronoun) to show what is happening in relation to that noun. For example: *to* and *for*, as in I gave the book *to* the librarian; The party was especially *for* you and me.

Several prepositions tell us <u>where</u> something is in relation to something else. Each preposition makes us look at something from a different angle or position. For example:

> **in   on   over   under   beside   behind   above   below   through**

Can you add any more to this list? _____

_____

Use these prepositions to help you write a description of something.

1   Write about something you can see from where you are working, for example:

> **the tree   the window   the door   the cupboard   my desk/table**
>
> **the teacher   the playground   the picture**

2   Choose a preposition from the list and place it before your subject to start your first line. Now write two lines to describe what you can see, for example:
     Outside the window the sun is shining through the broken clouds,
     Shadows flicker across the ground like frowns across a forehead;

3   Choose a different preposition to begin your next line and do the same thing, for example:
     Inside the window we sit dreaming of long summer beach days,
     Building castles, collecting shells, and swimming with seals;

4   Continue writing your description in the same way, using a different preposition each time – you do not have to use them all!

_____

_____

_____

_____

_____

_____

_____

_____

_____

_____

_____

_____

_____

_____

THE EXQUISITE CORPSE – TEACHER'S PAGE

The Exquisite Corpse was the name given to a game invented and played by Dadaist artists. It is a way of creating memorable images purely by chance.

The way they used to play was similar to a game of Consequences. Each person had a sheet of paper. Everyone would write down an article (*a* or *the*) in the top left-hand corner. They would then fold the papers vertically behind, so that the words could not be seen, and pass them on to the next person. Each would then write an adjective, fold behind, and pass on. These were followed by other parts of speech in an order that would make up a sentence. A simple example might be the following pattern: article / adjective / noun / verb / preposition / article / adjective / noun (e.g. a cunning bed sang to the fearsome feather).

After the papers had gone round and the sentences were completed, they would open them up and read out what they had created by chance. Incongruous and often very exciting images were made this way and could be used for creative work.

We can do this, too, and the images can give ideas for writing poems or stories. Some sentences will seem to have uncovered a real truth about life in a way that we would never have thought of on our own. Chance can be a great inspiration in creative writing.

However, whether you can play the game as described above will depend on your pupils' level of knowledge about sentence grammar, as well as the readability of their handwriting. Younger, and less able, pupils will find it easier to play the game one of two other ways which are set out on the pupils' page.

The activities there have been kept simple – using only adjectives, verbs and nouns – but you can make them more complicated if you wish and it is appropriate. Hence, the piece of paper they use could have more columns and employ other parts of speech. For example: article / adjective / noun / verb / adverb / preposition / article / adjective / adjective / noun (e.g. the respectable mudflat shot languidly through the fluffy automatic pig).

Pupils will need good dictionaries which give the parts of speech. They can be encouraged to find words here. This is another way of helping them to feel at home with the dictionary and to realise how it can enhance their writing. As long as they know what parts of speech they are looking for they will have the confidence to use the book. They will soon realise what a friend the dictionary can be!

With the **Lucky Dip** approach (with boxes) you can divide the class into three groups if this seems more appropriate. Each group will find words of a specific part of speech, write them on slips of paper and put them in the relevant box. Then the whole class can join in the fun of creating the sentences by taking it in turns to have a lucky dip.

> • **Sentence structure** • **Creative writing/making images by chance** • **Use of dictionary** • **Consolidating knowledge of parts of speech** • **Having fun with language**

• THE EXQUISITE CORPSE •

The title of this game comes from a similar game invented by a group of artists who liked to experiment with ways of creating unusual images. The effects are based on chance, but can surprise you with the fun and originality of the word pictures. Here is one way you can play like this with language.

CONSEQUENCES: for one player

Fold a piece of paper into five columns. Each column is headed with a part of speech.

ADJECTIVE	NOUN	VERB	ADJECTIVE	NOUN
1				
2				
3				
4				
5				
6				
7				
8				
9				
10				

1 Write ten adjectives in the first column. Then fold back the paper so you cannot see what you have written.
2 Write ten nouns in the second column and fold back.
3 Write ten verbs in the third column. Fold back.
4 Write ten adjectives in the fourth column. Fold back.
5 Write ten nouns in the fifth column. Now unfold the whole paper.

Read out the sentences across each line, putting in words like *a*, *the*, *under*, and *behind* wherever you need them to help the sentence make sense. For example:

	ADJECTIVE	NOUN	VERB	ADJECTIVE	NOUN
1	lazy	pumpkin	crept	enigmatic	ferret
2	velvet	candle	disappeared	borrowed	cloud
3	simple	fox	sings	blue	pyjamas

1 *A* lazy pumpkin crept *behind an* enigmatic ferret.
2 *The* velvet candle disappeared *under a* borrowed cloud.
3 *A* simple fox sings *about his* blue pyjamas.

What sort of words are *under*, *behind*, *in*, *on*, *over*, *beside*, *through*, *about* etc.? What job do they do in a sentence? Can you think of some more? Look in the dictionary to find what part of speech they are.

Choose your best sentences from above and illustrate them. You could even make a picture book.

• LUCKY DIP •

LUCKY DIP is a way of playing The Exquisite Corpse with a group of friends. You will need three cardboard boxes. Label one for nouns, one for adjectives and one for verbs:

1   Divide your group/class into three smaller groups.
2   Each small group will look for a different part of speech – either nouns, adjectives or verbs. It is easiest to work in pairs within each group.
3   Look in the dictionary to find your part of speech. Look for the word 'noun', 'adjective' or 'verb' which is printed after a word. For example:

ant (noun) a small insect   **glad** (adjective) pleased, happy

shout (verb) to call out loud   **poor** (adjective) having little or nothing

4   Write each word you and your partner find on separate slips of paper and put them in the correct boxes. Do this for about 20 minutes.
5   Then, take it in turns to pull out words in order, and write them into the grid.

ADJECTIVE	NOUN	VERB	ADJECTIVE	NOUN

Read out your 'chance' sentences, adding words like *a, the, in, on, under, behind, beside, over,* as needed, to help the sentences make sense.

SECTION 3

WRITING AND POETRY-BASED GAMES AND EXERCISES

NEW WORDS FOR OLD (1) – TEACHER'S PAGE

The next two pages look at ways of making up new words for things, or of using established words to stand for other things.

New Counting Systems. It is said that years ago shepherds used to make up their own counting systems for counting the sheep every day. This may have been to vary the routine for them. It also must be said that some of these counting systems were probably from local dialects. Some of the words in the list below bear a marked resemblance to the Welsh words for one to ten, for example.

WELSH				SHEPHERD'S			
1	un	6	chwech		1	aina	6	ithy
2	dau	7	saith		2	peina	7	mithy
3	tri	8	wyth		3	par	8	owera
4	pedwar	9	naw		4	peddera	9	lowera
5	pum	10	deg		5	pimp	10	dig

When pupils make up their own systems around a theme, they will need to say them aloud to hear whether they run to an easy rhythm. If any part is awkward to say, they will need to choose another word.

You might ask if any of your pupils can count to ten in another language. It can be interesting to compare the different words for each number and look for similarities.

Ladles and Jellyspoons. The full text of this rhyme is printed on page 70. (It is basically a nonsense rhyme which works by using the language of opposites.) The phrase, *Ladles and Jellyspoons*, stands for *Ladies and Gentlemen*. Pupils can play around with words in the same way by finding others that *sound like* the originals. The words they choose must exist. They must first choose a phrase which has two parts, such as *brothers and sisters*, and then replace the main words with two others which also go together in some way. It is somewhat like Cockney rhyming slang (see page 78). For example: brothers and sisters – bubbles and blisters; chalk and cheese – talk and tease.

Why not collect playground counting rhymes for dipping or skipping? These also use made-up words, for exampe, 'eeny meeny mackeracker air I dominacker' etc.

> ● **Playing with language** ● **Hearing rhyme** ● **Hearing rhythm** ● **Finding phrases of matching pairs** ● **Other languages** ● **Playground rhymes**

Ladles and Jellyspoons

Ladles and jellyspoons:
I come before you
To stand behind you
And tell you something
I know nothing about.

Next Thursday,
The day after Friday,
There'll be a ladies' meeting
For men only.

Wear your best clothes
If you haven't any,
And if you can come
Please stay at home.

Admission is free,
You can pay at the door.
We'll give you a seat
So you can sit on the floor.

It makes no difference
Where you sit;
The kid in the gallery
Is sure to spit.

Traditional English rhyme

• NEW COUNTING SYSTEMS •

Back in history shepherds sometimes made up new counting systems for themselves. They often had to count their sheep and it was probably more interesting for them to count in different ways. Here are two examples of how they counted from one to ten:

1	een	aina
2	teen	peina
3	tuther	par
4	futher	peddera
5	fip	pimp
6	sother	ithy
7	lother	mithy
8	porter	owera
9	dubber	lowera
10	dick	dig

MAKE UP your own new counting systems with favourite words or words on a theme. You can use the dictionary to help you. Say them aloud to yourself to make sure they have a good rhythm and are easy to say quickly.

EXAMPLES		MAKE UP YOUR OWN	
Favourite words	**Animals**		
1 ooze	ox	1 _____	1 _____
2 toddle	tiger	2 _____	2 _____
3 tango	weasel	3 _____	3 _____
4 fumble	ferret	4 _____	4 _____
5 filch	fox	5 _____	5 _____
6 splutter	camel	6 _____	6 _____
7 clutter	lion	7 _____	7 _____
8 butter	llama	8 _____	8 _____
9 wriggle	lemur	9 _____	9 _____
10 rump	pig	10 _____	10 _____

LADLES AND JELLYSPOONS

Ladles and Jellyspoons is a SOUNDALIKE phrase for *Ladies and Gentlemen*.

Your teacher will read you the rhyme from which this comes. MAKE UP some new soundalike phrases of your own. Find a phrase with two connected parts, for example, *uncles and aunts*; *brothers and sisters*. Then replace it with soundalike words which are also connected, for example, *chuckles and grunts*; *bubbles and blisters*.

NEW WORDS FOR OLD (2) – TEACHER'S PAGE

Portmanteau Words. A portmanteau word is one made from the parts of two (or more) other words. Lewis Carroll's famous poem, '*Jabberwocky*' (from *Through the Looking-Glass and What Alice Found There*), has examples of all sorts of made up words, including portmanteau words. This is always a popular poem with pupils and can inspire them to write their own. One of the reasons why '*Jabberwocky*' is so successful is that although there are many nonsense-type words, readers still understand in essence what is happening. The invented words are strategically placed within normal structures and although we might be hard pushed to explain in detail what each one means, we know instinctively. It is worth looking at this with pupils so that when they come to write their own poems they will not be tempted to make the whole thing nonsense.

Not all the words in '*Jabberwocky*' are portmanteau. We can look at some that are and see how Carroll made them from parts of other words. *Slithy* is made from *lithe* and *slimy*. The two words are compressed so that their two meanings are packed into the one word. *Galumph* is made from *gallop* and *triumph* and means 'to bound along exultantly'.

We still make up words in this way which eventually enter the language and the dictionaries. For example:

brunch   from a combination of *breakfast* and *lunch*

Oxbridge   from a combination of *Oxford* and *Cambridge*

Introduce pupils to the portmanteau word and practise making some up together. For example:

shicker (to *shout* and *bicker*);
crangry (*cross* and *angry*);
froad (a cross between a *frog* and a *toad*);
quilent (*silent* and *quiet*);
lairy (*light* and *airy*).

Then they can attempt to write their own poems using words they make up.

● **Creative writing**   ● **Making up new words**   ● **Language play**

Jabberwocky

'Twas brillig, and the slithy toves
Did gyre and gimble in the wabe;
All mimsy were the borogoves,
And the mome raths outgrabe.

'Beware the Jabberwock, my son!
The jaws that bite, the claws that catch!
Beware the Jubjub bird, and shun
The frumious Bandersnatch!'

He took his vorpal sword in hand:
Long time the manxome foe he sought –
So rested he by the Tumtum tree,
And stood awhile in thought.

And as in uffish thought he stood,
The Jabberwock, with eyes of flame,
Came whiffling through the tulgey wood,
And burbled as it came!

One, two! One, two! And through and through
The vorpal blade went snicker-snack!
He left it dead, and with its head
He went galumphing back.

'And hast thou slain the Jabberwock!
Come to my arms, my beamish boy!
O frabjous day! Callooh! Callay!'
He chortled in his joy.

'Twas brillig, and the slithy toves
Did gyre and gimble in the wabe;
All mimsy were the borogoves,
And the mome raths outgrabe.

Lewis Carroll (from *Through the Looking-Glass,* and *What Alice Found There*)

READ this poem with a friend. What happens in the poem? Make a list of all the words you think Lewis Carroll made up. You might want to learn the poem by heart.

_____

_____

_____

_____

_____

_____

_____

_____

_____

_____

• PORTMANTEAU WORDS •

In his famous poem, *'Jabberwocky'*, Lewis Carroll uses many made-up words.

Some of them are called PORTMANTEAU words because they pack more than one meaning. (A portmanteau is an item of luggage into which you pack things.) For example:

slithy comes from *lithe* and *slimy* and combines both meanings
mimsy comes from *flimsy* and *miserable*
galumph comes from *gallop* and *triumph* and means 'to bound along exultantly'

MAKE UP YOUR OWN PORTMANTEAU WORDS

1   Start by choosing from the following lists of words, and then find your own.
2   Choose two words (they may come from two different parts of speech).
3   Take part of one and add it to part of the other to make a new word.
4   Write a definition of what it might mean.

NOUNS   giraffe telephone ballerina horse trumpet thistle lorry
             catapult camera hurricane duvet pillow chocolate robot

ADJECTIVES happy beautiful upright single delightful unusual
             reliable charming naughty knobbly grumpy wrinkled

VERBS   to wander to remember to warble to brandish to juggle
             to somersault to writhe to chew to screech to cycle

FIRST WORD	SECOND WORD	NEW WORD	MEANING
brandish	juggle	to bruggle	to show off how clever you are
telephone	grumpy	telegrump	

Now try to write your own poem which tells a story and uses some of your new words. Notice that Lewis Carroll does not use invented words all the time. This makes it easier for readers to feel they understand what is happening.

RHYME GAMES – TEACHER'S PAGE

Most poetry for children is written in rhyme. So, naturally, when writing their own poetry, children often want to rhyme. The problem with this, though, is that they cannot usually do it very well. They tend to use any old word that rhymes, regardless of whether it makes sense – the 'moon, June, prune' syndrome. For example:

> **I walked beneath the silvery moon,**
> **One sultry evening in June,**
> **And then I ate a stewed prune!**

It is generally better for children to concentrate on other poetic techniques when writing, such as alliteration, rhythm, syllabics and patterned language, and to forget rhyme altogether unless it occurs naturally. What they have to *say* is the most important aspect in the earlier stages.

However, rhyme is an attractive technique, and one of the best ways of helping children to think about its implications, and how to find appropriate rhymes, is to play some rhyme games. There are two particular games which work well at this level.

The first is **Mime the Rhyme**, in which one group of children (around four) leaves the room. They decide on a word that the rest of the class will have to guess (e.g. *key*). When they return to the room they tell the others that the word rhymes with, say, *three*. Members of the class then think of words that rhyme with this *sound* and mime them. Possible words might be *tree, sea, flea, me, bee, tea, free*, etc. The group of four must watch each mime, identify the word that is being depicted, and then say, for example, either 'No, it isn't *tree*.' 'No, it isn't *bee*.' or 'Yes, it is *key*.'

Clearly it is better if the small group chooses a word for which there are a number of rhymes as this will make the game more interesting. Playing a game like this gives children the opportunity to practise finding a number of rhymes for a sound and alerts them to the fact that, in English, there are some sounds for which there are several rhymes, many for which there are only a few, and others for which there are no full rhymes at all. Later, when they come to use rhyme in their own writing, they will have some knowledge of the sounds to avoid and those which will give them more scope. For example, it would definitely be a mistake to try rhyme with the word *elephant*, but more productive to use a word like *cat* or *bear*.

I'd Rather ... Than ... Is explained on the pupils' page and should be played orally first, as a whole class – perhaps two or three times with different words. After this the children can be encouraged to write their own versions where they have to think of all the rhymes themselves – they can work in pairs, too, if they want.

The best of these will be those that have really explored all the possible rhymes, so do not let them give in after only a few. The longer the piece, the more the children will have learnt about how to find and use rhymes.

● **Hearing and finding rhymes** ● **Writing in rhyme**

• I'D RATHER … THAN … •

This is an oral game which you can play with a group of friends. One person says a sentence on the pattern of *I'd rather … than …* For example:

1st person: I'd rather have silver than *gold*

The last word sets the rhyme for the whole game. Everyone must now take it in turns to say a sentence on the same pattern but with a different rhyme. For example:

2nd person: I'd rather be young than *old*
3rd person: I'd rather drink tea hot than *cold*
4th person: I'd rather run away than be *bold*, etc.

This continues until there is one person left in the game who is the winner. People are out if (a) they cannot think of a new word or (b) they repeat a word already used.

HOW TO FIND RHYMES

The best way is to run through the alphabet in your mind putting different letters in front of the sound to make words: *bold, cold, fold, gold, hold, mould, old, polled, rolled, sold, told, wold*. Then move on to more than one consonant letter: *scold*. Then to two-syllable words: *behold, cajoled, withhold, untold, consoled*. Then three-syllable words: *marigold, centrefold, Cumbernauld*. And so on.

a b c d e f g h i j k l m n o p q r s t u v w x y z

NOW WRITE YOUR OWN VERSION OF THIS GAME. See how long a piece you can write. How many rhymes can you find?

I'd rather have coffee	than *tea*
I'd rather	than
I'd rather	than
I'd rather	than
I'd rather	than
I'd rather	than
I'd rather	than
I'd rather	than
I'd rather	than
I'd rather	than
I'd rather	than
I'd rather	than
I'd rather	than
I'd rather	than
I'd rather	than

RHYMING COMPOUNDS AND RHYMING SLANG – TEACHER'S PAGE

Rhyming compounds abound in English – more than you might think. This is probably because rhyme is pleasing on the ear and helps to make things more memorable.

Words like *hugger-mugger, humdrum, hotchpotch, hoity-toity, abracadabra, namby-pamby, hurdy-gurdy, helter-skelter, hocus-pocus, niminy-piminy, willy-nilly* and *roly-poly* all have a satisfying ring to them when spoken; some are even magical (abracadabra and hocus-pocus). Several are also onomatopoeic or at least expressive in some way of what they are describing.

Such rhyming compounds are used frequently in nursery rhymes, stories and comics for the very reason that they are fun to say and easy to remember. Rhyme always appeals to children. Such names as Humpty Dumpty, Andy Pandy, Henny Penny, Incey Wincey Spider, Beryl the Peril, Dennis the Menace, Roger the Dodger and the like, have been part of many children's early literary experiences! (Alliteration – another form of rhyme – is also popular, as in Postman Pat, Desperate Dan, Teletubbies, Roland Rat, Peter Pan, and Bob the Builder.)

We still coin new rhyming compounds today, such as *arty-farty, gender-bender, sinbin, bigwig, hotshot, AllyPally* (Alexandra Palace), *desres* (<u>des</u>irable <u>res</u>idence), *hifi* (<u>hi</u>gh <u>fi</u>delity).

Ask your pupils to see how many rhyming compounds they can find. A trawl through a decent dictionary will yield quite a number – interestingly several begin with the letter H. They can work alone or in pairs.

They may also find **tautonyms** – compounds using exactly the same rhyme word, such as tom-tom, cancan, dumdum, beriberi, hulahula, gogo, never-never; or **vowel-change compounds**, such as shilly-shally, flipflop, jingle-jangle, ding-dong.

Rhyming slang usually refers to the secret language made up by street sellers in London during the Victorian era. It was just one of the ways they devised to communicate with each other so that customers could not understand what they were saying. It is known as Cockney rhyming slang, as most of the costermongers were from the East End of London. Thieves also made use of rhyming slang to keep plans secret from informers and from the police.

Some of the rhyming compounds above might also be said to be slang expressions, particularly the modern ones. Slang, although not always acceptable in polite company or written work, is nevertheless very colourful and a lively use of language.

The next exercise introduces pupils to Cockney rhyming slang and encourages them to make up some of their own. Apart from the fun of doing this, pupils will be practising hearing and using rhyme – thus training their ear and laying the foundations for future writing when they may wish to employ rhyme.

> ● **Research using the dictionary** ● **Finding and hearing rhyme** ● **Creative writing**

•RHYMING COMPOUNDS AND RHYMING SLANG •

Rhyming compounds are words made of two rhyming parts, such as:

> **hugger-mugger   hobnob   abracadabra   Humpty Dumpty   teeny-weeny**

Look through a good dictionary to see how many you can find. There are actually quite a number. Several begin with the letter H.

COCKNEY RHYMING SLANG is the term applied to the secret language made up by London street sellers in Victorian times so they could hold conversations without their customers knowing what they were saying. It was also used by petty thieves to stop informers or the police knowing what they were planning! It is still used today by all sorts of people, particularly some Londoners, but not for the original reasons!

Rhyming slang has two parts and the whole phrase rhymes with the word it conceals:

> ***apples and pears*** = stairs   ***tea leaf*** = thief
>
> ***jam jar*** = car   ***whistle and flute*** = suit

Sometimes only the first part is said: He went down the *apples* in his new *whistle*. New rhyming slang has been added over the years, often using the names of well-known people of the times. For example, *Ruby Murray* = curry (Ruby Murray was a singer).

This rhyme uses many rhyming slang phrases. Can you work out what they mean?

As she walked along the street with her little plates of meat
And the summer sunshine falling on her golden Barnet Fair,
Bright as angels from the skies were her dark blue Mutton Pies;
In my East and West Dan Cupid shot a shaft and left it there.

She'd a Grecian I suppose and of Hampstead Heath two rows,
In her Sunny South they glistened like two pretty strings of pearls,
Down upon my bread and cheese did I drop and murmur, 'Please
Be my storm and strife, dear Tottie, O, you darlingest of girls.'

Then a bow wow by her side who 'til then had stood and tried
A Jenny Lee to banish, which was on his Jonah's Whale,
Gave a hydrophobia bark, she cried, 'What a Noah's Ark,'
And right through my rank and riches did my cribbage pegs assail.

Ere her bulldog I could stop she had called a ginger pop
Who said, 'What the Henry Meville do you think you're doing there?'
And I heard as off I slunk, 'Why, the fellow's Jumbo's trunk.'
And the Walter Joyce was Tottie's with the golden Barnet Fair …
Traditional.

Find the phrases that mean the following words:

> voice   mouth   wife   devil   feet   tail   legs   eyes   nose
>
> britches   breast   cop   lark   hair   knees   drunk   flea   teeth

MAKE UP some new rhyming phrases of your own. Remember, the two parts should be linked in some way. For example, *mutton pies*, *rabbit and pork* (talk), *butcher's hook* (look). Or they should use names of people or places. For example, *Uncle Dick* (sick), *Barnet Fair*, *Jenny Lee*, *Khyber Pass* (a rhyming part of the body!), Would you *Adam* and *Eve* (believe) it!

RHYME TENNIS (1 & 2) – TEACHER'S PAGE

Simple Rhyme Tennis. Both Rhyme Tennis games give practice in finding rhymes. The more pupils do this before they are asked to use rhyme in their writing, the better. Such practice enables people to realise much about the nature of rhyme, and how, in English, a surprisingly large number of words do not actually have any full rhymes. (A full rhyme is where the word chimes exactly on the ear, as with *simple*, *pimple* and *dimple*; half rhymes are where part of the word echoes the sound, for example in *simple*, *ample*, *crumple* and *temple*.) These rhyme games will also help to train the ear to hear full rhymes, something which not all children can do immediately. They often supply half rhymes without realising. The more musical pupils will usually find this easier to do since there is obviously a strong connection between music and poetry, both in rhyme which is akin to harmony, and in metre which is a sense of rhythm and equates with time signature.

Both games are scored as in lawn tennis, as the examples on each pupils' page show. Play the games as a class first, perhaps even a number of times, so that pupils become familiar with how to play. This can be done by dividing the class into two teams. This will also give you an opportunity to point out (gently) where rhymes are not full. Often children will not hear the difference between 'N' and 'M' and will try to rhyme, say, *home* with *bone*, or *time* with *line*. If they do this, it is a good idea to show how such words do not rhyme fully, but to boost pupils' confidence by telling them they have used another rhyming technique which you had not planned to tackle yet, namely half rhyme. This will stop other children from scoffing at them and make them feel they are one step ahead. It should also help them learn the difference between rhyme and half rhyme. Simple Rhyme Tennis only demands one rhyming word each time and should enable all pupils to take part. The way to win is to find words for which there are no rhymes, as well as finding rhymes for your opponent's words. This will also help pupils' later writing since it is as well to be aware that it is not a good idea to end a line with a word such as *elephant* if you are intending to use rhyme. Such practice will inform their later choices. (You can also play Rhyme Tennis using half rhymes instead so that everyone has to practise these too.)

Rhyme Tennis. The second version of this game differs in that players must find as many rhyming words as possible in order to stay in the game. Once a word has been said, a rally follows with players 'batting' rhymes to and fro until one player cannot think of one. They then lose a point. Just as in lawn tennis, players take it in turns to serve for a whole game. Decide in advance how many sets (1 to 5) are to played. If a player serves a word which has no rhyme, that would be considered an ace. However, the same word cannot be use again during the whole match. The game should be played as fast as possible which will keep them on their toes! Again, play this first with two class teams, before they try it amongst themselves. Hearing what other people say is also a good way of training the ear to hear rhymes.

> • **Practice in finding rhymes** • **Introduction of full and half rhyme as poetic techniques** • **Realisation of the potential and limitations of rhymes in English**

• SIMPLE RHYME TENNIS •

This is a rhyme game for two people which is played and scored rather like lawn tennis. Rallies go as follows:

The first player serves (i.e. says) a word.

The second player must return the service by saying a word which rhymes, followed by a new word of their own choosing.

The first player then replies with a rhyming word and another new word.

This goes on until a player cannot find a rhyme. The other player scores points, and then begins another serve. A player wins a set when they are winning 6 games to 4 or less, or 7 games to 6. You can play a 3-set match, or a 5-set match. Any winning words you serve (e.g. *elephant,* as shown below) can only be used *once* in each *match*.

EXAMPLE

1st player serves:	HOPE	
2nd player returns:	ROPE and RIGHT	
1st player:	FIGHT and SIMPLE	
2nd player:	PIMPLE and ELEPHANT	
1st player:	? (no rhyme)	Score: Love–15
2nd player serves:	GAME	
1st player returns:	NAME and RAVIOLI	
2nd player:	? (no rhyme)	Score: 15 All
1st player serves:	PRINCE	
2nd player returns:	RINSE and GRUNGE	
1st player:	LUNGE and HIPPOPOTAMUS	
2nd player:	? (no rhyme)	Score: 30–15
1st player serves:	INTERGALACTIC	
2nd player returns:	? (no rhyme)	Score: 40–15
1st player serves:	STINGING	
2nd player returns:	RINGING and SILVER	
1st player:	? (no rhyme)	Score: 40–30
2nd player serves:	SLENDER	
1st player returns:	TENDER and PLUMP	
2nd player:	LUMP and COTTON	
1st player:	FORGOTTEN and CLOCK	
2nd player:	LOCK and SAUSAGE	
1st player:	? (no rhyme)	Score: Deuce
2nd player serves:	PIG	
1st player returns:	BIG and ALGEBRA	
2nd player:	? (no rhyme)	Score: Advantage 1st Player
1st player serves:	NORTHERN	
2nd player returns:	? (no rhyme)	Game! To 1st Player

NEW GAME 2nd player to serve.

PLAY SIMPLE RHYME TENNIS against a friend. REMEMBER YOU MUST keep the game going so you cannot spend time thinking of words to say. You must say each word quite quickly. If you take too long, you will be out and your opponent will win the game.

• RHYME TENNIS •

Another rhyme game for two people, this is a variation on Simple Rhyme Tennis.

The object is to keep rallies going with the SAME RHYME for as long as possible. When a player cannot find a rhyme the point is lost. One player serves throughout a whole game, the other player serves throughout the next game.

Scoring is the same as for any lawn tennis game. A set is over when a player has won 6 games to 4 or less, or 7 games to 6. Matches can be 3 sets or 5 sets long. Games must be played quite fast!

EXAMPLE

1st player serves:	REAL
2nd player:	FEEL
1st player:	KNEEL
2nd player:	SEAL
1st player:	KEEL
2nd player:	WHEEL
1st player:	DEAL
2nd player:	MEAL
1st player:	STEAL
2nd player:	? (no rhyme) 15–Love
1st player serves:	THINK
2nd player:	PINK
1st player:	STINK
2nd player:	WINK
1st player:	DRINK
2nd player:	? (no rhyme) 30–Love
1st player serves:	LOVE
2nd player:	GLOVE
1st player:	ABOVE
2nd player:	? (no rhyme) 40–Love
1st player serves:	BABY
2nd player:	MAYBE
1st player:	? (no rhyme) 40–15
1st player serves:	WISH
2nd player:	DISH
1st player:	FISH
2nd player:	SWISH
1st player:	? (no rhyme) 40–30
1st player serves:	WIGGLE
2nd player:	WRIGGLE
1st player:	GIGGLE
2nd player:	? (no rhyme) Game! To 1st Player

NEW GAME: 2nd player to serve.

PLAY RHYME TENNIS against a friend. How long can you keep the rhyme rallies going? Some words have many rhymes, others very few – and some have none!

QUESTIONS, BATTLE LINES AND ONOMATOPOEIA – TEACHER'S PAGE

Questions is really a writing game of invention. It is fun to play and should encourage pupils to use their imaginations, both in the phrasing of the question and in the subsequent answers they give. The reason for swapping questions is to make it more interesting. Answering someone else's question is often easier than trying to answer your own. It is the answers that need to be inventive, not necessarily the questions, although imaginative questions are more likely to elicit imaginative answers.

For example, '*Why am I here?*' is a fairly straightforward question which could be answered in a number of ways ranging from '*Because the law says I have to come to school*' to '*In order to prove that the rest of you are alive*' or '*I'm not really – I'm a figment of your imagination*'.

'*How do worms sing?*' might result in '*In a very earthy way*' or '*They duet with themselves*' or '*Mouthing the words silently so the hedgehogs won't hear them*'.

It can sometimes take pupils a few tries at this game to get into the swing of it. They need to be able to let themselves go and take risks. Do not despair if it does not work first time. It is really worth trying it again a few times – they will get better at it.

The variation which is suggested at the bottom of the pupils' page is fascinating to do, but should only be tried after they are familiar with playing it the first way. As with any consequences game, sometimes it will work and sometimes not. However, it is surprising what can emerge purely by chance!

Battle Lines is best played as a team game, although it works well with two people as suggested on the pupils' page. It concentrates on likes and dislikes, or loves and hates, and forces pupils to think long and deeply about the subject. This will be helpful for later writing as it gives practice in dwelling on a subject instead of skirting over it as so many children do. The resulting list can be considered to be a poem which is based on alternative views of something. It is fun to play but its more serious intent is to encourage pupils to think about something in very great detail.

Onomatopoeia is a language technique where words in some way reproduce the sound of what they are describing. The effect may be produced by individual words, such as those suggested on the pupils' page, or via a cumulative effect achieved by a number of words with repeated letter sounds, as suggested at the bottom of the pupils' page, about the sea. This might also include alliteration. For example, *She sells seashells on the seashore* is both alliterative and onomatopoeic – reproducing the shushing sounds of the tide on the shore and within a shell when held to the ear.

The pupil's page is designed to alert children firstly to the term, 'onomatopoeia' through obvious animal sounds, and then to get them to consider other 'sound' words, such as *murmur* and *grumble*. It is then suggested that they write a piece where the sounds of the words used help to suggest what is being written about. Other subjects might include, *an electric storm, milking time on the farm, bathtime, a summer breeze, the washing machine, traffic jam, an owl hunting, a hurricane, the flood, cooking.*

> ● Introduction to, and reinforcement of, question words ● Use of imagination in writing ● Looking in detail at a subject from different angles ● Understanding and use of onomatopoeia as a writing technique

· QUESTIONS ·

The main question words are *how? when? what? why? where? who?* and *which?*

We can also ask questions by changing the order of words in a sentence. For example:

He is the boy who is coming to Anna's party = a statement
Is he the boy who is coming to Anna's party? = a question

Practise writing questions by playing QUESTIONS.

1   WRITE down eight questions using the eight types of question described above. Try to make up unusual questions, although any question will be all right because it is the answers that are the most creative.
2   Now swap papers with a friend and answer each other's questions. Try to be as inventive as possible with your answers.

1   HOW _____?

_____

2   WHEN _____?

_____

3   WHAT _____?

_____

4   WHY _____?

_____

5   WHERE _____?

_____

6   WHO _____?

_____

7   WHICH _____?

_____

8   _____?

_____

Now swap papers back and read out both questions and answers. Collect the best ones together into a piece of creative writing, or use one idea for writing a poem.

A VARIATION on this game is played like consequences. Each person writes down a question in the first space. (You will be asking seven questions in all using the same order as at the top of the page). They fold it back so the question cannot be seen and pass the paper on. Then, each person writes down an answer to a possible question beginning with HOW? and then writes a question in the second space. Each time the papers are passed on, the questions are folded back out of sight. At the end, the paper is unfolded and read out. It can be fascinating, and often amusing, to see what interesting ideas emerge purely by chance!

• BATTLE LINES •

BATTLE LINES is a writing game for two or more people.

1   Choose a subject about which there are strong feelings, either for or against.
2   One person (or a small group) writes ten positive things about the subject, beginning with the words 'What I love about ...'
3   The other person (or small group) writes ten negative things about the subject, beginning with the words 'What I hate about ...' When you are finished, face each other and take it in turns to shout out each of your lines. The person (or group) with the most persuasive arguments wins.
4   Write out the whole piece, alternating positive and negative lines, to make a poem.

EXAMPLE

1st: What I love about cats is the way they can scratch very fast behind their ears.
2nd: What I hate about cats is that they will insist on scratching the furniture.
1st: What I love about cats is that they purr very loudly when they are contented.
2nd: What I hate about cats is when they're sick on the carpet.
1st: What I love about cats is the way they move so silently on padded paws.
2nd: What I hate about cats is that they bring dead mice into the house.
1st: What I love about cats is their sense of humour.
2nd: What I hate about cats is that they dig up the flower beds when they go to the loo (and so on).

PLAY battle lines with a partner. Choose one of the subjects below, or find one of your own. One of you write ten positive things, the other ten negative things.

> dogs   school   teachers   ink   zoos   balloons   rain   picnics
>
> spiders   liver   holidays   being ill   trees   the sea   thunderstorms

What I _____

What I _____

What I _____

What I _____

What I _____

What I _____

What I _____

What I _____

What I _____

What I _____

Now join in the battle of words with your partner.

· ONOMATOPOEIA ·

ONOMATOPOEIA is the name given to words that sound like what they represent. For example: *slurp*, *splash*, *crunch*, *squelch*, *whizz*, *plonk* and *crash*. Say them aloud so that you can hear these 'sound' words.

There are onomatopoeic words for all the animal sounds. What sounds do the following make?

Cats   m _ _ _ _ and also p _ _ _

Dogs	w _ _ _	Sheep	_ _ _	
Cows	_ _ _	Snakes	_ _ _ _	
Pigs	_ _ _ _	Ducks	_ _ _ _ _	
Birds	_ _ _ _ p	Turkeys	_ _ _ _ _ _	
Hens	_ _ _ _ _	Doves	_ _ _	
Mice	_ _ _ _ _ _	Owls	_ _ _ _	
Parrots	_ _ _ _ _ _	Wolves	_ _ _ _	

Many words for the way we might say something are also examples of onomatopoeia. For example, *whisper* and *guffaw*. How many onomatopoeic ways of speaking can you find? Work on your own or with a friend. Say the words aloud to hear if they sound like what they describe.

Poems also show the use of onomatopoeia when the sounds of the words used suggest what is being described. For example, poems describing the sea might use words which contain many S or SH sounds to reproduce the sound of the waves.

WRITE A POEM about the tide coming in on the shore. Use as many S or SH sounds at the beginnings of or inside your words as you can.

OR

Write a poem about walking through mud. Think about the sound this makes and find words to reproduce it. You may want to use a number of CH and SH sounds.

OR

Write about a concert with a full orchestra. What sounds do all the instruments make? Describe what happens using words that suggest the musical sounds.

Sea Shell

Lift to your ear
The gleaming wave-washed shell,
Its song may tell
Strange ocean fantasies
Of silver pearls,
Glimpsed through the restless surge,
Of slender sinuous weeds
That golden patterns weave
By banks of bright anemones;
Of fishes, rainbow finned;
Of secret twilight caves
Where tides, their fury tamed,
Go stealing tip-toe in.

Enid Madoc-Jones

The Main-Deep

The long-rolling
Steady-pouring
Deep-troubled
Green-billow:

The wide-topped
Unbroken,
Green-glacid,
Slow-sliding

Cold-flushing,
-On-on-on-
Chill-rushing
Hush-hushing,

… Hush-hushing …

James Stephens

CONSEQUENCES AND LEXICON/ALPHABET STORIES – TEACHER'S PAGE

Consequences. This is such a well-known game and many teachers will probably have played it as children. Sadly, such games seem to have all but disappeared in the wake of Gameboys, Pokemon and the like. When we played as children it was not a game associated with school; indeed, some of the things we wrote might not have gone down too well with adults. However, children today still find it fun if introduced to it, and it has great potential for helping them with story-writing. The method of play is set out on the pupils' page and, clearly, the chance nature of the game is one of its strengths. What you end up with, though, is basically a short story – complete with beginning, middle and end. The stories are odd and imaginative, too. Consequences can, therefore, provide a plan and impetus for getting pupils to write stories that take them out of the usual rut and offer a chance of actually finishing them – something which too many children never experience. They will know where to start and how it all ends. Their task will be to fill in the details and bring the story really to life.

Another related idea based on chance, which also helps with story-writing, is a game invented (as far as I know) by the author Russell Hoban. It is called **Person, Place, Weather, Time.** You choose four people in the class. Each one must think of one of the elements in the game's title. It can be any type of person, living or dead; any place in the world; any kind of weather; and any time – time of day, season, in history, or all three. When they have thought of something you ask each one in turn to tell the class. You then have four ideas which, when combined, will be the skeleton of a story. Everyone now writes a story (or poem) using each of these elements and adding details of their own. For example:

* Queen Boadicea; on a bus; in a snowstorm; at 9 o'clock on a winter's morning.

* A retired policeman; on Hadrian's Wall; during an earthquake; in 1892.

* A baby; under an oak tree; in pouring rain; last night.

Lexicon stories is explained on the pupils' page and is an exercise in thinking quickly to come up with words based on beginning letters. The object is to make up sentences and, in so doing, to use up your cards before anyone else. The sentences tell a story, albeit arbitrary in construction, but which forces players to be aware of narrative, as well as the role and usefulness of punctuation. The sentences must make sense and follow on from previous sentences. There is, again, an element of chance involved with this game which can throw up unusual ideas. These can be taken up later and worked on to produce stories, if desired. It is a way of jolting people's minds out of the everyday and mundane, and is also good practice in making the mind more flexible in its choice of language.

Alphabet Stories is another exercise in writing a short story. This is, however, more focused as each word must begin with the next letter of the alphabet. The whole story will be just 26 words long. It is not so easy to do and a dictionary will probably be indispensable. It is good concentrated practice in making meaning with language.

> * Ways in to planning story-writing ● Imaginative writing ● Disciplined writing
> ● Finding words beginning with specific letters ● Use of dictionary

· CONSEQUENCES ·

CONSEQUENCES is a fun game which makes up short stories by chance. It is a game that works best with between four and eight players.

TO PLAY

1   Each person has a sheet of paper (use this piece and fill in the spaces below). On the first line everyone writes the name of a male person (or type of male person, e.g. a postman; or type of male animal, e.g. an elephant). The paper is folded over so that what has been written cannot be seen. Pass the papers one place to the left so everyone receives a different paper.
2   Then, the name of a female person (or type of female person, e.g. an actress; or animal, e.g. a pig) is written on the next line. This is folded over and passed on.
3   Where they met is written next, folded and passed on.
4   Then write: He said …   Fold and pass on.
5   Then write: She said ….   Fold and pass on.
6   Then write: He gave her …   Fold and pass on.
7   Then write: She gave him …   Fold and pass on.
8   Lastly write: The consequence (outcome) was … Fold and pass on. Then, everyone opens up the pieces of paper and reads out the chance stories. The game often works best when players carry on their own story each time they write something on the next piece of paper.

MALE: _____

MET

FEMALE: _____

AT/BY/IN/ON etc. _____

HE SAID: _____

_____

SHE SAID: _____

_____

HE GAVE HER: _____

SHE GAVE HIM: _____

THE CONSEQUENCE WAS: _____

_____

For example:

Harry Potter met Queen Victoria in the middle of a hedge. He said, 'Have you any frozen peas?' She said, 'You can't expect me to know that.' He gave her a kick in the shins; she gave him a slurpy kiss. The consequence was that they dined on worms that evening. **You can use consequence stories as plans for longer stories. You will need to add more details and description, but you already have a beginning, a middle and an end.**

• LEXICON STORIES •

To play LEXICON STORIES, a game for two to six players, you will need a pack of lexicon cards. These are like ordinary playing cards but with letters of the alphabet instead of numbers or pictures.

Alternatively, you can make your own, using ordinary playing cards as your base. Stick a self-adhesive white envelope label on the face of each of the 52 cards. Leave the jokers as these will be used in the game to represent any letter you wish. Write a letter on each label. The number of cards for each letter is as follows:

A	B	C	D	E	F	G	H	I	J	K	L	M	N	O	P	Q	R	S	T	U	V	W	X	Y	Z
4	2	2	2	4	2	2	2	3	1	1	2	2	2	3	2	1	2	2	3	2	1	2	1	1	1

Jokers are wild:
they can be any letter you wish

TO PLAY

1   Someone deals everybody five cards (players may look at their cards). The rest of the pack is placed face down on the table.

2   The player on the right of the dealer starts by placing any one of their cards face up on the table and saying a word that begins with its letter – the word should be the beginning of a sentence. They then replace the card by taking one from the pack.

3   The next player must place one of their cards on top of the first and say a word which could follow in making a sentence. They then replace it by taking a card from the pack.

4   Each player, in turn, adds a word to the sentence, and replenishes their hand from the pack. If players cannot go, they must still pick up a card. When the face-down pack is finished, the first person to use up their cards is the winner.

5   Anyone can say 'full stop' at any appropriate time and begin a new sentence.

The game must be played quite fast. Unusual and often amusing sentences are made in this way. You could even have a 'scribe' to write down your emerging stories!

ALPHABET STORIES is a game to play on your own, or working with a friend. The idea is to see if you can write a simple story, of 26 words in length, where each new word begins with the next letter of the alphabet. Try to make as good sense as possible, even though it can be quite difficult, especially near the end of the alphabet! Dictionaries will be a great help in this game. For example:

A big cuddly dog emerged from Geraldine's house in jolly Kidderminster last month. Nobody observed. People quietly relaxed, sampling television's usual viewing, watching X-rated yelling zombies.

ACROSTICS AND KENNINGS – TEACHER'S PAGE

Acrostics seem to be well-known now in schools and have proved to be a popular means of encouraging pupils to write. They provide an easily understood framework where the first letters on each line spell a word (usually the subject of the poem). In fact, acrostics do not have to be based on the first letters – sometimes it is each second letter, sometimes the third, or any other up to all the last letters. The word spelt can even be done diagonally starting with the first letter of the first line, then the second letter of the second line, and so on. The Victorians were very keen on acrostics which were generally presented as puzzles. There were also 'double acrostics', usually two words – the first read down the page from the first letters, and the second read from the last letters.

However, it has to be said that the acrostic has not necessarily done school pupils much of a service! Too many teachers and pupils have latched onto this form and tend to write in it every time they tackle poetry writing. What is written is also too often of inferior quality and not even poetry. It is not enough just to write lines starting with particular letters – anybody can do that. There must be some more poetic structure and there must be sensible meaning. The following are examples of the sort of thing that is seen too often:

S chool is a place where you	S itting at desks	S it down!
C an meet friends,	C ounting	C ome out
H ave fun	H ow many	H ere!
O n the football pitch	O ranges for	O pen your books to page
O r in the playground. I	O ne pound.	O ne
L ike school.	L et's go.	L ook at me!

None of the above has any real literary merit. There is no sense of rhythm, no rhyme (not absolutely necessary), no startling images, no insights and virtually no meaning. But, the acrostic can be useful as a form in a couple of ways at least. Firstly, it provides a framework so that pupils know exactly how long the piece will be, where to start and where to finish. This takes away one of the problems confronting any writer and acts as a kind of puzzle which they have to solve, thus intriguing them into writing. Secondly, as they must begin each line with a predetermined letter, it forces them to think that little bit harder about what they are going to say. Please emphasise, though, that they should make each line interesting, use images, be aware of some kind of rhythmic feeling for the poem, and that it must make sense grammatically.

Kennings are described fairly fully on the pupils' page and should be easy enough to understand. The beauty of these is that they are another way of making pupils dwell on a subject rather than skirting over it as they too often do in their writing. Work on one as a class first so that everyone has a chance to see how to find these new names. You might want to give some more modern examples, as we still use this construction today. For example, gold-digger, gob-stopper, ambulance-chaser, go-getter, hair-raiser, bodice-ripper, time-waster, globe-trotter, home-maker.

> ● **Writing in a predetermined framework** ● **Creating a list poem** ● **Looking at a subject in detail** ● **Creating riddles**

• ACROSTICS •

ACROSTICS are usually rhymes or poems where the subject of the poem can be read down the page – the letters are embedded in the piece. Most often it is the first letters of every line which spell the word or words. Sometimes, though, it might be the second, third or, last letters, or they might even be read diagonally. For example:

A crostics are popular poems to write,
C hildren, especially, experience delight.
R hyming, of course, they usually forgo,
O pting for easy ways out; although
S ome don't remember when they commence
T hat acrostic poems have to make sense.
I nitial letters should make you think hard,
C arefully choose what to keep or discard –
S o your final poem is viewed with regard.

C ats have whiskers,
C **a** ts have paws;
Ca **t** s have teeth, and
Cat **s** have claws!

WRITE AN ACROSTIC POEM

To write a good acrostic poem you MUST take care to write lines that make sense. The ideal acrostic would be one where a listener would not be aware of the form – they would just hear it as a poem and listen to what it is saying. So, you must make sure that your lines conform to normal sentence grammar.

Choose a subject to write about and spell the word down the left-hand side of the page before you begin. You do NOT have to rhyme, but you can if you wish, as long as it does not spoil what you want to say.

_____

_____

_____

_____

_____

_____

_____

_____

_____

_____

In a group, read your acrostics aloud to each other to hear how well they sound.

• KENNINGS •

KENNINGS are new descriptive names for things. Instead of calling something by its actual name, you make up new names based on some attribute – what it looks like, sounds like, what it does, how it moves, etc. The Anglo-Saxons and Vikings used kennings in their stories and poems – for example, *whale-road* and *swan's-way* were both kennings describing the sea, and *Skull-splitter* is the sort of name a Viking might have given his sword. The famous hero of an Anglo-Saxon story, Beowulf, was also known as *Dragon-slayer* (Draca-slaegend in Anglo-Saxon) after one of his deeds. Another enemy was called Grendel or *Shadow-walker* (*Sceadu-genga* in Anglo-Saxon).

You can write list poems from kennings. They can be about anything. Choose a subject for your poem. Now ask yourself questions about it so that you can make up new descriptive names for your subject. For example:

Subject = A cat	Kenning (new name)
Question: What do cats like to eat? Answer: fish	Kenning = fish-eater
Question: What do cats like to drink? Answer: milk	Kenning = milk-drinker
Question: What does a hunting cat catch? Answer: a mouse	Kenning = mouse-catcher
Question: Where do they like to walk? Answer: on walls	Kenning = wall-walker
Question: What do they do after eating? Answer: lick their fur	Kenning = fur-licker
Question: Answer:	Kenning =
Question: Answer:	Kenning =
Question: Answer:	Kenning =

Finish this poem by asking yourself more questions to make up your new names.

WRITE another kennings poem about something else of your own choice.
Here are a few suggestions for subjects to help you, but you can find your own, too:

> **an elephant   my brother (sister, mother or father)   the sea   a foot**
>
> **a football match   a car   a thunderstorm   a book   a hand**

KENNINGS POEMS make very good RIDDLES. When you have written yours, take turns to read them out to friends WITHOUT saying the title. Everyone must listen hard and picture the descriptions in your kennings in order to guess what you have written about. Here are two for you to guess.

        ?   **?**

nose-picker	button-pusher	bird-shelterer	spring-sprouter
guilt-pointer	phone-dialler	light-shader	autumn-fruiter
back-poker	sherbert-dipper	sun-processor	long-liver
friend-beckoner	ring-wearer	earth-rooter	squirrel-houser

TONGUE-TWISTERS AND ALLITERATION (1 & 2) – TEACHER'S PAGE

Tongue-Twisters are phrases or rhymes which are difficult to say – they can seem to tie your tongue into a knot. Most often they use alliteration to achieve their effect, but not always, as some of the examples on the pupils' page show.

One of the best known is 'Peter Piper' and you could have some fun as a class seeing how fast you can say this rhyme without making a mistake. Ask the class if they know any other tongue-twisters; these you can also try saying aloud. Can your pupil's say why they think they are difficult to say? Are some letters or sounds more difficult than others? It is worth making up a tongue-twister together on the board before they attempt the pupils' page.

Alliteration (1) uses the numbers one to ten as a framework. The idea is to write a sentence for each number where as many words as possible begin with the same sound as the number. Firstly, this will be practice in writing sentences, although these are surreal sentences and not possible in the real world. It is actually much easier to write surreal sentences and also, of course, more fun. Secondly, this will give pupils a good reason for using the dictionary and will, therefore, encourage them to see the dictionary as a wonderful source of words they can use in their writing. We need to show pupils that the dictionary is a treasure chest of language and if they have the key to open it up the words are there for the taking. All they have to do here is to identify the sound at the beginning of each number and find that section in the dictionary. Since the sentences are surreal, pupils are free to put together any interesting words they find to make fantasy pictures.

All pupils love this exercise and it is one of the best ways I know of introducing them to alliteration. Of course, in their later writing we would not want so much alliteration. Two or three words here and there are enough to add texture to a piece and help to make it more memorable and effective, but overdoing it like this, in a fun way, is going to help them to remember the technique. Let them work in pairs, as suggested on the pupils' page, and put two or three pairs together for a feedback session. Take a tip – do not try to mark all these, it will drive you mad! Reading so many sentences of this type will have you screaming from a surfeit of surrealism. However, you can utilise the feedback session by asking the (now larger) groups to condense their one to tens into just one version. This will necessitate their discussing which work best and making choices. Stipulate that each pair must be represented in the final piece. This is the beginning of getting them to do workshops and learning to develop their critical capacities. Follow up by asking them to write sentences that are possible in the real world – these are harder. Then they can try writing about something they know – pets or people – where they can decide when to use some alliteration.

Alliteration (2) is another chance for pupils to use alliteration and links this writing technique with its origins in Anglo-Saxon language and literature. The exercise is clearly explained and should be easy to understand. Do this after they have played with alliteration as described above.

- Introduction to, and use of, alliteration as a writing technique
- Use of dictionary ● Writing whole sentences ● Collaborative workshop
- The difference between the real and the surreal ● Wordplay

· TONGUE-TWISTERS ·

> Peter Piper picked a peck of pickled peppers,
> A peck of pickled peppers Peter Piper picked.
> If Peter Piper picked a peck of pickled peppers
> Where's the peck of pickled peppers Peter Piper picked?

TONGUE-TWISTERS are rhymes or phrases which are difficult to say. You can easily tie your tongue in a knot if you try to say them quickly. Take it in turns with friends to see how fast you can each say the 'Peter Piper' rhyme without making a mistake. You could time yourselves with a stopclock.

Do you know any other tongue-twisters? You can try saying the following:

Swan swam over the sea,   Say these three times each, as fast as you can:
Swim swan swim;   1   **Red leather, yellow leather**
Swan swam back again,   2   **The Leith Police dismisseth us**
Well swum swan.   3   **Sister Susie's sewing shirts for sailors**

Tongue-twisters often have many words beginning with the same sound. This is called ALLITERATION.

MAKE UP some tongue-twisters of your own.
You might find it helpful to collect a lot of words beginning with the same sound before you start. Use the dictionary and note them down below.

_____ _____ _____ _____
_____ _____ _____ _____
_____ _____ _____ _____
_____ _____ _____ _____
_____ _____ _____ _____
_____ _____ _____ _____

Now use them to write your tongue-twister. You can put in small words which do not begin with your chosen letter in order to help what you write make sense. For example:

shine   shipmate   shank   shape
ship   shipshape   show   shall
sharp   share   shammy   shovel
shake   shark   shillyshally   shindig

> Shape up, shipmates, shake a shank sharp!
> No shillyshallying, shine up the ship;
> Shammy till the ship's in shipshape shape,
> For shipmates make for a shipshape ship.

· ALLITERATION (1) ·

When a phrase, line or sentence has a number of words beginning with the same sound, as in some tongue-twisters, we call this ALLITERATION. For example:

'**S**ister **S**usie's **s**ewing **s**hirts for **s**ailors'

WRITE a sentence for each number from one to ten using as many ALLITERATIVE words as possible. It is easier, and much more fun, to write fantasy sentences where what you describe could not happen in real life. Note that all vowels alliterate with each other – see eight in the example below:

> **One witless wildebeest wished he were wicket-keeper for Warwickshire;**
> **Two tearaway teapots took to terrorising the tablecloth;**
> **Three thwarted thistles threatened to think the unthinkable;**
> **Four fabulous face flannels were flabbergasted by the flippancy of the bath-foam;**
> **Five flaunting ferrets flounced around in frilly frocks;**
> **Six unsociable spoons sat stubbornly silent, resisting the temptation to stir;**
> **Seven strawberry sorbets soldiered on through supper;**
> **Eight arrogant oiks interviewed each other underground;**
> **Nine knobbly knees denounced the Nobel Prize for knitting;**
> **Ten treacherous treacle tarts were not to be totally trusted.**

NOW WRITE your own 'one to ten' using alliteration. Work with a partner. Look in the dictionary to find interesting words.

ONE _____

TWO _____

THREE_____

FOUR _____

FIVE _____

SIX _____

SEVEN_____

EIGHT_____

NINE _____

TEN _____

When you have finished, join with other pairs and read your sentences to each other.

It is worth trying the same exercise again, but this time write about things that are possible in the real world. This is harder to do. Use the dictionary for this, too.

• ALLITERATION (2) •

When a phrase, line or sentence has a number of words beginning with the same sound we call this ALLITERATION. For example, 'Full fathom five thy father lies'.

ALLITERATION is a form of rhyme and is used particularly in poetry.
A more accurate definition is: 'repeated initial sounds before stressed syllables'.
'The flame flickered into life and before long firelight filled the farmhouse'.

The Anglo-Saxons used alliteration in their poetry. One famous poem is about the hero, Beowulf, who has to fight against different monsters. One of them was a dragon guarding a hoard of gold. This extract describes when they finally come face to face:

> ... Straightaway
> The breath of the dragon billowed from the rock in a hissing gust;
> the ground boomed.
> The temper of the twisted tangle-thing was fired to close now in battle.
> It came flowing forward, flaming and coiling, rushing on its fate.

Read it aloud and listen for the alliteration. Can you find all the words beginning with the letters B, G, T, C and F?

WRITE YOUR OWN ALLITERATIVE DRAGON

Describe the different parts of the dragon. It may help to list them first – for example: eyes, teeth, wings, breath, snout/nose, mouth, body, head, legs, claws, spines, etc. You can also describe how it moves and what it does. Use alliteration wherever you can – the dictionary will help you find suitable words.
The minimum number of words you need beginning with the same sound is just two. However, if you can use more than two, the effect on the ear will be even greater. For example:

> My dragon breathes and belches out
> Blistering, burning bellows and blasts.
> His enormous eyes are insidious and evil,
> His teeth are tremendous and terrible,
> And his noisy nostrils are nozzles
> Which flourish fierce and ferocious flames of fiery flux.

MY DRAGON_____

_____

_____

_____

_____

_____

_____

_____

_____

DRAW a picture of your dragon.

· THE FAR FAMED FAIRY TALE OF FENELLA ·

A Famous Fish Factor Found himself Father of Five Fine Flirting Females: Fanny, Florence, Fernanda, Francesca, and Fenella. The First Four were Flattering, Flat Featured, Forbidden Faced, Freckled Frumps; Fretful, Flippant, Foolish and Full of Fun.

The Fisher Failed, and was Forced by Fickle Fortune to Forgo his Footman, Forfeit his Forefathers' Fine Fields, and Find a Forlorn Farmhouse in a Forsaken Forest. The Four Fretful Females, Fond of Figuring at Feasts in Feathers and Fashionable Finery, Fumed at their Fugitive Father, Forsaken by Fulsome, Flattering Fortune hunters, who Followed them when Fish Flourished. Fenella Fondled her Father, Flavoured their Food, Forgot her Flattering Followers, and Frolicked in Frieze without Flounces.

The Father, Finding himself Forced to Forage in Foreign parts For a Fortune, Found he could afford a Fairing to his Five Fondlings. The First Four were Fain to Foster their Frivolity with Fine Frills and Fans, Fit to Finish their Father's Finances. Fenella, fearful of Flooring him, Formed a Fancy For a Full Fresh Flower. Fate Favoured the Fish Factor For a Few days, when he Fell in with a Frog. His Faithful Filly's Footsteps Faltered, and Food Failed. He Found himself in Front of a Fortified Fortress. Finding it Forsaken, and Feeling himself Feeble and Forlorn, with Feasting he Fell upon the Fish, Flesh and Fowl he Found, Fricasseed and Fried, and when Full, Fell Flat on his Face on the Floor.

Fresh in the Forenoon he Forthwith Flew to the Fruitful Fields; and, not Forgetting Fenella, he Filched a Fair Flower, when a Foul, Frightful, Fiendish Figure Flashed Forth. 'Felonious Feller, Fingering my Flower, I'll Finish you! Go! Say Farewell to your Fine Felicitous Family, and Face me in a Fortnight!'

The Faint-hearted Fisher Fumed and Faltered, and Fast was Far in his Flight. His Five daughters Flew to Fall at his Feet, and Fervently Felicitate him. Frantically and Fluently he unfolded his Fate; Fenella, Forthwith Fortified by Filial Fondness, Followed her Father's Footsteps, and Flung her Faultless Form at the Foot of the Frightful Figure, who Forgave the Father, and Fell Flat on his Face; For he had Fervently Fallen in a Fiery Fit of love For the Fair Fenella.

He Feasted and Fostered her till, Fascinated by his Faithfulness, she Forgot the Ferocity of his Face, Form, and Feature, and Finally, Frankly, and Fondly Fixed Friday, the Fifth day of February For the affair to come off. There were present at the wedding, Fanny, Florence, Fernanda, Francesca, and the Fisher; there was Festivity, Fragrance, Finery, Fireworks, Fricasseed Frogs, Fritters, Fish, Flesh, Fowls, and Furmity, Frontinac, Flip, and Fare, Fit For the Fastidious; Fruit, Fuss, Flambeaux, and Flowers; Four Fat Fiddlers and Fifers. Then the Frightful Form of the Fortunate and Frumpish Fiend Fell From him, and he Fell at Fenella's Feet, a Fair Favoured, Fine, Frank Freeman of the Forest. Behold the Fruits of Filial affection!

Anon

LIST POEMS (1 & 2) – TEACHER'S PAGE

List Poems (1): Names on a Theme. List poems come in various forms (see also kennings, page 92). They are very useful for giving pupils practice in hearing poetic techniques of rhyme and rhythm, as well as meaning, but within a context of found words. We often ask pupils to do too much too soon and it is very difficult to sustain a particular rhythm and rhyme scheme, while trying to say something worthwhile, when you are not experienced. Finding words, proper names on a theme, will give the raw material for a list poem. Once the names have been found, it is the sorting process that helps to teach the techniques. Pupils are asked to group words according to certain criteria – rhyme, alliteration, number of syllables, repeated sounds and rhythm. It would be a good idea to look at the example on the pupils' page, '*Birds of Britain and Europe*', and analyse its make-up in the light of these criteria. Say it aloud, too, to hear the regular rhythm of four main beats reproduced in each line.

When pupils have obtained their list and sorted the words, they are ready to write their list poem. They must decide on a rhythm and then stick to it for each line. Any rhyming words can be used in strategic places (often as rhyming couplets) to enhance the effect. If they only have two that rhyme, these will probably be best at the end to round the piece off. At the end of such an exercise they will have a better feeling for rhythm and rhyme (whether full, half, alliteration or repetition) because they have only had to concentrate on that without needing to worry about the subject.

List Poems (2): Place Names. This is a similar exercise but with a slight difference. This time place names are collected. These can be from any country in the world and might very well tie in with some geography project or give children from other countries a chance to use names of places they know. The idea is to put the words together to reproduce the sound of a train journey. So the main difference between this and the former exercise is that you vary the pace and rhythm through the poem.

It is a good idea to write all the place names out on slips of paper so they can be moved around the table top or floor when being put into groups. This makes it easier to manipulate them and use them in the writing. The poem can be laid out with the slips first and then written down when the writer is satisfied with the effect. Actually, it is best done in a small group of three or four, and it is essential that the poem is constantly read aloud as it is being made up.

The best list poems are long, but because they are long you do need to vary the pace. Each of the different categories into which the words have been sorted will assist in this. Spend some time looking at the example on the pupils' page together first. Get the class to identify the different techniques being used and to see and hear where and how the rhythm changes. When pupils have completed their own, these can be very good performance poems. Individual voices, group renditions, musical instruments, whistles and other background sounds, can all contribute to the performance.

> • **Use of reference books** • **List poems** • **Sound poems** • **Performance poems**
> • **Use of poetic techniques - rhyme, rhythm, alliteration, repeated sounds, number of syllables** • **Use of atlases or road maps** • **Collaborative writing**

• LIST POEMS: NAMES ON A THEME •

The following is a LIST POEM using names on a theme.

Birds of Britain and Europe

Dipper, Diver, Dotterel, Knot,
Godwit, Goshawk, Goose, Guillemot;
Bittern, Quail, Bustard, Rail,
Nightingale, Nightjar, Owl, Pintail;
Egret, Eider, Ibis, Auk,
Hobby, Harrier, Shrike, Sparrowhawk;
Blackcap, Whitethroat, Redwing, Pigeon,
Little Tern, Turnstone, Stonechat, Wigeon;
Kingfisher, Kittiwake, Woodpecker, Chough,
Yellowhammer, Cormorant, Coot, Chiffchaff.

WRITE YOUR OWN LIST POEM USING NAMES ON A THEME

1   First, cut up some rough paper into small slips.
2   Then, choose your theme. Work with a partner.

The following are some suggestions, but you can choose your own:

> **girls' names   boys' names   flowers   trees   fruit   fish**
>
> **aircraft   football teams   animals   car names**

You can use any reference book from your library which lists the names of your chosen theme. Collect as many as possible and write them on the slips of paper.

3   Sort all your slips into different groups according to the following sound effects:

> **rhyme   alliteration   number of syllables   repeated sounds   rhythm**

These groups will help you when you come to write the poem.

4   Now, write your poem just using words you have found. Put the words together so that they keep a regular rhythm or number of beats for each line. You will need to say it aloud to yourselves as you work to make sure the poem runs smoothly. If you can use a few rhyming names to round off some lines, so much the better.

_____

_____

_____

_____

_____

_____

_____

_____

LIST POEMS: PLACE NAMES

The following LIST POEM is a SOUND POEM. It is made entirely of proper nouns (in this case, place names in the British Isles). The words reproduce the sound of a train journey.

Place Names

Hove,
Ballybrack, Chirk, Adlestrop, Cork,
Amersham, Ashby, Faversham, Derby
Billericay, Harrowbarrow, Ballymurphy, Tobermory,
Little Gidding, Little Snoring, Little Walsingham,
Piddletrenthide, Wetwang …
Brancaster, Lancaster, Doncaster, Tadcaster,
Winchester, Liss, Chichester, Diss, Rochester, Foss, Manchester, Ross,
Willingham, Eltham, Gillingham, Feltham,
Immingham, Marlow, Trimingham, Barlow,
Uppingham, Nacton, Colchester, Clacton, Ilchester, Bacton,
Silchester, Cotterstock, Barnacle, Powerstock,
Blaenau Ffestiniog, Toller Porcorum, Gedney Drove End, Bovey Tracey …
Norwich, Ipswich, Harwich, Nantwich,
Tonbridge, Uxbridge, Cambridge, Redbridge,
Dundreggan, Dundee, Dundonald, Dundrod, Drumcree, Drumclog,
Hull, Ballyhack, Dull, Kettletoft,
Lowestoft, Poole,
Goole.

LOOK in an atlas to collect place names. You can choose any country in the world. Or you might like to collect underground stations from the London tube map. Work with two friends and write all the names you collect onto slips of paper.

Before you start to make your rhythmic (and sometimes rhyming) poem, sort your slips into groups according to their different sound effects. For example:

> **alliteration   rhyme   rhythm   repeated sounds   numbers of syllables**

Use these different groupings to vary the pace and rhythm of your poem.

_____
_____
_____
_____
_____
_____
_____
_____
_____
_____

SIMILES (1) – TEACHER'S PAGE

A **simile** is a figure of speech used to show a similarity between two different things. It uses a 'bridge' word – *as* or *like* – to link the two and make the comparison.

As wet as a fish – as dry as a bone;
As live as a bird – as dead as a stone;
As plump as a partridge – as poor as a rat;
As strong as a horse – as weak as a cat;
As hard as flint – as soft as a mole;
As white as a lily – as black as coal;
As plain as a pikestaff – as rough as a bear;
As tight as a drum – as free as the air;
As heavy as lead – as light as a feather;
As steady as time – uncertain as weather;
As hot as a furnace – as cold as a frog;
As gay as a lark – as sick as a dog;
As slow as a tortoise – as swift as the wind;
As true as the gospel – as false as mankind;
As thin as a herring –as fat as a pig;
As proud as a peacock – as blithe as a grig
[grasshopper];

As fierce as a tiger – as mild as a dove;
As stiff as a poker – as limp as a glove;
As blind as a bat – as deaf as a post;
As cool as a cucumber – as warm as toast;
As flat as a flounder – as round as a ball;
As blunt as a hammer – as sharp as an awl;
As red as a ferret – as safe as the stocks;
As bold as a thief – as sly as a fox;
As straight as an arrow – as bent as a bow;
As yellow as saffron – as black as a sloe;
As brittle as glass – as tough as gristle;
As neat as my nail – as clean as a whistle;
As good as a feast – as bad as a witch;
As light as is day – as dark as is pitch;
As brisk as a bee – as dull as an ass;
As full as a tick – as solid as brass.

Anon.

One of the best ways of introducing similes is to ask children how many they know. These will probably be in the same form as the examples above. There can be several similes for the same adjective. For example:

As *white* as – a sheet, a ghost, snow   As *black* as – night, coal, Newgate's knocker.
As *old* as – time, the hills, Methuselah   As *plain* as – a pikestaff, the nose on my face.

Do the children know any different ones from those in the rhyme above?

Discuss the similes and how they work. Can they make up some of their own? Then, collect all the similes together and make a class book illustrated by the children.

When children are doing creative writing – prose or poetry – they are more likely to use the other 'bridge' word, *like*.

How a Good Greyhound is Shaped
He needs
A head like a snake, a neck like a drake,
A back like a beam, a belly like a bream,
A foot like a cat, and a tail like a rat.

Trad.

The exercises on the pupils' page are ways of helping them to begin to train their minds to notice and create similes. This is continued in **Similes (2)** and naturally leads on to another important figure of speech – metaphor.

• **Understanding of Similes and how they work** • **Creative writing**

• SIMILES (1A) •

A SIMILE is a figure of speech used to show a similarity between two different things. It uses a 'bridge' word – *as* or *like* – to link the two and make the comparison.

As sick as a parrot!   As like as two peas in a pod.   Like father, like son.

My girl's a corker, she's a New Yorker,
I'd give her anything to keep her in style;
She's got a mop of hair, just like a grizzly bear,
That's where the money always goes.

… **She's got a pair of eyes just like two custard pies** …
… **She's got a runny nose just like a fireman's hose** …
… **She's got a pair of lips just like two greasy chips** …
… **She's got a pair of hips just like two battle ships** …
… **She's got a pair of feet just like two plates of meat** …   **Trad.**

WRITE ABOUT someone you know well – your mother, father, brother, sister, friend, grandparent, neighbour, teacher (!) – using similes to describe the person. DO NOT TRY TO RHYME, but you can be funny if you want. Whether you show it to them afterwards is up to you! But you can draw a picture.
Choose items from the following list and find similes to describe each one.

head	hair	eyes	nose	mouth	teeth	voice	ears	chin
hands	arms	fingers	body	legs	feet	knees		

Add other things if it seems appropriate – for example, if someone has bushy eyebrows or a funny walk which is especially noticeable, you will want to write about that using similes.

His/her eyes are like two round brown truffle chocolates
His/her nose is like a squashed piece of pink Plasticene

His/Her eyes are like _____

nose is like _____

mouth is like _____

like _____

like _____

like _____

like _____

like _____

like _____

like _____

• SIMILES (1B) •

How To Make A Monster

It needs
A head like the dome of St Paul's Cathedral,
A body like a hot-air balloon,
Ears like great sheets flapping in the wind,
A mouth like a huge cavern,
Teeth like pirates' curved cutlasses,
Eyes like bulging footballs,
Legs and arms like tree trunks made of rubber,
Claws like bent knitting needles
And a tail like an express train.

MAKE A MONSTER OUT OF SIMILES

First, make a list of all the parts of your monster or dragon. Choose from the following list:

head body eyes nose snout mouth teeth ears whiskers tongue legs tail
paws toes claws arms hands fingers wings fur scales skin voice

Your title will be: 'How to make a monster' or 'How to make a dragon'.

Begin with the words 'It needs', then select items from your list and find similes for them. For example:

A head like the dome of St Paul's Cathedral,
A body like a hot air balloon,
Ears like … etc.

It needs

A _____ like _____

A _____ like _____

_____ like _____

_____ like _____

_____ like _____

_____ like _____

_____ like _____

_____ like _____

_____ like _____

_____ like _____

Now draw a picture of your creature based on the similes you have used.

SIMILES (2) – TEACHER'S PAGE

There was a man of double deed
Sowed his garden full of seed.
When the seed began to grow,
'Twas like a garden full of snow;
When the snow began to melt,
'Twas like a ship without a belt;
When the ship began to sail,
'Twas like a bird without a tail;
When the bird began to fly,
'Twas like an eagle in the sky;

When the sky began to roar
'Twas like a lion at the door;
When the door began to crack,
'Twas like a stick across my back;
When my back began to smart,
'Twas like a penknife in my heart;
When my heart began to bleed,
'Twas death and death and death indeed.

Anon.

At first the infant
Mewling and puking in the nurse's arms;
Then the whining school-boy, with his satchel
And shining morning face, **creeping like snail**
Unwillingly to school. And then the lover,
Sighing like furnace, with a woeful ballad
Made to his mistress' eyebrow. Then a soldier,
Full of strange oaths, and **bearded like the pard** [leopard],
Jealous in honour, sudden and quick in quarrel …

Jaques' speech on **the seven ages of man**, from *As You Like It* by
William Shakespeare (Act II, Scene 7)

There are many examples of similes in use in both poetry and prose and it is a good idea to find and read some of these to pupils. Discuss how well they work.

Ask them to find examples to read out to the class from books they are currently reading, or poems they have found. Are there any differences between the similes found in prose books and those in poems? Which of the ones they found do they think work best?

Introduce your pupils to the concept of the **cliché**. A phrase that is fresh and new has a creative effect. But when it becomes well-known, it is no longer fresh and becomes a cliché – an overworked phrase. Similes of the kind all the pupils probably knew, and which you first collected, are so well-known that they are no longer effective in original writing. They have become clichés. Creative writing demands the creation of new images. We need to practise alerting our minds to seeing similarities so that we can create new similes in our writing.
The exercises on the pupils' page are designed to encourage pupils to do this.
Each provides another way of writing a description. For the first, make sure you have enough pictures of animals available in the classroom so pupils do not waste time looking elsewhere.

> • **Understanding of similes** • **Creative writing** • **Understanding of cliché**

• SIMILES (2A) •

How To Make A Giraffe

She needs
Long soft eyelashes like fringed canopies,
Legs like jointed bamboo
And a neck stretched like a high crane towards the leaves.
Her body must be like an elongated deer
With an orange and white skin pattern
That tessellates like crazy paving.

MAKE AN ANIMAL FROM SIMILES

1   Choose an animal that you wish to make.
2   Find a picture of your animal.
3   Now make a list of all the parts of your animal that you may wish to write
    about. For example:

head   body   eyes   nose   mouth   jaws   teeth   ears   legs   tail   fur   feathers
        scales   skin   neck   wings   fins   gills   paws   claws   talons   etc.

4   Your title will be: How to Make a …
5   Begin with: He, she or it needs …
6   Now choose items from your list (you do not have to use all of them) and find
    similes for them. Look hard at your picture and ask yourself, 'What in the
    whole world could I take to be the head of my animal?' Anything that reminds
    you of it might be suitable. Then do the same for the body. Then other parts of
    the animal.

_____ like _____

_____ like _____

_____ like _____

_____

_____

_____

_____

_____

_____

_____

7   When you have finished, read your descriptions out to each other as riddles.
    Do not say the title; your friends must picture your simile images to guess
    what you have written about.

• SIMILES (2B) •

How To Make March

It needs
A strong blustery wind like the rush of a train in a tunnel,
Willow catkins like yellow powdery tassels,
Sunshine like the gentle warmth of a genuine smile
And a carpet of bluebells like a lavender sea.

(List: strong winds, sunshine, new shoots, catkins, buds on trees, spring flowers)

If you have already made an animal from similes you can try something more difficult.
Try writing about more abstract ideas using similes.

For example, how would you make happiness, a city, or the night sky?
Other possible ideas might be:

> the sea   peace   autumn (or any other season)   daylight
> august (or any other month)   jealousy   a dream   dawn
> your mouth water   time stand still   worms laugh   hope

1   Choose one of the ideas above, or come up with one of your own.
2   Make a list of all the things that characterise your subject.
3   Then describe, using similes, how you would make it.

_____ like _____

_____ like _____

_____ like _____

METAPHOR (1 & 2) – TEACHER'S PAGE

Idioms. A good way to introduce pupils to how metaphor can work is to collect idioms which show how a phrase can operate on two levels. There are many idioms in common use which say one thing on the surface (the literal meaning) but actually mean something else. These idioms tend to refer mostly to everyday areas of life, such as food, animals, clothing, colours, the home and sport. The sea is also a fruitful subject for metaphorical language. Some examples from each of the above areas:

food: have your cake and eat it too; to be in the soup; to butter somebody up
animals: stop badgering me; a snake in the grass; a dog in the manger
clothing: to lose one's shirt; put a sock in it; to wear the trousers
colours: to feel blue; every cloud has a silver lining; to see red
the home: the pot calling the kettle black; out of the frying pan into the fire
sport: he's had a good innings; to hit below the belt; to score an own goal
the sea: to desert the sinking ship; to hit a rough passage; to weather the storm

Discuss the above with the class to see if they can say why these idioms came about and what they really mean when used metaphorically. Can they suggest any more expressions for each category?

The pupils' page concentrates on expressions which use parts of the body. These offer a chance to have some fun with the language by illustrating them literally. A wall display can be made with the idiom written above each picture, and the real meaning written below. It is amusing to depict literally what someone would look like who has eyes in back of their head, or has not got their head screwed on right.

The Furniture Game. This is much more of a writing game where pupils describe people in terms of other things – i.e. they use metaphor. It should be played orally first, probably a few times, so that they become used to the idea of seeing people this way. How to play this is described on the pupils' page. Any questions are admissible, for example, What flower? What time of day? What animal? What season of the year? What car? What item of furniture? What item of clothing? What sort of footwear? What month? What food? What drink? What character in literature? What sort of house? What newspaper? What fruit? What vegetable? What tree? What material? What weather? etc.

We answer such questions with something that reminds us of the person in some way. This can also show the connection between similes and metaphor. Whereas the simile uses the words *like* or *as* to connect the two parts of it, the metaphor makes the leap of saying that something (or someone) **is** something else. However, basically the same process is going on in the mind – that of seeing a similarity between two disparate things. When your pupils come to write about people in this way, encourage them to expand their answers, as shown on the pupils' page. It is easy to see that there is a difference between saying that someone is 'a brand-new white leather *sofa* which has just been delivered' and 'an old threadbare *sofa* that has seen better days'.

- **Introduction to metaphor via idioms** • **Analysis of how idioms work**
- **Wordplay** • **Creative writing – descriptions of people using metaphor**

Foolish Questions

Where can a man buy a cap for his knee?
Or a key for the lock of his hair?
And can his eyes be called at school?
I would think – there are pupils there.
What jewels are found in the crown of his head,
And who walks on the bridge of his nose?
Can he use, in building the roof of his mouth,
The nails on the ends of his toes?
Can the crook of his elbow be sent to jail –
If it can, well, then what did it do?
And how does he sharpen his shoulder blades?
I'll be hanged if I know – do you?
Can he sit in the shade of the palm of his hand,
And beat time with the drum of his ear?
Can the calf of his leg eat the corn on his toe? –
There's somethin' pretty strange around here!

American Folk Rhyme, Adapted by William Cole

List of Body Idioms

to put someone's back up
to pick someone's brains
I'm all ears
to give someone the elbow
to keep your eye on the ball
to pull the wool over someone's eyes
to have eyes in the back of your head
to bat an eyelid
to laugh on the other side of your face
to have two left feet
to have a finger in every pie
butterfingers
to be light-fingered
to be all fingers and thumbs
to split hairs
head not screwed on properly
to laugh your head off
my heart was in my mouth
to pull someone's leg

to give someone a piece of your mind
put your money where your mouth is
to pay through the nose
she gets up my nose
cut off your nose to spite your face
to have a chip on your shoulder
to jump out of your skin
to hold on by the skin of your teeth
to be a bit long in the tooth
to jump down someone's throat
to have a frog in your throat
to speak with forked tongue
to tie your tongue in a knot
to have butterflies in your tummy
to be all mouth and trousers
my heart was in my boots
my heart sank
to wear your heart on your sleeve
cat got your tongue?

• METAPHOR: IDIOMS •

IDIOMS are expressions that seem to say one thing but really mean something completely different. Many of these are METAPHORS. For example, if someone 'lets the cat out of the bag', it does *not mean* they have literally opened a bag and let a cat escape! It really means they have given away information that was supposed to be secret.

WHAT DO THE FOLLOWING REALLY MEAN? You can discuss with a partner.

It's no good crying over spilt milk means: _____

_____

Get your skates on means: _____

She's got ants in her pants means: _____

To be wearing your birthday suit means: _____

I'd love to be a fly on the wall means: _____

_____

Every cloud has a silver lining means: _____

She's in the doghouse means: _____

You're flogging a dead horse means: _____

Many of the idioms below are about the body. Do you know what these mean?

I gave him a piece of my mind: _____

It cost an arm and a leg: _____

I'm all ears: _____

To pull the wool over someone's eyes: _____

She gets up my nose: _____

How many more idioms based on the body can you find with a partner? For example, *She's got eyes in the back of her head.*

_____
_____
_____
_____
_____
_____
_____
_____
_____

Draw pictures of some of these as if they were to be taken literally. What does someone look like if they are all ears? Or if they have eyes in the back of their head?

• METAPHOR: THE FURNITURE GAME •

THE FURNITURE GAME is an oral game for any number of people from three upwards. It works well as a whole class game.

TO PLAY

One person thinks of someone in the class. Everyone else has to guess who it is by asking certain sorts of questions, such as: What piece of furniture is this person? What animal is this person? What flower is this person? What time of day? What month? What character from literature? etc. The first person must answer quickly with whatever comes into their mind. From their answers, people guess who it is.

When we describe people (or things) in terms of other things we are using METAPHOR. Clearly somebody is not, for example, a rocking chair or a kangaroo, but we see a similarity in some way.

WRITE ABOUT SOMEONE USING METAPHORS

You can write about someone you know well by asking yourself the same sort of questions as we use in the Furniture Game. Write your answers down and build up a description of the person with these metaphors. Don't just say a simple answer, such as *a puma*, but add more to it to make it more interesting and specific. For example, *a large black puma who likes to roam in the fields*. OR:

My Gran

She is an old comfortable sofa covered in velvet material,
And a soft purring cat asleep on your lap.
She is the warm month of June and the evening sunset over the sea,
The cooing of pigeons on a summer's day and a shiny black Rolls-Royce vintage car.

TITLE: _____

_____
_____
_____
_____
_____
_____
_____
_____

If you write about someone in your class your piece will make a good riddle. Read it out to others without saying the title so they can guess who's being described. You can also write about famous people (past or present), or characters in literature.

RIDDLES (1 & 2) – TEACHER'S PAGE

Riddles (1). Riddles are always popular with children because of the puzzle element, and they come in various forms. The first pupils' page looks at riddles as jokes and this can tie in with other activities involving jokes (see spoonerisms, page 26; palindromes, page 27; homophones, page 35; punny book titles, page 28; and Tom Swifties, page 61). A famous riddle which might intrigue the class is the one which Lewis Carroll put in *Alice Adventures in Wonderland*: Why is a raven like a writing desk? There was no answer but this did not stop many people from trying to find one. Your class might like to see if they can solve it, too. The other famous riddle is that of the Sphinx, which is reproduced among other examples of riddles on the pages after the activities. It would be worth looking at these examples and discussing the nature of writing riddles, and what sort of things make them work, before pupils attempt their own.

The writing exercise looks at the kind of riddle which buries the letters, spelling the answer within the rhyme. Look at this with the class to see how each line contains two elements which are in some way related – either opposites or connected in some other way. The letter obtained from each line is present in one of the words but not in the other. Sometimes it is in both. The last line of such riddles usually sums up the whole answer as an extra clue. Try writing one as a class together on the board, this will uncover any misunderstandings and also provide practice in thinking of pairs of words to use in these rhymes. These sort of riddles usually rhyme which will also cause a few problems for some children. They do not have to rhyme, but if rhyme is dispensed with the rhythm must be particularly regular throughout the whole piece in order to hold it together. However, if they are prepared to work a little harder at finding how to phrase their lines, there is no reason why they cannot find suitable rhymes. Creative writing is, to a large extent, a craft, and, as with any craftsmen, we learn to write by practising writing. The more we do, the better we usually become. It does not necessarily come easily, but the satisfaction of having wrestled with a piece to make it the best we can is a feeling surpassed by very few others. This is the kind of success which breeds success and offers a growing confidence to pupils in their use of language. This goes for *all* creative writing, so suitable challenges can make for a productive learning situation.

Riddles (2). The examples here are more literary in tone and execution. They rely much more on images and dress the language with contradictions which help to conceal, but also depict, the subject of the riddle. There are other examples on the following pages which would bear some study before pupils try to write their own.

Whatever they decide to write about, it can be very helpful to do a little planning before they start. They should make a list of all the things they can think of in connection with the subject – where they found it; what it looks like; how it might be used; what it does; how it changes in different situations (e.g. at different times of the day or year, etc.). They then select from this information to create their poetic lines.

> - **Study of different types of riddles and how they work** • **Wordplay**
> - **Creative writing** • **Planning (as part of drafting)**

· RIDDLES (1) ·

A RIDDLE is a description of something in the form of a puzzle. There are different sorts of riddles.

JOKES (OFTEN USING PUNS)

LOOK in your joke books to find some riddles. For example:

- When is a thought like the sea?   When it's a notion.
- Why is the desert a good place to eat?   Because of the sand which is there.
- What's black and white and red all over?   A newspaper
- What do you call a crow with a machine gun?   Sir.
- Why do cats purr?   For a definite purr-puss.
- How do you know an elephant's been in the fridge?   Pawprints in the butter.

Make a collection of riddle-type jokes and make your own riddle joke book.
Can you make up some of your own to add to the ones you have found?

HIDDEN LETTERS

Some rhymes conceal the answer to a riddle, letter by letter. The whole answer is usually described at the end. For example:

> **My first is in rainbow but not in sun;**
> **My second's in bread but not in bun;**
> **My third is in floating but never in sinking;**
> **My fourth is in eating but never in drinking;**
> **My fifth is in nightmare and also in dream;**
> **My whole can be found in a puddle or stream.**

Answer: (WATER: **W** in rainbow; **A** in bread; **T** in floating; etc.)

MAKE UP your own riddle with hidden letters. It must rhyme. Notice that the two parts of each line are connected in some way e.g. *bread* and *bun*.

My first is in
_____

My second is in
_____

_____

_____

_____

_____

_____

_____

Swap riddles with someone else and try to solve each other's.

• RIDDLES (2) •

POETIC RIDDLES

These riddles describe things in poetic terms, hiding the identity of the subject in images based on what it looks like, sounds like, what it does, where you find it, etc. For example:

Forty teeth have I complete,
Yet I've never learned to eat;
Sometimes black and sometimes
    white,
Yet I cannot even bite.

Answer: (A comb)

Two brothers we are,
Great burdens we bear,
On which we are bitterly pressed;
The truth is to say,
We are full all the day,
And empty when we go to rest.
                    Answer: (A pair of shoes)

I am in the earth and out of the earth,
I dig down deep and I reach for the stars.
Sunlight and moonlight play shadow games with me.
I sing in the breeze, I groan in the storm,
And stand resolute against snow and ice.
I hide many secrets in cracks and holes,
Though you can root them out if you've a mind.
I am the sturdy ship of the land
With a thousand green sails unfurled to catch the wind.
                    Answer: (an oak tree)

WRITE A POETIC RIDDLE

Your riddle does not have to rhyme. Try to give hints to the identity of the subject in your description without giving the game away too easily. It is often helpful to imagine you are the subject speaking directly to someone, as in the riddles above.

I am _____

_____

_____

_____

_____

_____

_____

_____

Read your riddles out to each other to see if you can work out the answers.

• EXAMPLES OF RIDDLES •

What am I?

1

In marble walls as white as milk,
Lined with a skin as soft as silk;
Within a fountain crystal clear
A golden apple doth appear.
No doors there are to this stronghold
Yet thieves break in and steal the gold.

(Anon)

2

My breast is puffed up and my neck is swollen. I've a fine head and a waving tail, ears and eyes also but only one foot; a long neck, a strong beak, a back and two sides, and a rod right through my middle. My home is high above men. When he who moves the forest molests me, I suffer a great deal of misery. Scourged by the rainlash, I stand alone; I'm bruised by heavy batteries of hail, hoar-frost attacks and snow half-hides me. I must endure all this, not pour out my misery.

3

On the way a miracle: water became bone.

(Anglo-Saxon riddle)

4

I was round and small like a pearl,
Then long and slender and brave as an earl,
Since, like a hermit, I lived in a cell,
And now, like a rogue, in the wide world I dwell.

(Anon)

Answers:
1   (An egg)
2   (A weathercock)
3   (Ice)
4   (First an egg. Then a silkworm. Then a cocoon. Lastly a moth)

• EXAMPLES OF RIDDLES •

I will give my love an apple without e'er a core,
I will give my love a house without e'er a door,
I will give my love a palace wherein she may be
And she may unlock it without e'er a key.

My head is the apple without e'er a core,
My mind is the house without e'er a door,
My heart is the palace wherein she may be
And she may unlock it without e'er a key.

I will give my love a cherry without e'er a stone,
I will give my love a chick without e'er a bone,
I will give my love a ring, not a rent to be seen,
I will get my love children without any crying.

When the cherry's in blossom there's never no stone,
When the chick's in the womb there's never no bone,
And when they're rinning running not a rent to be seen,
And when they're child-making they're seldom crying.

                                                    (Anon)

What am I?

1
A milk-white bird
Floats down through the air,
And never a tree
But he lights there.

                            (Anon)

What am I?

2
As I went through a field of wheat,
I picked up something good to eat;
It had neither flesh nor bone,
But in twenty-one days it walked alone.

                            (Anon)

The Riddle of the Sphinx

3
What creature is that which moves on four feet in the morning, on two feet in the
noon-day, and on three towards the "going down of the sun"?

Answers:
1   (Snow)
2   (An egg)
3   (A man)

PARODY – TEACHER'S PAGE

There are different forms of **parody** – parody of someone's style of writing, parody of a genre of writing, and parody of a (usually) famous poem or piece of prose.

The type of parody dealt with here is parody of well-known poems or rhymes. These are always funny and are a way of taking the (affectionate) mickey out of something which is so famous it can usually weather any tampering with it. Occasionally the original is a popular poem which is not particularly good in the literary sense. Lewis Carroll loved parodying the sort of poems that Victorian children were made to learn. These poems were often intended to improve morals and behaviour and were set for their ability to teach lessons. In the *Alice* books most of the poems and rhymes are, in fact, parodies of such things. For example, *'How Doth the Little Crocodile'* is a parody of *'How Doth the Little Busy Bee Improve the Shining Hour'* by Isaac Watts.

Children delight in parodying popular songs of the day, as well as hymns and Christmas carols. Anyone who has listened hard in assembly will have noticed a few children at times singing slightly different words from the proper ones! Sometimes this is through not understanding the language of the original. For example, the famous 'Gladly my cross-eyed bear' instead of 'Gladly my cross I'd bear'. More often it is out of a sense of fun and wordplay. The two examples of Christmas carol parodies on the pupils' page have been around for a long time. There are also many examples of playground rhymes which are parodies of popular songs, ranging from rewritten nursery rhymes to wartime parodies often ridiculing the enemy, such as 'Hitler has only got one ball'! One which was current in my area in the fifties began, 'Say what you will / School dinners make you ill …' and ended with, 'All school dindins come from pigbins / Out of town.' The Opie's book, *The Lore and Language of Schoolchildren*, contains some good examples of such parodies. Ask your pupils if there are any which they sing now, based on current popular songs.

Some poems have been extensively parodied. A prime example of this is Thomas Hood's *'The Gazelle'*. Many writers have penned parodies which have probably ensured that the original poem is still remembered. You might try to find some of these to show the class. Look in books of parodies or in older books of comic verse (modern books do not often include these).

One of the most parodied nursery rhymes is *'Mary Had a Little Lamb'*. Nursery rhymes are good examples for children to try to parody. They choose one they know well and should write it out so that they can refer to it as they write. They keep to the original rhyme and rhythm scheme but change some of the words to create a new amusing rhyme. You might try one as a class first so that they get the idea of how to approach the task. Since they are using much of the original language they do not have to compose too much in order to achieve their goal. This is wordplay which they enjoy, partly because of its subversive element! Most writers do too.

> ● **Wordplay** ● **Creative writing** ● **Parody**

• PARODY •

A PARODY is a piece of writing that is written in the style or pattern of another, usually well-known, piece. Parodies are often comic rhymes based on poems or songs. For example:

> Oh dear, what can the matter be?
> Three old ladies were locked in the lavatory,
> They were there from Monday to Saturday –
> Nobody knew they were there!

> Mary had a little lamb,
> She also had a bear;
> I've often seen her little lamb
> But never seen her bear.

These two are parodies of well-known nursery rhymes. Do you know the originals?

Do you know any other parodies? You might have heard some in the playground. For example, these come from Christmas carols:

> We four Beatles of Liverpool are,
> John in a taxi, Paul in a car,
> George on a scooter beeping his
>   hooter
> Following Ringo Starr.

> While shepherds washed their socks by
>   night
> All seated round the tub,
> A bar of Sunlight soap came down
> And they began to scrub.

WRITE YOUR OWN PARODY

Choose a well-known song or nursery rhyme – you may want to find one in a book. Using the same pattern and some of the same words, write your own comic version.

It will help to copy out the original first so you can refer to it as you write.

ORIGINAL	PARODY

For example:

Mary had a little lamb Its fleece as white as snow; And everywhere that Mary went The lamb was sure to go.	Mary had a little lamb Born early in the spring; She would take it to school each day And so it died, poor thing.

• EXAMPLES OF PARODIES •

The London Bus Conductor's Prayer

Our Father which art in Hendon,
Holloway be thy name.
Thy Kingston come,
Thy Wimbledon,
In Erith as it is in Epsom.
Give us this Bray our Maidenhead;
And forgive us our bypasses
As we forgive those that bypass against us.
And lead us not into Thames Ditton,
But deliver us from Esher.
For thine is the Kingston,
The Purley and the Crawley,
For Iver and Iver,
Crouch End.
                    Anon.

Mary had a little lamb
Its feet as black as soot,
And into Mary's bread and jam
Its sooty foot it put.

Good King Wenceslas walked out
In his mother's garden,
Bumped into a Brussel sprout
And said, 'I beg your pardon.'

A London Sparrow's 'If'

If you c'n keep alive when li'l bleeders
    Come arter y' wi' catapults an' stones;
If you c'n grow up unpertickler feeders,
    An' live on rubbidge, crumbs an' 'addock bones;
If you c'n nest up in the bloomin' gutters,
    An' dodge the blinkin' tabby on the tiles;
Nip under wheels an' never git the flutters'
    Wear brahn an' no bright-coloured fevver-styles;
If you ain't blown b' nippers (Cor, I'd skin 'em!);
    Stop in y'r shells nah, warm-like, under me;
Yours is the eggs an' everyfink 'at's in 'em –
    An' when they 'atch, yor be cock-sparrers, see?

                                        J.A. Lindon

PATTERNS – TEACHER'S PAGE

There are all sorts of **pattern poems**. A pattern is a framework which is not an established form, but which offers a predetermined pattern to help the writer frame ideas. We can find these patterns in several ways, including making them up.

There are patterns all around us in everyday life. For example: the days of the week; The numbers 1–7, or 1–10; the colours of the rainbow; the points of the compass; the seasons of the year; the months of the year.

These can be used to provide a framework to help children write. The example on the pupils' page uses the days of the week and is based on the rhyme, *'Monday's Child is Fair of Face'*. Other nursery rhymes provide other patterns which can be adapted by giving them new themes and teachers can find their own. For example: 'Solomon Grundy, born on Monday'; 'Sneeze on Monday, sneeze for danger'; 'Ten little dicky birds sitting on a line'. (A fuller list is provided at the foot of the page, after the pupils' activity, containing the rhyme, *'Who killed Cock Robin?'*) (See also Alliteration (1), page 95, and the ABC rhymes on page 50).

Some of these patterns, such as the days of the week in *'Solomon Grundy'*, are really metaphors for someone's life – the seven ages, if you like, but with the final age being death, as are the numbers in the magpie rhyme: *'One for sorrow / Two for joy / Three for a wedding / Four for a boy / Five for silver / Six for gold / Seven for the secret never to be told'* (which is death).

You can also make up patterns of your own. For example, you envisage a magic window. Everyone who looks through this window sees something which is peculiar to them, what they are or what they do. You might begin with a couplet such as the following:

> *There once was a very small window*
> *Hidden away in the corner of a room.*

From then on, different people look through the window. These can be people the children know personally; or types of people, such as a postman, a politician, an architect; or famous people living or dead; or characters in literature; or even animals in a zoo, perhaps looking through the bars of their cages. Each person sees what they most want to see. With older pupils it might be that they look into their own personal Room 101 and see what they would least like to see. The following couplets repeat a pattern which leaves gaps to be filled with the creative element of the poem. For example:

> A politician *looked through the window*
> *And saw* the crowds cheering him to victory.

> A doctor *looked through the window*
> *And saw* another life she had saved.

- **Writing to a pattern** - **Finding patterns from established rhymes**

• PATTERNS •

Many poems, rhymes and songs are written to a PATTERN. The pattern provides a framework for your ideas. The following traditional rhyme tells what sort of life you should have according to when you were born. Do you know what day of the week you were born?

> **Monday's child is fair of face,**
> **Tuesday's child is full of grace;**
> **Wednesday's child is full of woe,**
> **Thursday's child has far to go.**
> **Friday's child is loving and giving,**
> **Saturday's child works hard for a living;**
> **But the child that is born on the Sabbath day**
> **Is bonny and blithe and good and gay [merry].**

We can use this pattern of the days of the week to write our own rhyme. For example:

> **English Weather**
>
> **On Monday the weather was clear and bright,**
> **On Tuesday it poured with rain in the night;**
> **On Wednesday the sun refused to shine,**
> **On Thursday they promised it would be fine;**
> **On Friday, however, the sun had gone,**
> **On Saturday drizzle went on and on;**
> **On Sunday thick fog enclosed the land**
> **And you couldn't see beyond your hand.**

WRITE YOUR OWN PATTERN POEM based on the days of the week.

Choose your own theme – there are some ideas below to help you if you want.
Keep to the same rhythm – saying it out loud will help you to hear this.
You do not have to rhyme but if you do, make sure that what you say makes sense.
Possible themes are:

> dinners, the school week, what clothes you wore, what happened on holiday, each day's colour, who called at the door, what happened to the bus, what the cat brought in, what you dreamt, the seven ages of man (birth to death).

Title: _____

(On) Monday('s) _____

_____ Tuesday _____

_____ Wednesday _____

_____ Thursday _____

_____ Friday _____

_____ Saturday _____

• EXAMPLES OF PATTERN POEMS •

The following traditional rhyme has been used by a number of poets as the basis of poems of their own. 'Leaves', by Ted Hughes, is a good example:

Who Killed Cock Robin?

Who killed Cock Robin?
I, said the Sparrow,
With my bow and arrow,
I killed Cock Robin

Who saw him die?
I, said the Fly,
With my little eye,
I saw him die.

Who caught his blood?
I, said the Fish,
With my little dish,
I caught his blood.

Who'll make the shroud?
I, said the Beetle,
With my thread and needle,
I'll make the shroud.

Who'll dig his grave?
I, said the Owl,
With my pick and shovel,
I'll dig his grave.

Who'll be the parson?
I, said the Rook,
With my little book,
I'll be the parson.

Who'll be the clerk?
I, said the Lark,
If it's not in the dark,
I'll be the clerk.

Who'll carry the link [torch]?
I, said the Linnet,
I'll fetch it in a minute,
I'll carry the link.

Who'll be chief mourner?
I, said the Dove,
I'll mourn for my love,
I'll be chief mourner.

Who'll carry the coffin?
I, said the Kite,
If it's not through the night,
I'll carry the coffin.

Who'll bear the pall [cloth on coffin]?
I, said the Wren,
Both the cock and the hen,
We'll bear the pall.

Who'll sing the psalm?
I, said the Thrush,
As she sat on a bush,
I'll sing the psalm.

Who'll toll the bell?
I, said the Bull,
Because I can pull,
I'll toll the bell.

All the birds of the air
Fell a-sighing and a-sobbing,
When they heard the bell toll
For poor Cock Robin.   Anon.

See also particularly the following patterned traditional rhymes in most good nursery rhyme books: 'This is the Key of the Kingdom'; 'This is the House that Jack Built'; 'The Bells of London'; 'Over in the Meadow in the Sand in the Sun'; 'Ten Little Indians', 'Green Grow the Rushes-O', and other number rhymes; 'Monday's Child is Fair of Face', and other weekday rhymes. 'A was an Archer who shot at a Frog', and 'There was a Man of Double Deed' can be found on pages 49 and 104 respectively.)

Rhymes or songs that are written to a pattern can offer a framework for pupils' own writing, just as 'Who killed Cock Robin?' did for Ted Hughes.

Leaves

Who's killed the leaves?

Me, says the apple, I've killed them all.
Fat as a bomb or a cannonball
I've killed the leaves.

Who sees them drop?

Me, says the pear, they will leave me all bare
So all the people can point and stare.
I see them drop.

Who'll catch their blood?

Me, me, me, says the marrow, the marrow.
I'll get so rotund that they'll need a wheelbarrow.
I'll catch their blood.

Who'll make their shroud?

Me, says the swallow, there's just time enough
Before I must pack all my spools and be off.
I'll make their shroud.

Who'll dig their grave?

Me, says the river, with the power of the clouds
A brown deep grave I'll dig under my floods.
I'll dig their grave.

Who'll be their parson?

Me, says the crow, for it is well-known
I study the bible right down to the bone.
I'll be their parson.

Who'll be chief mourner?

Me, says the wind, I will cry through the grass
The people will pale and grow cold when I pass.
I'll be chief mourner.

Who'll carry the coffin?

Me, says the sunset, the whole world will weep
To see me lower it into the deep.
I'll carry the coffin.

Who'll sing the psalm?

Me, says the tractor, with my gear grinding glottle
I'll plough up the stubble and sing through my throttle
I'll sing the psalm.

Who'll toll the bell?

Me, says the robin, my song in October
Will tell the still gardens the leaves are over.
I'll toll the bell.

Ted Hughes

ANSWERS TO PUZZLES

ANAGRAMS (PAGE 15)

CORK & ROCK

ARCS & CARS & SCAR

MEAT & MATE & TEAM & TAME

SEAT & SATE & TEAS & EAST & EATS

1 OPTS   2 POTS   3 POST   4 SPOT   5 STOP   6 TOPS

1 BRISTOL   2 BELFAST   3 NORWICH   4 NEWCASTLE
5 INVERNESS   6 BANGOR   7 HEREFORD   8 PADSTOW
9 MAIDSTONE   10 LANCASTER   11 SHEFFIELD   12 COVENTRY
13 STEVENAGE   14 SWANSEA   15 PAISLEY   16 OMAGH
17 SALISBURY   18 DOUGLAS (IoM)   19 BEMBRIDGE (IoW)
20 CARLISLE

WORDS WITHIN WORDS (page 19)

Here are 110 words made from the letters of the word EDUCATION.
Pupils may find others as this is not a definitive list.

act acted action acute aid and ant antic at ate auction aunt
cad can cane caned cant caution cautioned cat cent cite cited coat
coated code conduit cone coned cot cud cue cued cut cute
dance date daunt den dent dice die diet din dine dint do doe
don done dote ducat duct due duet dunce dune duo eat edit en
end in induce into ion neat net nice nit no nod node not note
noted nude nut oat octane ode on once one otic out tan ten tend
tide tie tied tin tine to toad toe ton tone toned tonic tun tuna
tune tuned tunic undo untie untied unto

MISCHMASCH (page 20)

One answer is given here for each puzzle - pupils will find several other possibilities.

a**wkw**ard   chi**ldr**en   ma**rke**t   te**chni**cal   ci**rcle**   mi**xture**   sa**ndwi**ch

gru**mble**   to**ngue**   pu**zzle**   tra**ffic**   sa**usa**ge   pa**rsle**y   op**tio**n

ha**ndb**ag   ba**ckgro**und   rai**lwa**y   schoolboy   ho**mewo**rk   ni**ghtma**re   e**yes**ight

BURIED WORDS (page 21)

1	A fish's **fin ch**urns up the water.	finch
2	The fishermen be**gan net**ting as many fish as they could	gannet
3	We all**ow l**ong-standing members to bring guests to meetings	owl
4	Let u**s wan**der wherever we want	swan
5	I'm fed up wi**th rush**ing about all the time	thrush
6	We climbe**d ove**r the stile and went into the field	dove
7	He made a terrifi**c row** when he practised the drums	crow
8	We were toget**her on**ly for a short time on that occasion	heron
9	We went to Mexico this year and had a fort**night in Gale**ana	nightingale
10	When I am ill I **crave n**othing more than peace and quiet	raven

WORDSEARCH (page 23)

UNIVOCALICS (page 30)

PERSEVERE YE PERFECT MEN

EVER KEEP THESE PRECEPTS TEN

WORD LADDERS OR DOUBLETS (Page 37)

The following are just examples of how these may be solved. There will be several other possibilities, perhaps in fewer steps than those below.

WILD	SOCK	NOSE	GIVE	DAWN	SLEEP	HOME
WILE	LOCK	NODE	LIVE	DARN	SHEEP	TOME
TILE	LOOK	MODE	LIKE	BARN	SHEER	TORE
TIME	LOOT	MADE	LAKE	BARK	CHEER	WORE
TAME	SOOT	MACE	TAKE	BASK	CHEEK	WIRE
	SHOT	FACE		BUSK	CREEK	WIRY
	SHOE			DUSK	CREAK	AIRY
					CREAM .	AWRY
					DREAM	AWAY

ONOMATOPOEIA (page 85)

Cats **MIAOW** and **PURR**

Dogs **WOOF**

Cows **MOO**

Pigs **OINK**

Birds **CHEEP**

Hens **CLUCK**

Mice **SQUEAK**

Parrots **SQUAWK**

Sheep **BAA**

Snakes **HISS**

Ducks **QUACK**

Turkeys **GOBBLE**

Doves **COO**

Owls **HOOT**

Wolves **HOWL**

SPIRALGUIDE

Publishing

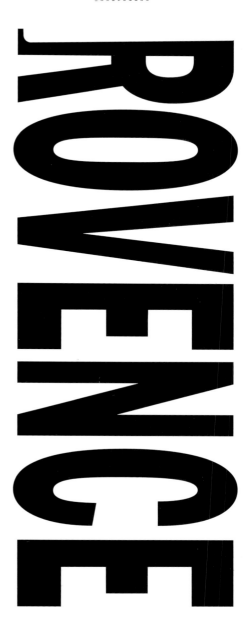

Contents

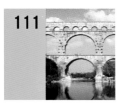

Compiled by Pam Stagg
Revised and updated by Neville Walker

Revision managed by Bookwork Creative Associates
Series Editor Karen Rigden
Series Designer Catherine Murray

Published by AA Publishing, a trading name of AA Media Limited,
whose registered office is Fanum House, Basing View, Basingstoke,
Hampshire RG21 4EA. Registered number 06112600.

ISBN: 978-0-7495-5974-8

A CIP catalogue record for this book is available from the British
Library.

Cover design and binding style by permission of AA Publishing
Colour separation by Keenes, Andover
Printed and bound in China by Leo Paper Products

Find out more about AA Publishing and the wide range of services the
AA provides by visiting our website at theAA.com/bookshop

A04171
Maps in this title produced from mapping © MAIRDUMONT/
Falk Verlag 2009
Transport maps © Communicarta Ltd, UK

The Magazine

A great holiday is more than just lying on a beach or shopping till you drop – to really get the most from your trip you need to know what makes the place tick. The Magazine provides an entertaining overview to some of the social, cultural and natural elements that make up the unique character of this engaging region.

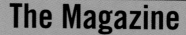

PROVENÇAL
Culture

Provence is rich in tradition. Not only noted for its landscapes and its climate, its cuisine and its perfumes, it is also celebrated for its very own regional language, literature, customs and costumes.

France was once divided linguistically into the Langue d'Oil, spoken in the north, and the Langue d'Oc (or Provençal), spoken in the south. This Latin-based language flourished during the Middle Ages, as this was the home of the troubadours who sang of courtly love in Provençal. The language gradually evolved and in 1854 a literary society called the Félibrige, founded by local poet Frédéric Mistral, was formed to preserve the language and the identity of Provençal customs and traditions – a group which still exists today. You are most likely to hear Provençal spoken in the Bouches-du-Rhône département, around Arles, Glanum and Baux,

Left: Moulin de Daudet near Fontvieille

with regional variants (Monégasque, Mentonnais and Nissart) in Monaco, Menton and Nice.

Provence has also made a significant contribution to French literature, through such local luminaries as Marcel Pagnol, Alphonse Daudet, Henri Bosco, Jean Giono and Frédéric Mistral, whose best-known work, the epic poem *Mirèio*, written in Provençal, won him the Nobel Prize for Literature in 1904. Pagnol is best known to English speakers following the successful films of his novels *Jean de Florette* and *Manon des Sources*. Admirers of his work can visit Manon's fountain and Pagnol's grave by following clearly signed tours of the countryside surrounding his home town, Aubagne. Jean Giono is the most popular Provençal author in France: his former home in Manosque, where he wrote *Horseman on the Roof*, can be visited. In Aubagne, the Little World of Marcel Pagnol is a re-creation of settings and characters in his works, produced by local *santon* makers. In Fontvieille, you can visit the mill in which Daudet wrote *Les Lettres de mon Moulin*.

CUSTOMS AND COSTUMES

Other aspects of Provençal life remain deep rooted in ancient regional rites and customs, especially during December, with its Christmas markets, *santon* fairs (➤ 105, 129), *pastorales* (theatrical representations of the nativity, sung and spoken in Provençal), folk dancing and

Traditional costumes feature in processions

Noëls (Provençal carols). Throughout the year, numerous villages host markets and arts and craft events, and traditional dress is often worn at such festivities.

The costumes of Arlesiénne women are most elaborate, with intricate lace over-blouses, distinctive embroidered *fichus* (caps) and flamboyant jewellery. Brightly coloured Provençal prints feature strongly.

Muséon Arlaten (➤ 121) in Arles – an ethnographic museum founded by Mistral in 1896 – has an impressive range of traditional clothing and jewellery, and the Costume Festival here (first weekend in July) is one of the region's most colourful affairs.

21ST-CENTURY PROVENÇAL

Provençal culture is making a comeback: certain regions insist on the daily use of the language; it is taught in schools, and it is now an option for the Baccalauréat (the French high school graduation exam). Throughout the region place names and often street signs, too, are written in both French and Provençal. In Nice, the local television news is presented in Nissart dialect (with French subtitles), and students study it at the university. Local culinary traditions remain alive and well, with such regional staples as *bouillabaisse*, *tapenade* and *ratatouille* as popular as ever on menus of modern Provençal chefs, and there is even a rekindled passion for Provençal bullfighting (Cours Camarguais) in Arles and the Camargue – a sport popular here since antiquity.

Provençal fashion even makes its mark on the catwalks of the world, thanks to designer, Christian Lacroix – born in Arles. His daring, boldly Mediterranean clothes are often inspired by traditional Arlésian costumes.

Christian Lacroix with two models

How to play
PÉTANQUE

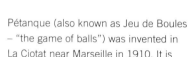

Pétanque (also known as Jeu de Boules – "the game of balls") was invented in La Ciotat near Marseille in 1910. It is a team game of great strategy and precision. The aim is to throw heavy metal balls as close as possible to a small wooden ball or *cochonnet* (piglet). The name is derived from the Provençal *pieds tanqués* (fixed feet), as your feet have to remain together within a small circle drawn on the ground when you throw your ball. The game is normally played on hard sand or gravel, and most villages have a special area called the *terrain de pétanque* or Boulodrome – typically outside a local café or in the main square.

Pétanque follows strict rules: everyone takes it in turns to throw their *boules*, either placing them as near as possible to the *cochonnet*, or shooting them in an attempt to displace your opponent's balls. When all the balls have been thrown, the team with the ball closest to the *cochonnet* scores a point. Most games are up to 13 points.

Pétanque is currently France's most played sport, enjoyed by about 17 million people, and it is also ranked as a world-class sport, played in over 50 countries. For further information on how and where to play, check the websites www.petanque.org or www.petanque.fr

SCENIC PROVENCE

Nature has been abundantly kind to Provence, providing it with a rich diversity of landscape, from the untamed marshes of the Camargue and the beautiful beaches of the Riviera to the snow-clad mountains of the Alps.

It is the beaches of the Riviera that have made the region what it is today, and the main reason for many to visit the region. From the shimmering heat of the Côte d'Azur beaches, with their bars and restaurants, to the secret sun-baked coves of the Esterel shoreline, with its ragged red cliffs set against a bright green backdrop of spruce, pine and scrub, there are beaches to suit all tastes. The tortuous Corniche de l'Esterel (➤ 77) between St-Raphaël and Théoule-sur-Mer is still largely untouched by development and embraces some of the Riviera's most grandiose scenery.

GO WEST

Further west, the dazzling white cliffs of the Calanques (➤ 97) are breathtaking, plunging into sparkling turquoise inlets – best seen by boat trip from Cassis (➤ 97) or on foot along a clearly signed cliff-top path. The Camargue (➤ 116–118) counts among Europe's most important wetlands – a wild, disparate region of brackish lagoons, flat rice fields, sand dunes and salty marshes famous for its white horses, black bulls, pink flamingos and exotic water birds.

EXPLORE INLAND

With such diversity, some holidaymakers seldom leave the coast. Those who do explore the *arrière pays* (hinterland) are rewarded with lush hills, forests, gorges and mountains. Head off the beaten track and you will find tiny sun-kissed vineyards splashed with poppies, olive groves and scented stripes of lavender, stretching like mauve corduroy across the countryside – the very essence of Provence.

A special treat is to ramble through the scrubland habitats known as *garrigue*, where the air is fragrant with the wild *herbes de Provence* so prominent in regional cuisine – basil, rosemary, marjoram, tarragon and thyme. The white limestone crags of the Châine des Alpilles, with their sun-bleached garrigue, is a walker's paradise.

NATIONAL PARKS

The verdant Parc Naturel Régional du Lubéron (➤ 152–154) is one of Provence's most visited areas: a protected park of cedar and pine countryside draped across small mountains between Cavaillon and Manosque, with quaint hilltop villages, almond and olive groves, vineyards and lavender fields. For even more dramatic scenery, head east to the Gorges du Verdon (➤ 74–76), the deepest, longest, wildest canyon in Europe and one of the great natural wonders of Provence.

Anywhere in this area, the snow-capped peaks of the Provençal Alps are never far away. The Parc National du Mercantour (➤ 52–53) is a beautiful alpine reserve, while the Parc Régional de Quayras is a wild, forgotten corner, its hillsides ignited by rare wild flowers in summer.

Winding roads cross across the hills of Provence

Painters
in Provence

Provence's rich palette of landscapes and almost magical, incandescent light has inspired artists for centuries, but never more so than in the late 19th and early 20th centuries, when painters, both native and adopted, were drawn to the region, with its stunning sun-drenched scenery.

PIERRE AUGUSTE RENOIR (1841–1919)

The crisp Provençal light fascinated Impressionist painter Renoir, who lived in Haut-de-Cagnes from 1903. In 1907, he fell in love with a small piece of land planted with 100-year-old olive trees, and built a large house there in which he remained until his death. In the Mediterranean sunshine, his work took on a new lease of life, and the warmth soothed his rheumatic joints. He would sit in his wheelchair at his easel beneath his olive trees for hours on end, his brushes strapped to his rheumatic fingers. His house (Musée Renoir, ➤ 56) has remained as it was at his death, and his palette and other mementoes have been preserved, together with several of his paintings, drawings, sculptures and bronzes.

La Montagne Saint-Victoire by Cézanne (left); *The Night Café at Arles* by Van Gogh (above)

PAUL CÉZANNE (1839–1906)

Cézanne spent much of his life in and around Aix-en-Provence, painting the limestone hills of the surrounding countryside. His "studio" was the great outdoors, and he was so fascinated by Mont Ste-Victoire (➤ 98–99) that he painted it more than 65 times, from all angles and at all hours. Hardly surprising that some of his greatest canvases include *La Montagne Sainte-Victoire* and *Le Paysage d'Aix*. The city today honours its most famous citizen with a special circuit Cézanne, marked by bronze pavement plaques. It concludes at the studio (9 avenue Paul-Cézanne, tel: 04 42 21 06 53) where he spent the last seven years of his life – still exactly as he left it, with unfinished canvases, palettes and his old black hat.

VINCENT VAN GOGH (1835–1890)

Dutch artist Vincent Van Gogh moved to Arles in 1888, believing "the entire future of the new art is in the Midi." Here he lived with Gauguin in the yellow house which he immortalised on canvas in *La Maison Jaune*. He was so inspired by the brilliant light and intensity of colour in the region that he created over 200 paintings in Arles (including his celebrated *Sunflowers* and *Café de Nuit*) and 150 in St-Rémy-de-Provence. It was here, too, that he cut off his ear and gave it to a surprised prostitute. The city was outraged, and greatly relieved when he voluntarily entered the local hospital in 1889. Ironically, no original Van Gogh paintings remain in Arles today.

HENRI MATISSE (1869–1954)

Matisse moved to Nice in 1917. Shortly before his death in 1954, he bequeathed his personal collection to the city – on view at the Musée Matisse (► 43) – an ensemble of canvases spanning his working life, from early Old Master copies through Impressionism and Fauvism to the bright colours and simple shapes of his maturity. This final phase of creativity reached its pinnacle in the Chapelle du Rosaire in Vence (detail pictured above), with its simple interior and sublime stained-glass windows. Matisse considered this masterpiece his "ultimate goal, the culmination of an intense, sincere and difficult endeavour."

PABLO RUIZ Y PICASSO (1881–1973)

Following the war years in Paris, Spanish artist and sculptor Picasso returned to his beloved Mediterranean in 1946, where the mayor of Antibes lent him a room in the Château Grimaldi to use as a studio. In gratitude, Picasso left his entire output of that period on permanent loan to the castle museum (Musée Picasso, ► 55) – 25 paintings, 44 drawings and 150 ceramics designed in the nearby village of Vallauris. Although Picasso only spent three months here, it was one of his most prolific periods. After the melancholy of war, he was hypnotised by the brilliant sunshine and the sparkling air and his work reflected the joie de vivre of the Mediterranean through bold and innovative use of line and sunny colours. From 1961 until his death, he lived in Mougins.

RAOUL DUFY (1877-1953)

Born in the Norman port city of Le Havre, Raoul Dufy was associated with the fauvists, though as he matured he developed his own, distinctive style. Dufy first came to the south of France before the World War I, to Martigues

THE NICE SCHOOL

Art has long thrived in Nice. Examples of the postwar Nice School of painters – a group of New Realists, including Raysse, César, Arman, Ben, Tinguely and, most famously, Yves Klein (1928--1962) – can be seen at MAMAC (► 43). Many of their works involved smashing, burning or distorting everyday objects as a spoof on society and the highbrow art world.

near Marseille, but he is forever associated with the fashionable seaside life of the Riviera, which he depicted in joyous, vibrant watercolours and oils. The city's Musée des Beaux Arts has a selection of his works.

PAUL SIGNAC (1863-1935)

Born to prosperous parents in Paris, Signac originally intended to become an architect but abandoned the idea while still young. An anarchist and follower of the pointillist painter Georges Seurat, he is regarded as the "discoverer" of St-Tropez, which in Signac's day was a humble Provençal fishing village. St-Tropez featured in several of his works, examples of which you can see in the town's Musée de l'Annonciade (➤ 68).

The renowned *Sunflowers* by Vincent Van Gogh

Gourmet
Provence

La cuisine Provençale is typified by bold, sun-drenched flavours and hearty Mediterranean dishes full of personality, enriched by olive oil, tomatoes, garlic and aromatic *herbes de Provence*.

But there's more to Provençal cuisine than *bouillabaisse* and the monumental salade Niçoise of olives, anchovies, tuna, eggs, potatoes and lettuce. On the coast, fish dishes reign supreme, with such delicacies as *telines Camarguais* (tiny shellfish served with aïoli) and *oursins* (sea urchins) alongside such local favourites as *loup* (bass) or *rouget* (mullet). Look for lesser-known dishes such as *beignets de courgettes* (frittered courgette flowers); *pain bagnat* (salad Niçoise inside a loaf of bread) and *mesclun* (a flavoursome salad of peppery leaves) – try them all at Lou Pilha Leva, a simple "fast-food" hole-in-the-wall at the heart of Old Nice – or piping hot slices of *pissaladière* (onion tart with anchovy and olives) and *socca* (chickpea pancake) from the stalls of nearby cours Saleya market. It is the region's

> It is the food markets that have given Provençal cuisine its excellent reputation

celebrated food markets that have given Provençal cuisine its excellent reputation, together with the intimate local bistros of the hilltop villages, where simple meals are served in hearty portions.

GOURMET DINING

At the opposite end of the spectrum, Provence boasts more than its fair share of gourmet restaurants. Auguste Escoffier, the great French "chef of kings and king of chefs" learned to cook in Nice and, ever since, many of the country's top chefs have flocked to the region to perfect the art of Provençal haute cuisine. Most famous of all, the legendary chef Alain

Ducasse has a restaurant with three Michelin stars – Le Louis XV – in the Hôtel de Paris, Monte Carlo (tel: 0377 98 06 88 64). Other top chefs in the area include Christian Sinicropi at La Palme d'Or restaurant in Hôtel Martinez, Cannes (tel: 04 92 98 74 14), renowned for his seasonal specialities; and Alain Llorca at Le Moulin de Mougins (tel: 04 93 75 78 24). The culinary extravaganzas at these restaurants represent the pinnacle of Provençal cuisine – the experience justifies the expense.

THE WINES OF PROVENCE

Provence is one of France's largest and oldest wine-growing regions, first introduced by the Greeks 2,600 years ago. The main wine-producing areas, on the rocky hillsides (*côtes*) in southwest Provence, use a number of traditional grape varieties including Grenache, Cinsault, Carignan, Syrah and Sémillon. The resulting wines range from the intense, heady reds and rich, buttery whites of the Rhône valley to light, fresh, fruity whites and rosés in the south.

Popular *appellations* include Côtes-de-Provence, Côtes-du-Ventoux, Les Coteaux d'Aix-en-Provence and Les Coteaux-des-Baux. About 75 per cent of all Provençal wine is rosé. Indeed 50 per cent of all French rosés come from here, and the Bandol appellation is generally considered the best. Also of special note are the delicious, little-known wines of Bellet, a stamp-sized wine-pocket just behind Nice; the prestigious white wines

TUCK IN AND TUCK UP

What could be better than to enjoy a delicious meal followed by tumbling into bed upstairs afterwards? This is increasingly the trend with new gourmet restaurants in the region – they offer Michelin-starred cuisine with rooms. For instance, two-star Michelin chef Edouard Loubet's farmhouse, La Bastide de Capelongue at Bonnieux, offers 17 rooms and a restaurant serving inventive Lubéron cuisine (www.capelongue.com). Auberge La Fenière (Lourmarin, tel: 04 90 68 11 79, www.reinesammut.com) is managed by Reine Sammut, one of France's top female chefs. Accommodation here consists of seven stylish garden rooms and two gypsy caravans. At the Bastide de Moustiers farmhouse (Moustiers Ste-Marie, tel: 04 92 70 47 47, www.bastide-moustiers.com), charm and simplicity are the keys: the olive oil comes from the neighbouring *domaine*, the only cheese is local *chèvre* and you can see the vegetable garden from your bedroom window. "The produce alone is the star" is the maxim here, and the food is second to none. After all, this is the country home of that culinary superstar, Alain Ducasse!

of Cassis, the oldest *appellation* in Provence; and the world-class wines of Châteauneuf-du-Pape, Vacqueyras, Gigondas and Beaume-de-Venise (famous for its sweet muscat) in the Rhône valley. Many vineyards and cellars are open for *dégustations* (tastings) – you will usually be expected to buy at least one bottle!

THE ART OF DRINKING PASTIS

Ice cubes first, then pastis, then water…a hallowed trio for a great Provençal custom, the aperitif. Although consumed throughout France, this pale yellow anise-flavoured liqueur is typically associated with Provence, especially Marseille. Santé!

BOUILLABAISSE

Few visitors to Provence get to taste an authentic *bouillabaisse*, although many restaurants offer second-rate versions). This world-famous rust-coloured fish soup originated in Marseille. It is traditionally made with up to 12 different kinds of fish and cooked in a stock containing saffron, herbs and fennel. Try it in Marseillaise at Fonfon (140 rue Vallon des Auffes, tel: 04 91 52 14 38) or Le Miramar (quai du Port, tel: 04 91 91 10 40) by the Old Port. Bon appetit!

Page 17: Cours Saleya market in Nice. Below: Le Bastide de Capelongue

PLAYGROUND OF THE
RICH AND FAMOUS

From the Cannes Film festival to the decadence of St Tropez, Provence – and the Riviera in particular – is a paparazzo's paradise, where stars and millionaires perpetuate a well-deserved reputation for glamour.

Without its rich foreign champions, Provence might still be the impoverished border region it was before the British discovered it as a health resort at the end of the18th century. In the hundred years or so which followed, wealthy expatriates helped create the French Riviera, socially and architecturally. During the 19th and early 10th centuries opulence became the only consistent architectural style as European royals and the rich built exotic, fanciful mansions like the Villa Ephrussi de Rothschild (► 56) along the coast from the Esterel to the Italian border. The atmosphere of the old, aristocratic Riviera lingers along the Corniches (► 44), on Cap d'Antibes and Cap Ferrat, where billionaires still live discreetly behind high walls, as well as in the leafier suburbs of Cannes, Menton and Nice. These days, the celebrity mansion owners include Elton John, and Russian oligarch Roman Abramovich in the Cap d'Antibes château that was once home to the Duke and Duchess of Windsor.

From Brigitte Bardot on the beach at St-Tropez in *And God Created Woman* to Grace Kelly speeding along the Corniche in *To Catch a Thief*, cinema has helped shape Provence's image. The Cannes International Film Festival (► 55), which takes place every May, is the obvious place for a spot of star gazing. Late May is also the time when the annual Grand Prix in Monaco (► 48) turns the principality into a Formula One racing circuit.

For a taste of the Riviera lifestyle at its most hedonistic and extravagant, head for St Tropez (► 68) in high season. The port is lined with vast motor yachts, many of which serve as floating platforms for the most extravagant parties. By day, Nikki Beach (► 71) is the place to rub shoulders with the likes of Paris Hilton, while by night you'll need confidence, deep pockets and a fashionable wardrobe to mix it with the same high-spending set at Les Caves du Roy or the VIP Room (► 88).

SOME OF THE BEST

HILLTOP VILLAGES

1 Èze (➤ 45)
2 Gordes (➤ 150–151)
3 Grimaud (➤ 78–79)
4 Moustiers-Ste-Marie (➤ 80–81)
5 St-Paul-de-Vence (➤ 51)

ACTIVITIES

1 Canoe the Verdon Gorge (➤ 74–76)
2 Horse-ride in the Camargue (➤ 116–118)
3 Hang-glide off Mont Ventoux (Association Vaucluse Parapente, Avignon, tel: 04 90 85 67 82)
4 Take a helicopter ride from Nice Airport to Monte-Carlo (Héli Inter Riviera, tel: 04 93 21 46 46)
5 Ski at Serre-Chevalier (tourist office, tel: 04 92 24 98 98)

BEACHES

1 Cannes – best for star-spotting
2 Cassis (Calanques) – most scenic
3 Îles d'Hyères (Plage de la Palud, Port-Cros) – best island beach
4 Marseille – best water sports
5 St-Tropez (La Voile Rouge) – the trendiest

CHILDREN'S ACTIVITIES

1 Musée Océanographique, Monaco (➤ 49)
2 Marineland, Antibes (➤ 57) – a great marine show
3 Visiobulle, Juan-les-Pins – a glass-bottomed boat trip
4 Grottes de St-Cézaire – a fairy-tale world of red caves
5 Massalia Théâtre, Marseille – marionnette theatre

CAFÉS

1 Café de la Place (St-Paul-de-Vence), locals' café
2 Café Excelsior (St-Raphaël), France's first live-music café
3 Sénéquier (St-Tropez), one of the Riviera's top celebrity haunts. Try the nougat!
4 Café de France (Isle-sur-la-Sorgue), historic hot spot for poets, philosophers and artists
5 Les Deux Garçons (Aix-en-Provence), the city's first café and watering-hole of Cézanne, Piaf, Picasso, Sartre et al

MARKETS

1 Aix-en-Provence (Tue, Thu, Sat am) – fruit, vegetables, cheese and flowers galore
2 Arles (Sat am) – fruit, vegetables, soaps and fabrics sold by locals in traditional dress
3 Marseille Fish Market (daily am) – boatside stalls
4 Nice's cours Saleya (daily am) – colour and fragrance
5 Grand Marché Truffes et Gastronomie (truffle and gastronomy market), Rognes (December)

Finding Your
Feet

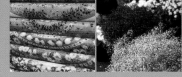

First Two Hours

There is ready access to France through the northern coastal ports, such as Calais, and via rail routes, including the Eurotunnel and Eurostar links with the UK. Nice and Marseille are Provence's main international airports. If you are staying in the Vaucluse, the Bouches-du-Rhône or the Var, it is more convenient to fly into Marseille.

Arriving by Road from the UK

Eurotunnel
■ The **Eurotunnel** shuttle train (tel: 08705 353 535; www.eurotunnel. com) takes vehicles and their passengers under the English Channel from Folkestone, in the UK, to Calais/Coquelles, in northern France. The journey takes 35 minutes and is the shortest vehicular journey time from the UK to mainland Europe.

Ferries
■ Well-equipped **car ferries** link France with the UK (Brittany Ferries tel: 08709 076 103; www.brittanyferries.com. LD Lines tel: 0844 576 8836; www.ldlines.com. P&O Ferries tel: 08716 645 645; www.poferries.com. Seafrance tel: 0871 663 2546; www.seafrance. com. Speedferries tel: 0871 222 7456; www.speedferries.com). The cost varies according to the time, day and month of travel. Book early for the cheapest fares.

In France
■ Once in France, a comprehensive system of *autoroutes* **(motorways/ expressways)** fanning out from Paris enables you to cross the country with relative ease. Your motoring organisation can recommend a suitable route to your final destination; or visit www.theAA.com/travel to plan your route online.

Arriving in Nice

By Air
■ Most international flights come into **Nice-Côte d'Azur Airport** (tel: 0820 423 333; www.nice.aeroport.fr), in eastern Provence, on the coast 6km (4 miles) west of Nice. The second busiest airport in France, it is well situated for visitors to the Riviera resorts of Antibes, Cannes and Monaco. There are two terminals, with information desks, shops, restaurants, banks, bureaux de change and car-rental firms.
■ A **taxi** into Nice will cost around €20–€28 and takes 20 minutes. There's **no rail** link, but buses run to the centre of Nice every 20 minutes (€4). Take bus 23 or 98 to the **bus station** (*gare routière)* near Vieux Nice; or bus 99 to the Nice **train station** (*gare SNCF*).

By Train
■ The easiest option is to take the **Eurostar** from **London** to **Lille** (1 hour 40 minutes) and change platforms for the direct **TGV** (*Train à Grande Vitesse*) to **Nice** and all key stations in Provence. Through tickets from the UK are available from Rail Europe (tel: 08448 484 0641; www.raileurope.co.uk).

■ **Nice Tourist Offices**
✉ 5 promenade des Anglais, Nice ☎ 0892 707 407;

www.nicetourisme.biz ⊕ Jun–Sep Mon–Sat 8–8, Sun 9–7; Oct–May Mon–Sat 9–6

✉ Nice-Côte d'Azur Airport, Terminal 1 ⊕ Mon–Sat 8am–9pm
✉ SNCF Railway Station, Avenue Thiers ⊕ Jun–Sep Mon–Sat 8–8, Sun 9–7; Oct–May Mon–Sat 8–7, Sun 10–5

Arriving in Marseille

By Air
■ **Marseille-Provence Airport, also called Marseille-Marignane** (tel: 04 42 14 14 14; www.mrsairport.fr), is 30km (19 miles) northwest of Marseille and operates international and regional flights. It has three terminals with shops, restaurants and bureaux de change.
■ **Taxis** to the city centre take 45 minutes, and cost around €40 by day and €50 by night. **Shuttle buses** to St-Charles train station run about every 20 minutes from 6:10am to 10:50pm. After 8:50 they tie in with flights (€8.50, 25 minutes).

■ **Marseille Tourist Office** ✉ 4 La Canebière, Marseille ☎ 04 91 13 89 00; www.marseille-tourisme.com ⊕ Mon–Sat 9–7, Sun 10–5 (longer hours in peak season)

Arriving in Toulon

By Air
■ **Toulon-Hyères** (tel: 08 25 01 83 87; www.toulon-hyeres.aeroport.fr) is 23km (14 miles) east of Toulon and receives daily flights from Paris and weekly flights from London Gatwick. There is one terminal, with a café/bar.
■ A **taxi** into Toulon will cost around €45 and take 40 minutes. A **bus** service to the city runs several times during the day, but it does not necessarily coincide with the flight arrivals.

■ **Toulon Tourist Office**
✉ 334, avenue de la République, Toulon ☎ 04 94 18 53 00; www.toulontourisme.com ⊕ Jul–Aug Mon, Wed–Sat 9–8, Tue 10–8, Sun 10–-12; Sep–Jun Mon, Wed–Sat 9–6, Tue 10–6, Sun 10–12.

Arriving in Nîmes

By Air
■ **Nîmes-Arles-Camargue** (tel: 04 66 70 49 49; www.nimes-aeroport.fr) is a small airport 12km (7.5 miles) southeast of Nîmes, with services from London Luton, Liverpool and East Midlands by Ryanair. There is a car rental office at the small terminal.
■ A **taxi** into Nîmes will cost around €20 and take 25 minutes. A **bus** service meets flights and takes passengers into Nîmes. It costs €5 and the journey time is 25 minutes.

■ **Nîmes Tourist Office**
✉ 6 rue Auguste, Nîmes ☎ 04 66 58 38 00; www.ot-nimes.fr
⊕ Jul–Aug Mon–Fri 8:30–8, Sat 9–7, Sun 10–6; Apr–May, Sep Mon–Fri 8:30–7, Sat 9–7, Sun 10–6; Oct–Mar Mon–Fri 8:30–6:30, Sat 9–6:30, Sun 10–5.

Getting Around

By Car

- **Driving** is a good way to discover the rural areas of Provence. The roads in the region are generally in excellent condition with good signposting. Traffic jams can be a problem on the coast at any timeof year.
- If **bringing your own car** to France, you must always carry the following documentation in addition to your passport: a full, valid national driver's licence, a certificate of motor insurance and the vehicle's registration document (plus a letter of authorisation from the owner if it is not registered in your name). Third-party motor insurance is the **minimum requirement**, but fully comprehensive cover is strongly advised. Check that your **insurance** covers you against damage in transit, and that you have adequate **breakdown cover** (for information contact the AA, tel: 0800 444 500; www.theAA.com, or your own national breakdown organisation). You must also display an **international sticker** or distinguishing sign plate on the rear of the car by the registration plate. **Headlights** of right-hand-drive cars must be adjusted for driving on the right.
- **To rent a car** you must be at least 21 years old and have held a full driver's licence for at least a year. You will have to produce your licence and passport or national ID card.
- You'll find most major **car rental** agencies at airports, main rail stations and in the large towns and cities. Book ahead in high season.
- Make sure you have **adequate insurance** and that you are aware of what you are covered for in the event of an accident. Low-cost operators may have a high excess charge for damage to the vehicle.
- Check that your vehicle comes with **roadside assistance**. In the event of a breakdown, refer to your documentation or to the information regarding breakdowns, which is often kept in the glove compartment or under the sun visor.
- If your car **breaks down** on an *autoroute*, phone from the emergency telephones located every 2km (1.25 miles) on the roadside.

Driving Know-How

- Drive on the **right-hand side** of the road (*serrez à droite*).
- Drivers must be **18 or over**, and you'll need to be **21 or over to rent** a car.
- **Speed limits** are 50kph/31mph on urban roads, 90kph/56mph outside built-up areas (80kph/49mph in rain), 110kph/68mph on dual carriageways/divided highways and non-toll motorways (100kph/62mph in rain), and 130kph/80mph on toll motorways (110kph/68mph in rain). Visiting drivers who have held a licence for less than two years must follow the wet-weather limits **at all times**, even when it's dry. Drivers from within the EU who **exceed the speed limit** by more than 40kph/25mph may have their licences confiscated by the police on the spot.
- In **built-up areas** you must **give way** to traffic coming from the right (*priorité à droite*). At roundabouts/traffic circles with signs saying *Cédez le passage* or *Vous n'avez pas la priorité*, traffic already on the roundabout has priority. On roundabouts without signs, traffic entering has priority.
- **Do not overtake** where there is a solid single line in the centre of the road.
- If you have **an accident or break down** it is compulsory to place a **warning triangle** at a suitable distance from the rear of your car. It is also compulsory to carry a reflectorised jacket in your vehicle.
- The **blood alcohol limit** is 0.5 per cent (US blood alcohol content 0.05). If you drink, don't drive.

- **Fuel** is unleaded (95 and 98 octane), lead replacement petrol (LRP or *supercarburant*), diesel (*gasoil* or *gazole*) and LPG. Many filling stations **close on Sundays** and at 6pm other days. Some self-service pumps are operated by debit/credit cards, but not all acccept cards issued outside France.
- For information on **road signs**, see www.permisenligne.com and the French highway code.

Trains

- Train services within France are run by the state railway company, the Société Nationale des Chemins de Fer (**SNCF** www.sncf.com), and are generally fast, comfortable and efficient.
- The **TGV** (*Train à Grande Vitesse*) high-speed train links major towns and cities at speeds of up to 300kph/186mph. **TER** (*Transport Express Régional*; tel: 0891 70 3000) provide a local service (*Lignes Régionales*). Reliable services link Nice, Cannes and Fréjus with Marseille. The Rhône valley towns of Avignon, Orange, Arles and Nîmes are also connected by train. Lines from Nice run through the Roya valley and northwest into the pre-Alps. For journey planning try www.ter-sncf.com, and in Provence look for the brochure *Guide reégional des transports*.
- **Buy tickets** at stations. You must validate your ticket in the designated machine on the platform before you board the train. If there is no ticket office or it is closed, you can pay the conductor on board the train. Some TER platforms do not have validation machines. In this case, the conductor will validate your ticket on the train.
- You can take **bicycles** onto all suitable trains outside the peak hours (Mon–Fri 7am–9am and 4:30pm–6:30pm).
- Under-26s can get a 25 per cent **discount on travel** (*Carte 12–25*), and discounts are also available for older people and by booking well ahead (*Carte Escapades J30*). A variety of discount **rail passes** is available for travel within France, or within the whole of Europe, and should be bought before arrival in France from travel agents or Rail Europe (in the UK www.raileurope.co.uk; in the US www.raileurope.com).
- You can arrange to have your luggage delivered to your onward destination using SNCF's Service Bagages à Domicile – book at the same time as you buy your ticket, or call 3635 and dial 41.

Long-Distance Buses

- **Long-distance bus routes** within France are generally slightly less expensive than the trains, but much slower. You'll usually find the **bus station** (*gare routière*) close to the railway station (*gare SNCF*). **Eurolines** (tel: 08 92 89 90 91; www.eurolines.fr) operates services between major towns and cities within France and to other destinations within Europe. **SNCF** (tel: 3635) also runs services as extensions to rail links.

Local Buses

- **Local bus services** link the key towns in Provence. Services are limited on Sundays and official holidays. Buses usually leave from either the **bus station** or the **town square**. You should find timetable details here or at the bus company offices. The **route number** and final **destination** are dispalyed on the front of the bus. You can normally **buy tickets** on the bus or at kiosks/*tabacs* around the town. You must validate tickets in the machine on the bus.
- In **Aix-en-Provence** a shuttle bus links the town with the TGV station, 15km (9 miles) away. It runs from 4:40am to 11:25pm, every 15 minutes at peak times and every 30 minutes at other times. Aix en Bus (tel: 04 42

26 37 28) operates more than 20 lines around town and the suburbs. Buses depart from the bus station at avenue de l'Europe. You can buy tickets (1 ticket €1.10, 10 tickets €7.70) from the office at the bus station or on the buses (you must have the exact change).

■ In **Arles** tel: 0810 000 816 for information. Buses depart from the **bus station** at 24 boulevard Clemenceau in Arles. Societé des Transports d'Arles runs four lines. Buses between Arles and Ste-Maries de la Mer, Tarascon or Marseille are operated by Cartreize (www.lepilote.com). Tickets for town buses cost €0.80 each, or €6.50 for 10.

■ In **Avignon** Transports en Commun de la Region d'Avignon (TCRA) operates buses from avenue de Lattre de Tassigny (tel: 04 32 74 18 32; www.tcra.fr), and runs 31 routes around Avignon and to surrounding towns. Buses do not run within the walls of Avignon. Buses run from 7am to 8pm. STDGard runs services linking Nîmes, Avignon and Tarascon. Tickets cost €1.10 and can be purchased on the bus or from the office of the bus company. A Ticket Carnet valid for 10 trips costs €9.40

■ In **Cannes** Bus Azur (www.busazur.com) runs 20 services in the town and to surrounding towns. You can get information at the bus station at place Cornut Gentille, next to the town hall (tel: 0825 825 599). Buses run from 6am to 9pm. Sillages runs services from Cannes north into the hills around Grasse (tel: 04 92 42 33 80; www.sillages.eu).

■ You can download the **Trans Vaucluse public transport route map** of all bus links through and across Vaucluse at www.provenceguide.com.

■ Bus and tram services in and around Nice are operated by Ligne d'Azur, 3 place Masséna (tel:08 1006 1006, www.lignedazur.com). Single trip tickets can be bought on the bus and cost €1; a one-day pass costs €4. TAM inter-town services along the Riviera are operated by Rapides Côte d'Azur (www.rca.tm.fr); Noctam'bus night bus services link the coastal towns and Cannes to Grasse.

■ Bus, tram and metro services in Marseille are operated by RTM, 6 rue des Fabres tel 04.91.91.92.10, www.rtm.fr). A single ticket costs €1.70, a one-day pass €4. Night bus services fan out from the Vieux Port, while metro services run until after midnight at weekends.

■ SODETRAV (www.sodetrav.fr) operates infrequent coastal bus routes in the Var, linking resorts with Hyères, Toulon and St-Raphaël

Taxis

■ **Taxis** are a convenient but generally expensive option.

■ You'll pay a pick-up charge and a charge per kilometre (0.6 miles), plus extra for items of luggage and travel in the evening or on Sundays. All taxis use a **meter** (*compteur*). Make sure that this is reset for your journey. You may be charged for the driver's journey to collect you.

■ Some taxi firms provide **chauffeur-driven cars** by the day, if you wish to visit several locations around Provence.

■ The best way to find a taxi is to head to a **taxi stand** (indicated by a blue Taxi sign). Phoning for a taxi means the meter starts from the moment it sets off to pick you up.

■ Some taxis accept credit cards, but it is best to have **cash** available. It is usual to give a 10 per cent **tip**.

Admission Charges
The cost of admission for museums and places of interest mentioned in the text is indicated by the following price categories:
Inexpensive under €5   Moderate €5–€8   Expensive over €8

Accommodation

There's a wide variety of accommodation available to visitors to Provence, and you should find something to suit your budget and your taste. Accommodation ranges from the extremely grand hotels on the Riviera to old stone buildings in the country areas. For an authentic experience of France, you may like to try a campsite, stay in a rented gîte or perhaps try a family-run auberge. Certain cities including Aix en Provence and Avignon offer cheap accommodation deals for weekend stays; check with the individual city tourist websites for details.

Types of Accommodation

Hotels

■ Hotels are inspected and are **classified into six categories**, from no stars (at the bottom) to four stars and four-star luxury hotels. They must display their rates inside and outside the hotel. **Charges** are usually **per room** rather than per person, and breakfast is generally charged separately.

■ If you're driving down to the south of France from the UK you may be glad to break the journey overnight in one of the many budget chain hotels that cluster by road junctions and in retail or industrial parks on the edge of most towns. The most basic, such as Formule 1 (www.hotelformule1.com) have simple but comfortable rooms with shared facilities for as little as €30 a night; there's more comfort on offer in the slightly more expensive Etap (www.etaphotel.com) and Première Classe (www.premiereclasse. com) chains. Some sat nav systems will be able to locate these hotels and if you arrive late without a reservation you can pay for a room at Etap or Formule 1 hotels with your credit card using the terminal at the door.

■ Family-run inns and small hotels, the **Logis de France**, usually offer some of the best accommodation if you're on a budget. All have a basic standard of comfort, and some are in particularly quaint or charming locations. Most have their own restaurant, serving good local food. In remote areas, some hotels offer deals including meals. If you are cycling or hiking **luggage can be transported** between Logis for you – very useful if you're planning a hiking break. As well as star gradings, Logis also have their own fireplace symbol of classification. Find them on the website www.logis-de-france.com, or get a list from the tourist office.

■ There are some great **luxury hotels**, if you want to treat yourself. The traditional *belle-époque* hotels of the Riviera, such as Hôtel Négresco ► 59, have a cachet which is hard to beat.

■ For something with a more modern twist, look at designer hotels, or for a stay in a luxurious château setting, contact Relais & Château (tel: 08 25 32 32 32; www.relaischateaux.com).

Bed-and-Breakfast

■ **Chambres d'hôte** offers a taste of life in a real French household, anywhere from a farm to a château. Ask at the tourist offices for local availability. Many of the best are affiliated to the **Gîtes de France** organisation, which grades them with one to four ears of corn (*épis*) according to the level of comfort and facilities. All the establishments listed in the **AA Bed & Breakfast in France** are inspected by **Gîtes de France.**

Self Catering (Gîtes)

■ Self-contained cottages, villas and apartments (**gîtes**) are widely available in towns, villages and country areas, and offer particularly good value for families. They are usually **rented by the week or fortnight**, and may range from simple and basic (bring your own linen) to more elaborate, with swimming pools and other facilities thrown in.

■ Many *gîtes* are administered through the **Gîtes de France** organisation, which also inspects and grades them according to comfort and facilities (www.gites-de-france.com). Local tourist offices also generally hold this information for their area.

Youth Hostels

■ There are around 160 youth hostels (*auberges de jeunesse*) across France, which are open to members from other countries if they have a membership card with photo. For a complete list and details of youth hostels in Provence, contact the Fédération Unie des Auberges de Jeunesse, 27 rue Pajol, 75018 Paris (tel: 01 44 89 87 27; www.fuaj.org).

Camping

■ The warm, dry climate in Provence makes camping a very popular choice for visitors both from abroad and from northern France, with a roll-call exceeding **9,000 fully equipped campsites**, plus around 2,300 farm campsites. Sites are **inspected and graded** with a star system like that of the hotels, and range from basic (with electricity, showers and lavatories) to luxurious, with swimming pools and other family sports activities, restaurants and bars, and kids' clubs. You don't even have to take your own tent as many have **pre-pitched tents and mobile homes** on site, complete with cooking equipment, fridge and beds.

■ You must **book well ahead**, especially in high season, which runs from April to September. For more information contact the **National Federation of Campsites** (tel: 01 42 72 84 08; www.campingfrance.com). **The** *AA Caravan and Camping in France* gives details of over 450 inspected campsites throughout the country.

■ Note that camping or overnight parking of caravans and motorhomes is **not permitted** on the beach or at the roadside. If you get caught out and need to find a campsite, the local tourist office should be able to advise you, and in case of an emergency, police stations can also let you have a list of local campsite addresses. Check with the local town hall if you intend to camp away from official sites, as it is often forbidden, especially in areas at risk from forest fires.

Finding a Room

■ If you haven't booked ahead, visit the **local tourist office**, as they will have a list of accommodation with prices.

■ When you **check in**, you may need to complete a registration form and show your passport. Ask to see the room first, especially in cheaper accommodation.

■ **Check-out time** is usually around 10 or 11am.

Seasonal Rates

■ Accommodation prices are likely to **vary widely throughout the year**, according to the season. In the resort areas of Provence, higher prices may be charged between April and September.

Prices
Expect to pay per night for a double room:
€ under €100 €€ €100–€200 €€€ over €200

Food and Drink

Few nations enjoy their food with quite the pride and relish of the French. Eating out is one of the "must do" experiences on a holiday in Provence, and there's no better way to discover the wealth of local dishes and culinary twists than at a local bistro.

Provençal Cuisine

■ Near the **coast**, fish dishes reign supreme – the ultimate fish dish here is, of course, *bouillabaisse*. *Moules frîtes* (mussels with french fries) are always good value, as are *telines Camarguais*, tiny shellfish served with *aïoli* (garlic mayonnaise). By contrast, meat dishes predominate inland. Try Sisteron lamb with its taste of wild thyme, game dishes or *boeuf gardian* (a spicy beef stew with olives, served with Camarguais rice).

■ The **Nice area** has its own distinctive cuisine. Pizzas and pasta taste every bit as good here as they do over the border in Italy. Look out also for *pissaladière* (olive and onion pizza) and *petits farcis* (savoury stuffed artichoke hearts, courgettes and tomatoes), *beignets* (aubergine or courgette fritters) and *socca* (chickpea pancake, sold hot from stalls in the street and incredibly cheap). Ice cream is often just as good as in Italy.

Vin de Provence

■ About 11 per cent of France's **wine** comes from Provence. The chalky soils and warm, dry Mediterranean climate produce the smooth, easy-to-drink wines such as Côtes du Ventoux and Côtes du Lubéron. Some of the more famous labels include Chateauneuf du Pape.

■ Provence is particularly famous for its rosé wines – fresh, crisp and fruity. Côtes de Provence and Bandol are among the best. For white wine try the dry, green-tinged Cassis wines or the fruity Bellet.

Where to Eat

■ You'll find a decent **restaurant** or several in every town, where the locals will go for a special occasion. Expect to **reserve your table in advance, dress smartly, and allow plenty of time** for the full gastronomic experience. If the dinner price is beyond your budget, look out for better-value set-menus at lunchtime. The ***menu dégustation*** offers a selection of the restaurant's signature dishes with accompanying wines at a fixed price.

■ **Brasseries** are **informal** establishments generally open long hours, where you can sample local dishes alongside staples such as *steak-frîtes* (steak with chips/fries).

■ **Bistros** tend to be **small, informal, family-run** restaurants serving traditional and local dishes, with a modest wine list.

■ Lunchtime menus tend to offer the **best value**, when a *menu du jour* (daily menu) of two or three courses is likely to cost much less than an evening meal. ***Prix-fixe*** meals of three or four courses also generally offer good value.

■ **Service** should be **included in the bill** (*l'addition*) – look for the words *service compris*, or *s.c.* If the service is exceptional, you may like to leave loose change (in a bar) or a tip of 5 per cent (in a restaurant).

Prices
Expect to pay for a three-course meal for one, excluding drinks:
€   under €25   €€   €25–€50   €€€   over €50

Shopping

Shopping in Provence can be a real pleasure, whether you're after local produce at the lively markets, looking for chic Riviera fashion in the boutiques or conversing with the small-scale cheese producers in the marché (market). Prices may not be cheap, but quality is usually high. Pottery, perfumes, soaps, herbs, olive oil and wine are among the best buys.

Opening Hours

■ **Opening times vary** according to the type of shop, the season and the location, and there are no hard-and-fast rules. Some shops close from noon until mid-afternoon (➤ 178).

■ **Daily and weekly markets** are a feature of cities and towns, and usually operate from around 7am to noon. Often the people who produced or grew the food are the people selling it too, and can tell you about their range of cheeses or produce.

Payment

■ Shops in towns and major tourist areas usually accept payment by **credit or debit card**. For markets and smaller outlets, carry **euros** in cash.

■ Visitors from outside the European Union can reclaim a 12 per cent tax on certain purchases. You'll need a **détaxe** form from the shopkeeper, which must be shown with the goods and stamped at customs

What to Buy

■ **Food** is taken very seriously in France. Most small food shops sell only one type of product – you're most likely to see the *boulangerie* (bakery), *pâtisserie* (pastry/cake shop), *fromagerie* (cheese shop), *boucherie* (butcher's shop), *charcuterie* (delicatessen) and *poissonnerie* (fishmonger's). Dried wild herbs and virgin olive oil are the musts for any food shopping trip. For a sweet treat try crystallised fruits in Apt, *berlingots* (stripey boiled sweets) in Carpentras and *marrons glacés* (glazed chestnuts) in Collobrières. If you're in the lavender-growing regions of rural Provence, particularly around the plateau de Valensole, look out for lavender honey and delicious soft nougat.

■ Visit the local **markets** for the freshest seasonal produce, including fruit, vegetables and cheeses, and products from basketware to pottery. Large cities hold at least one daily market and smaller towns have a weekly one. In autumn and winter look for wild *cèpe* mushrooms and truffles.

■ Hypermarkets sell an excellent range of **French wines**. It is also fun to buy from the vineyards (*domaines*) themselves – the Rhône and Lubéron have specialist wine routes. Go for a tasting at a vineyard and you will be expected to buy at least one bottle – and, of course, more if you find something you really like.

■ The area around Grasse is world-famous for its **perfumes**, while Marseille is known for its quality **soap**, often made with a base of olive oil. Terracotta pottery is also popular, and you'll find bright ceramics in any market square. For *faïences* (fine glazed ceramics) head to Moustiers-Ste-Marie, and for **glassware** try Biot.

■ France is known world-wide for its **stylish fashion**, and you'll find designer labels in the chic Riviera resorts and individual boutiques everywhere. You can buy traditional **Provençal cotton** fabrics either by the length or ready-made into scarves, tops and skirts. Souléiado and Les Olivades stores are good places to look.

Entertainment

Epic opera, concerts and drama in the Roman amphitheatres at Arles or Orange and major theatrical performances at the Avignon festival are all part of the arts scene in Provence. For something more intimate, try a fringe show in a café-theatre or jazz in a small, smoke-filled club. Magazines in hotel foyers and tourist offices are a good source of information about all forms of entertainment, including top sporting events.

Live Arts

- All major cities have a **theatre**. The season usually runs from October until late spring, although the fringe scene, specialising in works by local playwrights, has a year-round schedule.
- Avignon's International Theatre Festival in July offers top entertainment and fringe shows in venues ranging from the Palais des Papes to cafés.
- Provence's most famous **operatic and classical music festival** is the Chorégies in Orange. The Roman theatre is the setting for large-scale opera productions such as *Carmen* and *La Traviata*. In Aix-en-Provence, the Festival d'Art Lyrique is held in the courtyard of the Archbishop's Palace, where you are likely to hear performances of works by Mozart and Britten.
- The summer **music festivals** in Aix and Orange have orchestral concerts, as well as the more famous opera. In Nice, you can enjoy sacred music in churches and summer concerts at the Cimiez monastery.
- The world's leading **jazz** musicians are attracted to the Cimiez gardens for the Nice Jazz Festival and to La Pinède for Jazz à Juan.
- **Contemporary dance festivals** are held in Aix and Marseille in summer, and the Ballet Preljocaj (www.preljocaj.org) hosts performances throughout the year at the Pavillon Noir in Aix. For information on the Ballet National de Marseille, visit www.ballet-de-marseille.com

Nightlife

- There are **café-bars** all over Provence. In rural areas they are the place for locals to get together for a drink and perhaps enjoy a game of pool. In the cities and resorts they are likely to be more sophisticated places to stop for a drink either before or after dinner. You're likely to find tables outside during the summer, where you can watch the world go by. In cities, bars open at 7am to serve breakfast and don't close until the early hours of the morning. Out of season and out of the cities, bars may close at 9pm. Unaccompanied children under 16 are not allowed into bars. The legal age for drinking is 16, although children aged 14 to 16 may drink wine or beer if accompanied by an adult.
- Major cities and resorts have a vibrant **club** scene, and you'll find flyers at tourist offices, music stores and trendy cafés. Clubs may open from 10pm, but don't expect things to liven up until about midnight. Smart dress is the rule. There is an admission charge at weekends and on some week nights, but this usually includes your first drink.
- **Casinos** are part of the entertainment scene and you should dress up for the ocassion. Tables open around 10pm and close around 4am – expect to pay an entrance fee. The place to go is Monte-Carlo's Casino. Only foreigners are allowed to play here, so you'll need your passport and you must be over 18. At the glamorous Ruhl casino in Nice you can enjoy spectacular dinner cabarets, as well as take your chances at the gaming tables and slot machines.

Sports and Outdoor Activities

■ Most tourist offices publish separate booklets detailing their leisure facilities, whether it's a pétanque (boules) pitch, sports hall, swimming pool (*piscine*), tennis court or golf course. Look for details of local sporting facilities amid the tourist publications under *loisirs* (leisure).

■ The area around the Lubéron attracts **climbers** from all over the world. Contact the Club Alpin de Français (www.clubalpin.com) for information about climbing lessons, or for equipment rental if you are an experienced climber.

■ **Cycling** is a popular pastime, as well as a serious sport in France, and you can rent bicycles in towns and at major railway stations. Most tourist offices can offer itineraries for riders with mountain bikes (*vélo tous terrains – VTT*). The **Tour de France** is possibly France's most important sporting event (www.letour.fr). The three-week event crosses the country in July and often includes a stretch in Provence. Arrive early to find a suitable spot along the route, as the roads will be closed well before the race is expected to pass by. You don't need a ticket to watch.

■ Many of the rivers in Provence, including the spectacular Grand Canyon du Verdon, are excellent for **kayaking** and **canoeing**. You can rent equipment on site by the hour, the day or longer, or take a guided kayak trip. Fédération Française de Canöe-Kayak: www.ffck.org

■ The waterways of Provence offer plenty of opportunities for **angling** and **fly-fishing**. You will need a licence, available from fishing shops.

■ There are plenty of **golf** courses in Provence, especially on the coast. You can get details of special offers on green fees for visitors from tourist offices. They also have details of passes allowing holidaymakers to visit a selection of courses. Fédération Française de Golf: www.ffg.org.

■ **Football** is one of the most popular sports in France. Olympique de Marseille and AS Monaco are among the region's top teams. AS Monaco plays at Stade Louis II (tel: 377 92 05 74 73; www.asm-fc. com); Olympique de Marseille at Stade Velodrome 3, boulevard Michelet (tel: 3229; www.om.net). The season runs from August until end May.

■ **Horse racing** is popular in France and there are *hippodromes* (race courses) in some of the coastal towns and resorts in Provence. The main venues are at Cagnes-sur-Mer (www.hippodrome-cotedazur.com) and Marseille (www. hippodrome-borely.com).

■ **Horse-back riding** trips into the flat marshes of the Camargue are an ideal way to discover the area's spectacular scenery. You'll also find riding clubs close to major towns and cities, including Les Milles, near Aix. Fédération Française d'Équitation: www.ffe.com

■ **Motor racing** fans will look forward to the most glamorous race in the Formula 1 calendar, when the narrow streets of Monte-Carlo are turned into a race track (www.mcm.mc).

■ There are **sailing schools** and boats for rent at most of Provence's ports and marinas (www.voilecotedazur.com). Sailing is also popular in the mountain lakes of the Alpes-de-Haute-Provence, such as Lac de Quinson and Lac du Castillon.

■ There are **windsurfing** schools all along the coast. The best places to watch the experts are at Stes-Maries-de-la-Mer and l'Almanarre, near Hyères.

■ Provence is criss-crossed by **walking** and **hiking** trails. A series of *Sentiers de Grandes Randonnées* (long-distance trails) and *Petites Randonnées* (shorter walking routes) are marked on maps. Most tourist offices have information about trails and walks in their area, including marked trails around lakes, along river banks or linking historical monuments, and town halls usually have free maps of local walks.

The Alpes-Maritimes

Getting Your Bearings

The name Alpes-Maritimes portrays the very essence of this region – the perfect combination of sea and mountains, attracting millions of visitors annually. After all, the French Riviera is one of the world's most sophisticated holiday playgrounds, with its trio of chic seaside cities – Nice, Monaco and Cannes – each rivalling the other with their luxury hotels, award-winning restaurants, designer boutiques and glitzy marinas brimming with millionaires' yachts.

Ubaye □ Barcelonnette 🖾 D900

ALPES-DE-HTE-PROVENCE

2839 ▲ Le Grand Cheval de Bois

□ Allos

Despite the Riviera's popularity, it is still possible to escape the bustling tourist-courting coastal resorts and explore the *arrière pays* (hinterland): to ramble through hectares of wild *garrique* landscapes; to hike in the wild hills, forests and mountains of the unspoiled Parc National du Mercantour; and to explore such Picturesque hilltop villages as Èze, Biot and St-Paul-de-Vence.

Art has flourished here for centuries, and today the region boasts more than its fair share of magnificent museums and galleries, including Musée Matisse, Musée Chagall and MAMAC (Musée d'Art Moderne et d'Art Contemporain) in Nice; Musée Picasso in Antibes; Musée Renoir between Cagnes-sur-Mer and Haut-de-Cagnes; and the dazzling Fondation Maeght, one of the world's most distinguished modern art museums, at St-Paul-de-Vence.

From art treasures to sleepy villages, glamorous resorts and dramatic landscapes, the Alpes-Maritimes is a region of great contrasts. No wonder many visitors return here year after year for their annual fix of Mediterranean *joie de vivre*.

St- □ Auban

N85

Page 35: Palais Massena in Nice

Left: A floral extravaganza, Nice Carnival

3031 ▲ Mont Ténibre
St-Etienne-de-Tinée
D2205
2818 ▲ Cime de Pal
Isola

2241 ▲ Cime de l'Evêque

0   20 km
0   10 miles

Parc National du Mercantour 5

Guillaumes
D28
Beuil
St-Sauveur-sur-Tinée
3143 ▲ Cime du Gélas
St-Martin-Vésubie
2873 ▲ Mont Bégo
Tende
N204

D902

2137 ▲ Dôme de Barrot

Tinée
2085 ▲ Mont Tournairet
D2565

Roya
Saorge

ALPES-MARITIMES
Lantosque
D2566
Breil-sur-Roya

Puget-Théniers
N202
Var
Villars-sur-Var
D2205
D2565
1504 ▲ Cime de Rocca Seira
D2566
SS20

Roquesteron
Esteron
L'Escarène
Sospel
D2566

Montagne du Cheiron
▲ 1777 Cime du Cheiron
1264 ▲ Pic de Baudon

Gréolières
N202
D2204
Menton 13
E80 A8
Cap Martin

Vence 6
D2201
Les Corniches 2
3 **Monaco**

Fondation Maeght 4
N202
Nice 1
12 **Villa Ephrussi de Rothschild**
Cap Ferrat

N85
N2085
11

7 **Grasse**
N85
Cagnes-sur-Mer
E80 A8
10 **Biot**

Siagne
N7
8 **Cannes**
9 **Antibes**
Cap d'Antibes

N7
Mandelieu-la-Napoule
Îles de Lérins
Miramar

In Three Days

If you're not quite sure where to begin your travels, this itinerary recommends a practical and enjoyable three-day tour of The Alpes-Maritimes, taking in some of the best places to see using the Getting Your Bearings map on the previous page. For more information see the main entries.

Day One

Morning

Start your day in **❶ Nice** (➤ 40–43) at the cours Saleya (➤ 42). This sunny square is home to one of France's best outdoor flower, fruit and vegetable markets (below) and, with all the colours and fragrances of Provence, it is a veritable feast for the senses. Watch the world go by from the pavement terraces of one of the many cafés here, then spend the rest of the morning getting lost in the maze of narrow streets and shaded alleys of Vieux Nice (➤ 42). Here you will find some fascinating specialist boutiques, art galleries and an excellent choice of restaurants for lunch.

Lunch

If you're lucky, you may get a table at La Mérenda (4 rue Raoul Bosio, no phone), a tiny restaurant near cours Saleya, which specialises in Niçois dishes.

Afternoon

Visit one of Nice's major galleries: the beautiful Musée Matisse (➤ 43) set in olive groves overlooking the city, or the remarkable Musée d'Art Moderne et d'Art Contemporain (MAMAC), which traces the history of French and American avant-garde from the 1960s.

Evening
Stroll the palm-lined waterfront Promenade des Anglais before enjoying a performance at the Opéra de Nice (➤ 62). Dine near by, at elegant La Petite Maison (11 rue St-François-de-Paule, tel: 04 93 92 59 59).

Day Two

Morning
Visit the modern art collection at ❹**Fondation Maeght** (➤ 51), just outside St-Paul-de-Vence. This charming village (left) is also well worth a visit, with its art galleries and sophisticated boutiques which line the steep, cobbled streets.

Lunch
Grab a light lunch on the terrace at Café de la Place (place Général de Gaulle, St-Paul-de-Vence, tel: 04 93 32 80 03), and watch locals playing pétanque.

Afternoon
Drive the snake-like, cliff-hanging ❷**Moyenne Corniche** (➤ 44–47) from Nice to Monaco, for some of the Riviera's most spectacular scenery. En route, stop for refreshment in the picture-postcard hilltop village of Èze (➤ 45).

On arrival in ❸**Monaco** (➤ 48–50), head straight to the world-famous Musée Océanographique (➤ 49), with attractions to fascinate all ages.

Evening
The cobbled streets of Monaco-Ville with their fountain-filled squares and grand Italianate façades are especially atmospheric in the evening light. Experience traditional Monégasque cuisine at Le Castelroc (place du Palais, tel: 0377 93 30 36 68) opposite the Palais Princier (➤ 49), then join bejewelled gamblers to try your luck in the world's most famous Casino (place du Casino, Monte Carlo, ➤ 49, 50, 62).

Day Three

Take a picnic and spend the day exploring the ❺**Parc National du Mercantour** (right, ➤ 52–53). With its high mountains, lakes, forests and verdant meadows, this vast country park is an absolute must for nature-lovers.

⬛ Nice

Nice, one of the biggest and most vibrant cities along the Mediterranean coast, is the capital of the Riviera. There's an old Italian corner to discover, and if you're here in the two weeks before Lent you're bound to get swept up by the colourful frenzy of the Mardi-Gras carnival, the Riviera's biggest winter event. The entire city is cradled by the vine-clad foothills of the maritime Alps, and this charming setting has attracted many famous artists over the years. As a result, Nice is blessed with more museums and galleries than any French town outside Paris.

Nice's history has been influenced by successive owners, including the Ligurians, the Greeks and the Romans, and only became part of France when the Italians (who called it Nizza) handed it over in the 1860. In the 19th century it became a chic winter resort, with Queen Victoria among its illustrious visitors.

Nice Highlights

The palm-lined **promenade des Anglais**, which graciously sweeps round the Baie des Anges (Bay of Angels), is bordered by a busy highway and the grand façades of luxury *belle-époque* hotels, such as the world-famous **Négresco**. Stretching for several kilometres beside the town's stony beach, on

Left: Boats in the harbour at Nice
Above: The view from Colline du Château

fine days it is full of people taking a leisurely stroll, sitting in the sun or skating. The promenade ends at **Colline du Château**, a high headland which separates the beach and the port. There is no trace of the medieval fortress which once stood here, but you will find shady gardens and fabulous views of the crowded Old Port – busy with all kinds of craft – the sea and town.

The park-like Paillon promenade divides the Old Town from the New and is home to the MAMAC gallery. Around

HÔTEL NÉGRESCO

The Négresco, one of France's most magnificent hotels, features Churchill, Chaplin, Piaf, Taylor and Burton, Picasso and the Beatles on its guest list. Inside, the décor is inspired by Versailles, while from the outside, its pink-and-white turreted façade looks more like a wedding cake than a hotel. You may have trouble finding the main entrance, which is in a small back street.

the handsome main square, **place Masséna**, are the broad boulevards and designer shops of the modern city, and a pedestrian-only area of narrow streets lined with specialist shops and inexpensive restaurants. Set back from the sea at the eastern end of the beach is **Vieux Nice** (Old Nice),

Above: Enjoying an drink on a summer's evening on the cours Saleya

a maze of dark narrow streets, festooned with flowers and laundry and brimming with cafés, hidden squares and bustling markets. This is the trendiest part of Nice, lively day and night, especially around **cours Saleya**. This spacious square is scene of one of France's top fruit and vegetable markets – the tastes, fragrances and colours of Provence are a feast for the senses. In the evenings, cafés and restaurants fill the square, making it one of Nice's most animated night spots.

On higher ground to the north you'll find **Cimiez**, a district of luxury villas and palatial buildings considered to be the city's smartest residential area. Near by lies the site of a **Roman settlement**, and you can explore Les Arènes (a small

oval amphitheatre), paved streets, public baths and a museum of excavated remains. Europe's leading international Jazz Festival is held in Cimiez every July, in the beautiful olive grove beside the **Musée Matisse** (➤ 43).

The **Cathédrale Orthodoxe Russe St-Nicolas**, in the St-Etiénne district, is a magnificent pink-and-grey Russian Orthodox church, crowned by six gleaming green onion-shaped cupolas. Brimming with precious icons, frescoes and treasures, the church still conducts regular services in Russian.

A narrow stepped alley in Vieux Nice

NICE: INSIDE INFO

Top tips The Carte Musées Ville de Nice (€7 for 7 days), available from the tourist office, gives unlimited access to many of the galleries and museums.
■ Admission to the municipal galleries is free to all on the first and third Sundays of every month.

Hidden gems Two of the lesser-known museums, but well worth seeking out, are the Asian Arts Museum, at 405 promenade des Anglais, and the Anatole Jakovsky International Museum of Naïve Art, on avenue de Fabron, which houses naïve art from all over the world.

TOP GALLERIES AT A GLANCE

Musée d'Art Moderne et d'Art Contemporain
🚏 196 D2
📧 Promenade des Arts
☎ 04 97 13 42 01; www.mamac-nice.org
🕐 Tue–Sun 10–6
💰 Inexpensive, free 1st and 3rd Sun of month

This intriguing modern structure of four
towers linked by bowed girders and glass
holds a great collection of avant-garde and pop-art dating from the 1960s.
Highlights include works by Lichtenstein, Warhol and Christo, as well as
French New Realists (➤ 14). Visit the rooftop terrace for spectacular views
of Nice.

Musée Matisse
🚏 196, off C3
📧 164 avenue des Arènes de Cimiez
☎ 04 93 81 08 08; www.musee-matisse-nice.org
🕐 Wed–Mon 10–6
💰 Inexpensive

Matisse (1869–1954), who spearheaded
the Fauvist movement in the early 20th
century, moved to Nice in 1917, and is buried in the cemetery near by. This
gallery, in a handsome 17th-century villa in the gardens at Cimiez, contains
the artist's breathtaking collection of his own sinuous sketches and brightly
coloured gouache paintings.

Musée National Message Biblique Marc Chagall
🚏 196 C3
📧 Avenue de Dr Ménard, Boulevard du Cimiez
☎ 04 93 53 87 20
🕐 Wed–Mon 10–5 or 6
💰 Moderate

Located in the heart of a Mediterranean garden at the foot of Cimiez hill, this
museum was specially designed to hold the French Surrealist artist's biblical
works, with fabulous stained-glass panels, mosaics and paintings.

TAKING A BREAK

Dine on fabulous fresh seafood with a Mediterranean twist at
the moderately priced **L'Âne Rouge**, overlooking the harbour
(7 quai des Deux-Emmanuel, tel: 04 93 89 49 63).

Tourist Information Office
🚏 196 B1 📧 5 promenade des Anglais
☎ 0892 707 407; www.nicetourisme.com
🕐 Summer Mon–Sat 8–8, Sun 9–7; winter Mon–Sat 9–6

Musée Archéologique de Cimiez
🚏 196, off C3 📧 160 avenue des Arènes ☎ 04 93 81 59 57 🕐 Wed–Mon
10–6. Guided tours by appointment 💰 Moderate

Cathédrale Orthodoxe Russe St-Nicolas
🚏 196 A2 📧 Avenue Nicolas-II ☎ 04 93 96 88 02 🕐 Mon–Sat 9:15–12,
2:30–6 (winter 5 or 5:30) 💰 Inexpensive

② The Corniches

Three famous corniches (cliff roads) traverse the most dramatic and mountainous stretch of the Riviera between Nice and Menton. The Grande, Moyenne and Inférieure corniches each zigzag their way along vertiginous ledges at three different elevations, overlooking the resorts and beaches.

The Grande Corniche, at the highest level, was built by Napoléon along the route of the old Via Julia Augusta, and passes through picturesque hilltop villages. This is by far the best choice for picnickers and lovers of plants and wildlife. The steep Moyenne Corniche, in the middle, is a wide modern road. This cliff-hanging route, with hair-raising bends, sudden tunnels and astounding views, is frequently used for car commercials and movie car chases. The lowest

Below: The spectacular view from the Jardin Exotique

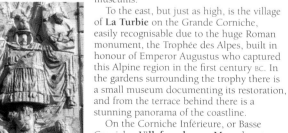

Above: The Roman Trophée des Alpes, detail of carving below, rises above La Turbie

route, the Corniche Inférieure, was built in the 18th century by the Prince of Monaco, and follows the coastal contours through all the wealthy coastal resorts and Monaco itself.

There are lots of highlights to explore along this stretch of coastline. The most strikingly situated and best-preserved Provençal hilltop village, **Èze** stands high on a rocky pinnacle ten minutes' drive from Nice and Monaco on the Moyenne Corniche. Known as the *Nid d'Aigle* (Eagle's Nest), it boasts spectacular views over the Riviera as far as Corsica. Tall, golden stone houses and a labyrinth of tiny vaulted passages and stairways climb steeply up to the ruins of the once-massive Saracen fortress, 429m (1,407 feet) above sea level, which is surrounded by an exotic garden, bristling with magnificent cacti, succulents and rare palms. Take time to explore the craft shops housed in small caves within the rock – tiny treasure troves of antiques, ceramics, pewter and olive-wood carvings. At the foot of the hill, the two perfume factories of Galimard and Fragonard both contain fascinating museums.

To the east, but just as high, is the village of **La Turbie** on the Grande Corniche, easily recognisable due to the huge Roman monument, the Trophée des Alpes, built in honour of Emperor Augustus who captured this Alpine region in the first century BC. In the gardens surrounding the trophy there is a small museum documenting its restoration, and from the terrace behind there is a stunning panorama of the coastline.

On the Corniche Inférieure, or Basse Corniche, **Villefranche-sur-Mer**, close to Nice, remains surprisingly unspoiled and little changed since it was founded in the 14th century as a customs-free port. Its picturesque natural harbour is fringed with old red and orange Italianate houses, tempting waterfront bars, cafés and restaurants. Take time to explore the maze of steep stairways and cavernous vaulted passageways which climb from the harbour through the *Vieille Ville* (Old Town), and the sturdy 16th-century citadel, with galleries of paintings and sculptures by local artists, including Picasso and Miró.

Jutting out into the Mediterranean, the peninsula of **Cap Ferrat** bristles with luxurious mansions and villas hidden away behind tall gates and impenetrable hedges. These include the peninsula's finest property, Villa Ephrussi de Rothschild, (► 56–57). The cape has long been a favourite haunt of the rich and famous, including writer Somerset Maugham, chanteuse Edith Piaf, the Duke and Duchess of Windsor, and movie stars Charlie Chaplin and David Niven. A delightful coast path leads from Villefranche around the cape, past countless tiny azure inlets (ideal for a refreshing dip), and makes a pleasant stroll before lunch in the former fishing village of St-Jean-Cap Ferrat.

On the eastern side of Cap Ferrat is **Beaulieu-sur-Mer**. Sheltered by a natural amphitheatre of hills, this is one of the warmest resorts on the Riviera. Its many attractions include an elegant palm-lined promenade, a glamorous casino, the elegant Edwardian Rotonde, and the extraordinary Villa

A bird's-eye view of Villefranche-sur-Mer and its harbour

THE CORNICHES: INSIDE INFO

Top tips The **Corniche Inférieure** is very busy in the main tourist season of July and August, so travel early if you want to visit one of the coastal resorts.
- Browse **Roquebrune-Cap Martin's** daily food and flower market.
- Drop into the **local tourist offices** and pick up a map detailing local coastal walks.

Hidden gem In Villefranche-sur-Mer, the tiny 14th-century **Chapelle St-Pierre**, by the quay, was decorated in 1957 with symbolic frescoes by Villefranche's most famous resident: writer and film director Jean Cocteau (tel: 04 93 76 90 70; open summer Tue–Sun 10–12, 3–7; winter 10–12, 2–6; admission inexpensive).

Grecque Kérylos – a faithful reproduction of an Athenian villa.

Sandwiched between Menton and Monaco, **Roquebrune-Cap Martin** is divided into two areas – Old Roquebrune, an attractive medieval hilltop village, and the smart coastal resort of Cap Martin. Old Roquebrune is a maze of ancient flower-filled lanes, steps and vaulted passageways clustered around its 10th-century château, which was built to ward off Saracen attack. A delightful coastal path (promenade Le Corbusier) circles the cape, passing sumptuous villas shrouded in dense foliage.

 TAKING A BREAK

Tuck into the *plat du jour* at **La Grotte** in place des Deux-Frères, at the entrance to Roquebrune village. This popular troglodyte restaurant has tables spilling out into the square (tel: 04 93 35 00 04, closed Tue evening and Wed). If you're in Èze then try the tasty *crêpes* on offer at **Le Cactus** in the old gateway (tel: 04 93 41 19 02, open Feb–Oct).

Tourist Offices
➕ 189 D2 ✉ Jardin François-Binon, Villefranche-sur-Mer
☎ 04 93 01 73 68
➕ 189 E2 ✉ 59 avenue Denis Semeria, Cap Ferrat ☎ 04 93 76 08 90
➕ 189 E2 ✉ Place de Gaulle, Èze
☎ 04 93 41 26 00
➕ 189 E2 ✉ Place Clemenceau, Beaulieu-sur-Mer ☎ 04 93 01 02 21
➕ 189 E2 ✉ 218 avenue Aristide Briand, Roquebrune-Cap Martin
☎ 04 93 35 62 87

❸ Monaco

After the Vatican, Monaco is the world's smallest sovereign state – a spotlessly clean, 2sq km (less than 1sq-mile) strip of skyscraper-covered land squeezed between sea and mountains. It has become an affluent and stylish haven for the world's rich and famous, who are drawn here by its attractive tax-free status.

Monaco is the name of the principality and also the district on the peninsula to the south. This contains the Old Town with its narrow streets and pastel-coloured houses, a startling contrast to the newer high-rise district of **Monte-Carlo**, centred round its glitzy casino and designer shops. With so much evident wealth and glamour, it is hard to imagine Monaco's turbulent past, but at various times it has been occupied by the French, the Spanish and the Dukes of Savoy. For the last 700 years, the principality has been ruled by the Grimaldi family, the world's oldest reigning monarchy.

The Old Town, **Monaco-Ville**, is reached via a long steep walkway from place d'Armes or by an elevator from parking des Pêcheurs on the seafront. This labyrinth of cool, cobbled streets perched on "the Rock" (a sheer-sided finger of land extending 800m/880 yards into the sea) has been well preserved, with lovely fountain-filled squares and fine Italianate façades.

The **Palais Princier** and surrounding gardens are situated at the western end of Monaco-Ville. In summer, when Prince Albert II is away, guided tours take visitors through the priceless treasures of the State Apartments and the small Musée Napoléon in the south wing of the palace. When he is in residence, the royal colours are flown from the tower

High-rise apartments overlook the Mediterranean in the millionaire resort of Monte-Carlo

The famous Casino

and you must be content with the Changing of the Guard ceremony (daily at 11:55am). Close by is the Cathédrale, built in 1875 and funded by casino profits. Among its treasures are two 16th-century retables by Niçois artist Louis Bréa, and tombs of the former princes of Monaco and the much-loved Princess Grace (1929–82).

Monaco's prestigious **Musée Océanographique**, a spectacular aquarium and museum of marine science, is located in a grandiose building on a sheer cliff high above the Mediterranean. Marine explorer Jacques Cousteau set up his research centre here and his remarkable films are regularly screened in the museum's cinema. Superbly lit aquariums hold thousands of rare fish, displays of living corals from all over the world and a state-of-the-art shark lagoon.

The Musée Océanographique is one of France's most popular museums

La Condamine, at the foot of the royal palace, is the busy commercial district. It is fun to wander along the quayside and marvel at the size and cost of the yachts, but take time to explore the back streets too, for they hide some superb shops and restaurants. **Fontvieille**, a modern residential and commercial development, built on reclaimed land below the rock of Monaco-Ville, has a marina, sports stadium and

excellent shops; it also has the Princess Grace Rose Garden, a peaceful oasis fragrant with the scent of 4,000 rose trees. Just off the Moyenne Corniche, above the residential district of Les Moneghetti, lies one of Monaco's finest attractions, the **Jardin Exotique**, bristling with thousands of cacti and succulents.

The world-famous **Casino**, in glitzy Monte-Carlo, is worth a visit even if you are not a gambler. Its opulent *belle-époque* interior is a riot of pink, green and gold, with marble floors and bronze sculptures. To the left of the casino is the Café de Paris and the casino's Salons Américains, a clattering room

of poker machines, with free entry. Ten euros will gain you entry to the Salons Européens in the casino proper, with blackjack, craps and roulette tables; and a further ten will take you into the lavish Salons Privés. Attached to the Casino is a tiny, ornate opera house, which has been graced by the world's most distinguished opera singers. The place du Casino, dazzlingly illuminated by night, is a Monaco must see.

TAKING A BREAK

You can rub shoulders with the beautiful people on the sun terrace at **Zebra Square**, a chic restaurant at 10 avenue Princesse-Grace, Monte-Carlo (tel: 377 99 99 25 50), or try **Stars'N'Bars** at 6 quai Antoine I, La Condamine (tel: 377 97 97 95 95, closed Mon in winter), a popular American-style bar-restaurant.

Tourist Information Office
✚ 197 C3
✉ 2a boulevard des Moulins
☎ 377 92 16 61 16;
www.visitmonaco.com;
www.monaco-tourisme.com
🕐 Mon–Sat 9–7, Sun 10–12

Palais Princier
✚ 197 A2 ✉ Place du Palais ☎ 377 93 25 18
31 🕐 Apr daily 10:30–6;
May–Sep daily 9:30–6:30; Oct 10–5:30. Closed Nov–Mar
💷 Moderate

Casino
✚ 197 C3 ✉ Place du Casino ☎ 377 98 06 21 21
🕐 Salons Européens from 2pm; Salons Privés from 4pm
💷 Expensive

Musée Océanographique
✚ 197 B1 ✉ Avenue St-Martin ☎ 377 93 15 36 00 🕐 Oct–Mar daily 10–6; Apr–Jun, Sep 9:30–7; Jul–Aug 9:30–7:30 💷 Expensive

Jardin Exotique de Moneghetti
✚ 197, off A3
✉ Off Moyenne Corniche
🕐 15 May–15 Sep daily 9–7 (closes 6 or nightfall in winter) 💷 Moderate

Above: The Jardin Exotique de Moneghetti

MONACO: INSIDE INFO

Top tips The currency in Monaco is the euro.
■ Don't visit Monaco during the **Grand Prix in May** unless you are a motor racing fan. The principality is crowded and many of the roads are closed.
■ You must be over 18 to visit the **Casino**. Don't forget to take your passport and wear a jacket and tie.
■ A frequent **bus service** runs the length of Monaco from 7am to 9:30pm.
■ For a different perspective of Monaco take one of the **boat trips** from quai des Etats-Unis, Port d'Hercule, tel: 377 92 16 15 15.

Hidden gem Seek out the tranquillity of **Jardin Japonais**, a Shinto garden near the Larvotto beach area.

④ Fondation Maeght

The Fondation Maeght, opened in 1964, is one of the most distinguished modern art museums in the world. It was the brainchild of Aimé and Marguerite Maeght, art dealers and close friends of Matisse, Miró, Braque, Bonnard and Chagall. It was their collection that formed the basis of the museum.

Miró sculpture in the museum's grounds

The gallery is hidden amid umbrella pines above the hilltop village of St-Paul-de-Vence. It is surrounded by a compact park which contains a collection of sculptures, mosaics and murals. The building itself blends into its natural surroundings, with massive windows, light traps in the roof, and extraordinary white cylindrical "sails" atop the building.

Fondation Maeght's remarkable permanent collection consists entirely of 20th-century art and includes works by nearly every major artist of the past 50 years. The star sights include the cour Giacometti – a tiled courtyard peopled with skinny Giacometti figures – Chagall's vast canvas *La Vie*, and Miró's *Labyrinthe*, a fantastic multi-level maze of fountains, trees, mosaics and sculptures.

The nearby hilltop village of St-Paul-de-Vence has strong links with the artistic community. In the 1920s, St-Paul was discovered by a group of young, impoverished artists – Signac, Bonnard, Modigliani and Soutine – who stayed at the modest Auberge de la Colombe d'Or, paying for their lodgings with their paintings. Other artists were also drawn to the village, including Marc Chagall, who is buried in the cemetery here. Today, the village's steep, cobbled streets are full of galleries, and it is one of the most beautiful and well-preserved villages in Provence.

TAKING A BREAK

The museum's **café** makes a pleasant place to stop for lunch.

🔳 189 D2
✉ St-Paul-de-Vence
☎ 04 93 32 81 63; www.fondation-maeght.com
🕐 Daily 10–12:30, 2:30–6, Oct–Jun; 10–7, Jul–Sep 💲 Expensive

FONDATION MAEGHT: INSIDE INFO

Hidden gem Don't miss the **chapel** in the grounds, which contains stained glass by Braque, Ubec and Marq. It was built in memory of the Maeght's son, who died in childhood.

5 Parc National du Mercantour

A short journey inland from the Riviera, on roads climbing through the Tinée, Vésubie and Roya valleys, are the majestic, snow-capped peaks of the Provençal Alps and the Parc National du Mercantour, the only remaining French National State Park. This beautiful mountain region stretches for over 128km (80 miles) along the Italian border and combines superb wildlife with the warm climate of the Mediterranean. It has no permanent inhabitants, but basic refuges on well-marked mountain trails offer shelter or overnight lodgings (these must be reserved in advance).

The small town of Tende, on the Roya river, is the main entry point to the park. The highly varied landscapes of the Mercantour range from gentle green pastureland and Alpine forests to glacial lakes, canyons and peaks. The park starts at an altitude of 490m (1,605 feet), and as you climb, the pines and larches of the lower slopes give way to Alpine meadows and rock-strewn scree, before reaching permanent snow on peaks at 3,000m (9,845 feet) high.

Popular with walkers and climbers, the park is carefully managed, with guides, park rangers and facilities. There are 600km (370 miles) of paths in the park and several nature trails, such as those at Lac d'Allos and Col de la Bonette. Two long-distance hiking trails, GR5 and GR52, also cross the area. Most of the park's higher reaches are covered in snow from mid-October to mid-June, limiting accessibility for all but the most experienced climbers.

Flora and Fauna
The park provides sanctuary for most of Europe's mountain

PARC NATIONAL DU MERCANTOUR: INSIDE INFO

Top tips **Picking flowers is forbidden** in the park, as are camping, fires, pets and waste disposal.

■ For information, to arrange accommodation or get advice on the difficulty and weather conditions on the park trails, visit one of the Maisons du Parc at Barcelonette, Valberg, St-Etienne de Tinée, St-Martin Vesubie or Tende; www.parc-mercantour.eu.

■ The ultra-modern **Musée des Merveilles** in Tende provides an introduction to the flora, fauna, archaeology and traditional culture and lifestyle of the Vallée des Merveilles.

Don't miss The most remarkable excursion into the Parc is the **trek to the Vallée des Merveilles**, a valley on a high tributary of the Roya, where thousands of drawings are etched on the rocks. Many more can be seen in the nearby **Vallée de Fontanalbe**. In a simple style resembling stick men, these images, thought to have been made in the Bronze Age (1800–1500 BC), depict hands, weapons, tools and horns. Guided tours leave Refuge des Merveilles at 7:30, 11 and 3 daily in July and August. On the D91 at Lac des Mesches there is a parking area at the start of the path to the Refuge des Merveilles (a 3-hour walk away).

Trekking the Vallée des Merveilles animal species, including wild boar, marmot, chamois, ibex and mouflon (wild sheep), as well as bright butterflies. In springtime the meadows are ablaze with bellflowers and blue gentians. There is also the rare big, spiky saxifrage (*Saxifraga florulenta*), the symbol of the park. Soaring overhead are birds such as eagles, kestrels, falcons and vultures. Smaller birds include the ptarmigan, great spotted woodpecker, hoopoe, citril finch, ortolan and rock bunting.

TAKING A BREAK

You can have meals at the **refuges** if you make a reservation. Alternatively, take a picnic with you.

189 D4
Mercantour Information Office
188 B4 ✉ Parc National du Mercantour, Centre Accueil Valberg, 1 rue St-Jean, 06470 Valberg ☎ 04 93 02 58 23; www.parc-mercantour.eu ⏰ Daily 10–1, 3–7, summer; hours vary in winter

Musée Départemental des Merveilles
✉ Avenue du 16 Septembre 1947, 06430 Tende ☎ 04 93 04 32 50; www.museedesmerveilles.com ⏰ Jul–Aug daily 10–6:30; May–Jun, Sep to mid-Oct Wed–Mon 10–6:30; mid-Oct to Apr Wed–Mon 10–5. Closed mid-Mar and mid-Nov 🎟 Free

BACKGROUND
In the 19th century, the Mercantour was Italy's royal hunting ground. In 1946, the area was split across national borders, and 68,000ha (168,000 acres) returned to France. Both nations granted the site national park status, and the park has been designated a protected nature reserve since 1979.

At Your Leisure

❻ Vence

Vence, only 10km (6 miles) inland from Cannes or Antibes, has long attracted artists. The town's main attraction, **Chapelle du Rosaire**, is in the modern suburbs to the north. The chapel was designed by Henri Matisse (1869–1954) as a thank you to Dominican sisters who

nursed him when he was seriously ill. The interior is decorated with powerful black line drawings of the Stations of the Cross, coloured by pools of light from the stained-glass windows.

At the heart of the lovely Old Town are place du Frêne and place du Peyra, where there are mineral-rich drinking fountains. From here head down the narrow rue du Marché, lined with mouth-watering food shops, to place Clemenceau, where you'll find Roman tombstones incorporated into the walls of the 10th-century cathedral – the site was formerly a Roman temple. In the baptistery at the back there's a mosaic by Marc Chagall (1887–1985).

➕ 188 C2

Tourist Information Office

✉ Place du Grand-Jardin ☎ 04 93 58 06 38; www.vence.fr

Chapelle du Rosaire

✉ Avenue Henri-Matisse ☎ 04 93 58 03 26 ⓘ Mon, Wed, Sat 2–5:30, Tue, Thu 10–11:30, 2–5:30 (Fri 2–5:30 during school hols), Sun service at 10am. Closed mid-Nov to late Dec 🎟 Inexpensive

❼ Grasse

Lavender fields are one of the memorable sights of Provence, and the flowers they produce are a key ingredient in the modern perfume

Top: A shady corner in Vence

industry. Molinard, Galimard and Fragonard are the great perfumeries located in Grasse, the **capital of the perfume industry**, which supplies perfumes to all the biggest names, including Chanel and Dior. All three offer factory tours. Roses and jasmine, flowers essential to the industry, are celebrated with their own festivals in May and August. The cathedral on place Godeau is worth a quick look inside for the three early paintings by Rubens, dating from 1601.

➕ 188 B1

Tourist Information Office

✉ Place du cours Honoré Cresp ☎ 04 93 36 03 56; www.grasse-riviera.com ⓘ Jul–Sep Mon–Sat 9–7, Sun 9–1, 2–6; Oct–Jun Mon–Sat 9–12:30, 2–6

8 Cannes

Cannes is a chic resort with excellent shopping, good entertainment, and major international cultural and business events, including the prestigious **international film festival** held each May.

The town is divided into two parts. To the west is the Old Port area with its waterside esplanade and narrow lanes which climb to le Suquet, the old hilltop quarter. To the east, modern Cannes is built round la Croisette, the elegant seafront promenade. Floodlit by night and lined with designer shops, this is the place to see and be seen, or perhaps try your own hands in the concrete prints of the stars, set in the pavement outside the Palais des Festivals.

Unfortunately, payment is required for access to many parts of the town's long, sandy beach, but there are public areas at both ends.

➕ 188 C1

Tourist Information Office

✉ Palais des Festivals, 1 boulevard de la Croisette ☎ 04 92 99 84 22; www.cannes. fr; www.cannes.com ⏰ Jul–Aug daily 9–8; Sep–Jun daily 9–7

9 Antibes

A small thriving resort, Antibes attracts its share of luxury craft in the large yacht harbour, Port Vauban. The most appealing parts of the town are in the central **historic quarter**, where Italianate buildings are crowded into the remains of a 17th-century defensive wall designed by the great military engineer Sébastien le Prestre de Vauban (1633–1707). This area is a maze of cobbled, winding lanes and crowded squares overflowing with shops, restaurants and bars.

The chief reason to visit Antibes is the **Musée Picasso**. Paintings, drawings, ceramics and sculptures, mostly dating to the three months in 1946 that Picasso spent here, are housed in a severe medieval fortress that once belonged to the Grimaldis of Monaco.

➕ 189 D1

Tourist Information Office

✉ 11 place Général de Gaulle ☎ 04 97 23 11 11 ⏰ Jul–Aug daily 9–7; Sep–Jun Mon–Fri, 9–12:30, 1:30–6, Sat 9–noon, 2–6

Musée Picasso

✉ Château Grimaldi ☎ 04 92 90 54 20 ⏰ Mid-Jun to mid-Sep Tue–Sun 10–6; mid-Sep–mid-Jun 10–noon, 2–6 🎟 Moderate

10 Biot

Set back from the sea between Antibes and Nice lies the charming hilltop village of Biot – a mass of steep cobbled lanes leading up to the famous arcaded main square. This little town has been a thriving pottery centre since Roman times, but today it is famous for its gold-

Bottom left: Bowls of scents in Grasse
Below: The colourful cours Masséna market, Antibes

and silverwork, ceramics, olive-wood carving and busy glassworks. Visitors can watch glass-blowers at the **Verrerie de Biot** demonstrating their unique *verre bullé* (bubble glass).

Near by, the striking **Musée national Fernand Léger**, with its huge mosaic façade and stained-glass windows, was founded in 1959 in memory of cubist painter Fernand Léger, who lived in Biot for a short time and inspired the growth of the craft workshops here. The museum contains nearly 400 of his works, including ceramics, tapestries, stained glass and mosaics.

🚩 188 C1
Tourist Information Office
✉ 46 rue St-Sébastien

by a 14th-century château which houses several exhibitions including a collection of portraits of the cabaret singer Suzy Solidor by famous artists. Renoir spent the last 11 years of his life near by at Domaine des Collettes, now the **Musée Renoir**. He would sit and paint beneath the olive trees, brushes strapped to his rheumatic fingers.

🚩 189 D2
Tourist Information Office
✉ 6 boulevard Maréchal-Juin
☎ 04 93 20 61 64; www.cagnes-tourisme.com
Musée Renoir
✉ 19 chemin des Collettes ☎ 04 93 20 61 07 ⏰ May–Sep Wed–Mon 10–12, 2–6; Oct–Apr Wed–Sun 10–12, 2–5. Closed Nov
💶 Moderate

Villa Euphrussi de Rothschild

☎ 04 93 65 78 00
Musée national Fernand Léger
✉ Chemin du Val de Pôme ☎ 04 92 91 50 30 ⏰ Jul–Sep Wed–Mon 10:30–6; Oct–Jun Wed–Mon 10–12:30, 2–5:30 💶 Inexpensive, free under 18

11 Cagnes-sur-Mer
Cagnes is divided into three areas: the old fishing quarter and main beach area of Cros-de-Cagnes; Cagnes-Ville, the commercial centre with its smart racecourse beside the sea; and Haut-de-Cagnes. This inviting hilltop village of is crowned

12 Villa Ephrussi de Rothschild
This rose-pink *belle-époque* palace and its gardens belonged to the flamboyant Baroness Béatrice Ephrussi de Rothschild (1864–1934), a woman of seemingly unlimited means. The remarkable interior is lavishly decorated with rare furniture (some pieces once belonged to Marie Antoinette), set off by rich carpets and tapestries. Rare *objets d'art* include one of the world's most beautiful collections of Sèvres and Vincennes porcelain. You can wander around the ground floor of the villa and through the stunning gardens at your leisure, but to see the

FOR KIDS

- **Antibes** Treat the whole family to a day at **Marineland**, where you can see dolphins, sea lions, sharks and more. The complex includes a farm, butterfly jungle, waterpark and crazy golf (Route N7, opposite Antibes Land, daily).
- **Grasse** Enjoy **go-karting** for children and adults, just outside Grasse at Fun Kart, Bar-sur-Loup (Route de Gourdon; www.fun-karting.com, open daily).
- **Cagnes-sur-Mer** Spend a memorable family night out at the **horse races** at the Hippodrome (tel: 04 93 22 51 00, open Mon, Wed, Fri from 8:30pm, early Jul–Aug).
- **Monaco** Jacques Cousteau's world-famous **Musée Océanographique** appeals to children of all ages (➤ 49). The **terraces of Fontvieille** were built to house numerous museums, including impressive collections of model boats and vintage cars, and a zoo (naval museum, tel: 0377 92 05 28 48; classic car exhibition, tel: 0377 92 05 28 56; zoo, tel: 0377 50 40 30). The **Musée National** is home to a huge collection of dolls dating from the 18th century to Barbie (17 avenue Princesse-Grace; open daily).

Festival takes place in the Jardins Biovès. The **medieval Old Town** has two magnificent churches – Église St-Michel and the Chapelle des Pénitents Blancs. Other notable sights include the Musée Jean-Cocteau, the Musée de la Préhistoire Régional, and Palais Carnolès – Menton's main art museum.

➕ 189 E2

Tourist Information Office

✉ Palais de l'Europe, avenue Boyer
☎ 04 92 41 76 76 ; www.menton.fr
🕐 Mid-Jun to mid-Sep daily 9–7; mid-Sep to mid-Jun Mon–Sat 8:30–12:30, 2–6, Sun 9–12:30

collections on the first floor you must take a guided tour.

➕ 189 E2

✉ St-Jean-Cap Ferrat ☎ 04 93 01 33 09 🕐 Mid-Feb to Nov daily 10–6/7; Nov to mid-Feb Mon–Fri 2–6. Closed 25 Dec
💷 Expensive

🔢 Menton

Close to the border, France's most Italianate resort, with its steep jumble of tall, honey-coloured houses, is wedged between a palm-lined bay and a dramatic mountain backdrop. The terraced slopes behind the town are smothered in citrus groves, and every February a spectacular **Lemon**

Where to... Stay

Prices

Expect to pay per night for a double room
€ under €100   €€ €100–€200   €€€ over €200

CANNES

Hotel Beau Séjour €€

Situated just west of the old quarter of Le Suquet and only minutes' walk from the port and the Plage de la Croisette, this smart, comfortable and modern three-star hotel has 44 contemporary-styled, air-conditioned rooms, well equipped with bathroom, hairdryer, wireless internet and satellite TV. The hotel has attractive, extensive gardens with an outdoor pool, terrace and sunbathing area, and it has a lounge bar as well as spa facilities on site.
188C1 ✉ 5 rue des Fauvettes ☎ 04 93 39 63 00; www.cannes-beausejour.com

ÈZE

Château Èza €€€

This enchanting hotel is a luxury "eagle's nest" formed from a 400-year-old private residence. Most rooms and all the suites have private balconies with panoramic views, which can also be enjoyed from the restaurant.
189 E2 ✉ Rue de la Pise ☎ 04 93 41 12 24; www.chateaueza.com

MENTON

Claridge's €

This two-star hotel in the centre of Menton is 5 minutes from the town's casino, the Promenade du Soleil and the beaches. The 39 simply decorated bedrooms are quite small, but they are comfortable and have TV and air-conditioning. Some rooms are suitable for families. Facilities include parking, a bar and a lounge, and there is a terrace which looks onto the street. Breakfast not included.
189 E2 ✉ 39 avenue de Verdun ☎ 04 93 35 72 53; www.claridges-menton.com

MONACO

Hotel Alexandra €€

The Alexandra is a good-value option for its location, less than 500m (550 yards) from the casino, restaurants, nightlife and elegant shops of Monte-Carlo, and with the beaches just a 10-minute walk away. The exterior of this three-star hotel has classic belle-époque features, while the 56 modern bedrooms have soundproofing, mini-bar, TV and a safe. Continental breakfast is served in the bedrooms.
197 C3 ✉ 35 boulevard Princesse-Charlotte, Monte-Carlo ☎ 377 93 50 63 13; www.monte-carlo.mc/alexandra

NICE

Le Grimaldi €€

Tucked behind an imposing belle-époque façade close to Nice's most stylish shopping streets, Le Grimaldi is a very good value four-star hotel, its 46 air conditioned rooms and suites individually decorated in tasteful Provençal style. Each offers mini-bar, safe, satellite TV, internet access, air-conditioning and bathroom. There are also facilities for business guests. Breakfast is not included in the price; parking is available nearby.
196 B2 ✉ 15 rue Grimaldi ☎ 04 93 16 00 24; www.le-grimaldi.com

Hôtel Armenonville €

A warm welcome awaits at this attractive, two-star hotel in a 20th-century mansion. The 13 bright rooms are tastefully decorated, some

Where to...
Eat and Drink

Prices

Expect to pay for a three-course meal for one, excluding drinks and service

€ under €25   €€ €25–€50   €€€ over €50

ANTIBES

Le Brûlot €

This authentic restaurant, with its antique baker's oven, beamed ceilings and stone walls, is full of character. In the vaulted basement there is another dining room, which dates from the 12th century. Many of the dishes are prepared on the wood oven, including grilled steak with Provençal herbs, and grilled scampi flambéed with pastis. A lovely *tarte au citron* with *pastis*. The house specials include couscous and naturally cured ham.

➕ 189 D1 ⌧ 3 rue Frédéric Isnard
☎ 04 93 34 17 76; www.brulot.com
⊘ Closed Sun and Aug

CANNES

La Brouette de Grand-Mère
€€

This dark, quirky little restaurant is something of a Cannes institution, with traditional fare such as home-made terrine, leg of rabbit and andouillettes – chitterling sausages – on the €35 *prix-fixe* menu, which includes an aperitif and a half bottle of wine per person.

---

with antique furniture, and have attractive tiled bathrooms. The hotel is set in flower-filled gardens where breakfast can be served. There is free secure parking within the hotel grounds.

➕ 196 A1 ⌧ 20 avenue des Fleurs ☎ 04 93 96 88 00; www.hotel-armenonville.com

Hôtel Négresco €€€

Prominently located on the famous promenade des Anglais, the pink dome of the Négresco is a much-loved Nice landmark dating back to 1912 (▶ 41). Inside, it's a luxurious palace of art, with works covering all periods from the Renaissance to the 21st century. The rooms are furnished to the highest standards and have internet access and the latest technology. Everything here is on a grand scale, and guests staying in the 121 rooms or 24 suites have access to the hotel's own private stretch of Mediterranean beach.

➕ 196 A1 ⌧ 37 promenade des Anglais ☎ 04 93 16 64 00; www.hotel-negresco-nice.com

ST-JEAN-CAP-FERRAT

Grand Hotel du Cap Ferrat
€€€

This is a sumptuous palace in lush, tropical gardens, amid some of the world's most expensive real estate. The 44 rooms and 9 suites either overlook pine trees or the sea. and are furnished to the highest standards. Le Cap restaurant makes good use of local ingredients. The seawater swimming pool is heated.

➕ 189 E2 ⌧ Boulevard Général-de-Gaulle ☎ 04 93 76 50 50; www.grand-hotel-cap-ferrat.com

ST-PAUL-DE-VENCE

La Colombe d'Or €€€

Once a modest 1920s café where Braque, Matisse, Picasso and Léger paid for their drinks with canvases, this is now a deluxe hotel offering all the services you would expect. Advance reservations essential.

➕ 188 C2 ⌧ Place du Général-de-Gaulle ☎ 04 93 32 80 02; www.la-colombe-dor.com

🖶 188 C1 ⊠ 9 bis rue d'Oran ☎ 04 93 39
12 10 ⓒ Dinner only; closed Sun, two weeks
in Nov and second half of Jun

Caffe Roma €€

This Italian bar-restaurant with a
great atmosphere, is an ideal place
for a break and a restorative ice
cream or cocktail, or if it's a meal
you're after, then try one of the
tempting Italian specialities, such as
ravioli stuffed with mushrooms and
foie gras, or veal with rocket and
tomato. Desserts include delicious
home-made tiramisu. You can
choose to eat alfresco on the terrace,
or in the elegant dining room.

🖶 188 C1 ⊠ 1 square Mérimée
☎ 04 93 38 05 04; www.cafferoma.fr
ⓒ Daily 7am–2am

GRASSE

La Bastide St-Antoine €€€

An 18th-century *bastide* on the
outskirts of Grasse is the setting
for celebrity chef Jacques Chibois'
renowned restaurant, where

luxury ingredients meet Provençal
inspiration in dishes such as braised
suckling lamb in a creamy fricassée
of vegetables and basil or lobster in
black olive fondue with beetroot jus.
There's an 800-bottle wine cellar to
draw on; for much of the year, you
can dine outside on the terrace.

🖶 188 C1 ⊠ 148 avenue Henri Dunant
☎ 04 93 70 44 44;
www.jacques-chibois.com ⓒ Daily noon–
1:30, 8–9:30pm

MONACO

Stars'N'Bars €€

The perfect place for families who
want a change from formal French
restaurants, this American-style bar-
restaurant offers a mainly Tex-Mex
menu. The bar has lots of games to
keep kids amused. In the evenings
there's live music or a disco.

🖶 197 B1 ⊠ 6 quai Antoine I,
La Condamine ☎ 377 97 97 95 95;
www.starsnbars.com
ⓒ Daily (closed Mon in winter), food served
11:30am–midnight, bar open to 1am

MOUGINS

Le Moulin de Mougins €€€

This 16th-century former olive mill
decorated with baroque chandeliers,
is the place to go for a gastronomic
treat. The menu is seasonal, with
sophisticated Mediterranean dishes,
while the excellent wine cellar has
more than 5,000 vintages.

🖶 188 C1 ⊠ Quartier Notre-Dame-de-Vie
☎ 04 93 75 78 24; www.moulin-mougins.com
ⓒ Tue–Sun 12–2, 7:30–9.30

NICE

L'Acchiardo €

One of the few authentic café bar/
restaurants remaining in Old Nice,
serving simple, nourishing dishes at
reasonable prices, and probably the
best fish soup in Nice.

🖶 196 D1 ⊠ 38 rue Droite
☎ 04 93 85 51 16 ⓒ Closed Sat and Sun

Aphrodite €€€

The imaginative culinary creations
of chef David Faure are a seductive

blend of classic French and Niçois
cuisine. His delectable desserts
would grace any modern art gallery.

🖶 196 C2 ⊠ 10 boulevard Dubouchage
☎ 04 93 85 63 53
ⓒ Closed Sun and Mon

Don Camillo Créations €€

There's a contemporary feel to
the decor and to Marc Laville's
Mediterranean-influenced cooking
at this smart restaurant, with dishes
like roast scallops with celery
mousseline and dried cranberries
or strawberry and rhubarb tiramisu
with strawberry and violet sorbet on
a good-value €40 carte.

🖶 196 D1 ⊠ 5 rue des Ponchettes ☎ 04 93
85 67 95 ⓒ Closed Sun, Mon

ST-PAUL-DE-VENCE

Mas d'Artigny €€€

Well known for its regional cuisine,
including *fougasse Provençale* and
fish dishes, and local wines.

🖶 188 C2 ⊠ Route de la Colle ☎ 04 93 32
84 54; www.mas-artigny.com ⓒ Daily

Where to... Shop

There are plenty of shopping opportunities in this area. Cannes and Monaco have a reputation for glamour, Grasse is at the heart of the perfume industry and excellent local markets abound.

MARKETS

Nice holds several markets on the animated cours Saleya, with its many shops and cafés. The **Marché Saleya** offers lots of locally grown produce, including olives, tomatoes and basil (open Tue–Sun 6am–1:30pm); for antiques try the **Marché à la Brocante** (open Mon 7:30–6), and the **Marché aux Fleurs** for exotic flowers and trees (open Tue–Sat 6–5:30, Wed and Sun 6–6:30).Stroll through the evening arts and crafts market if it is Provençal handicrafts

you're interested in (open Jun–Sep Tue–Sun 6pm–midnight).

SOUVENIRS AND GIFTS

Grasse, world-renowned as a perfume capital, is home to many perfumeries. **Fragonard**, one of the oldest and most prestigious, has a perfume museum and a shop (20 boulevard Fragonard, factory open 9–6:30, shop 9–6). The tiny, traditional perfumerie **Parfums Poilpot** in Nice (10 rue St-Gaëtan) also has a wide choice of scents from Grasse.

Biot is famous for its traditional bubble-flecked glassware, which is produced and sold at **Verrerie de Biot** (chemin des Combes, Mon–Sat 9:30–6:30, Sun 10:30–1:30, 2:30–6:30). You can buy beautiful hand-blown bottles, jars, dishes and

glasses and visit the workshop.

L'Herminette Ezasque in Èze (rue Principale, open summer 10–7, winter 10–6), in the walls of the old gateway, sells wonderful Christmas cribs and *santons*. For beautiful Provençal fabrics, sold by the metre or transformed into finished items, stop at **Les Images de Provence** in Menton (21 rue St-Michel, open Mar–Fri 9–12:30, 1:30–5).

FASHION

Jacques Loup is an institution for every *fashionista* in Cannes (21 rue d'Antibes, open Mon–Sat 9:30–8). In addition to its own collection, this shoe shop has the latest designs from international shoemakers. It also stocks clothes from Prada, Marni and Miu Miu.

In Vallauris, near Cannes, beautiful original pottery designs by Picasso are still made and sold in limited, numbered editions by the Madoura Gallery (av Suzanne & Georges Ramié, open Mon–Fri

10–12.30, 2:30–6/7). Hats for every occasion can be found at **La Chapellerie** in Nice (36 cours Saleya, open Mon–Sat 9.30–12, 2–6:30).

FOOD AND DRINK

In Nice the best place to buy traditional crystallised fruits is at **Maison Auer** (7 rue St-François-de-Paule). For olive oil, visit **Alziari** (14 rue St-François-de-Paule) or **Moulin à Huile Alziari** (318 boulevard de la Madeleine, open Mon–Fri 8–12, 2–6).

The **Caprioglio Wine** store in old Nice has wines to suit all purses, from *vin de table* to the top *crus* (16 rue de la Préfecture). Nice's best ice-cream maker is **Glacier Fenocchio** (2 place Rossetti); here you'll get big servings and truly original tastes.

In St-Paul-de-Vence, visit **La Petite Cave de St-Paul**, a 14th-century cellar containing a choice selection of Provençal wines (behind 47 rue Grande).

Where to...
Be Entertained

BARS, CLUBS AND CASINOS

La Siesta in Antibes offers every entertainment, from a casino to dance floors (route du Bord-de-Mer, tel: 04 93 33 31 31, open daily 10pm–5am, 4am in winter.

Casino Ruhl, Nice's glamorous casino, offers spectacular dinner cabarets, as well as private gaming rooms (promenade des Anglais, tel: 04 97 03 12 22, open 10am–4/5am). If you want to dance the night away to the latest sounds, from house to R&B, then try Nice's largest indoor nightclub, **L'Odace** (29 rue Alphonse Karr, tel: 04 93 82 37 66, open 7pm–2:30am); alternatively visit **Le Guest**, an established Niçois nightspot in the Old Port, with neo-baroque décor (5 quai des Deux-Emmanuels, tel: 04 93 56 83 83, open 11:30pm–5am).

Nocy-Be is a chic Moroccan café in Vieux Nice, with low lighting, floor cushions, organic tea, cakes and aperitifs (4–6 rue Jules Gilly, tel: 04 93 85 52 25, open Tue–Sun 5–12:30).

While living the high life in Monaco, visit the famous **Café de Paris**, which has a restaurant, as well as a gaming house (place du Casino, tel: 0377 98 06 77 77, open from 10 am). **The Casino de Monte-Carlo** is probably the most famous in the world and has featured in Bond movies (place du Casino, tel: 377 98 06 21 21). If you're still feeling lucky, head for the bright lights of Cannes and Casino **Croisette** (1 esplanade Lucien Barrière, tel: 04 92 98 78 00, open 10am–5am, games room from 8pm), or soak up the jet set ambiance at Cannes' most glamorous nightclub, Le Bâoli (Port Pierre Canto, bd de la Croisette, tel 04 93 43 03 43, open summer daily 8–5; winter Fri–Sat only).

THEATRE AND MUSIC

Cannes' modern **Palais des Festivals et des Congrès** hosts the annual film festival in May, but is also a year-round venue for international concerts, ballet, theatre and exhibitions (1 boulevard de la Croisette, tel: 04 93 39 01 01).

In Nice, the modern congress, arts and tourism centre **L'Acropolis**, is popular for theatre, films and concerts (1 esplanade Kennedy, tel: 04 93 92 83 00). The **Opéra de Nice** is home of the Nice Opera, the Philharmonic Orchestra and Ballet Corps (4–6 rue St-François-de-Paule, tel: 04 92 17 40 00). The modern **Théâtre de Nice** (TDN) presents world-class shows (promenade des Arts, tel: 04 93 13 90 90).

SPORTS AND ACTIVITIES

There are excellent beaches along the Mediterranean coast, the larger ones offering watersports, and most of the ports and marinas have sailing schools and boats for rent (www.voilecotedazur.com).

You can explore the Riviera's bays, capes and islands at a more adrenaline-charged pace by hiring a speedboat from **Locarama Rent a Boat** (13 rue Latour Maubourg, Cannes Tel 06 19 180 618).

Cannes Bowling (189 avenue Francis-Tonner, 06150 Cannes La Bocca, tel: 04 93 47 02 25) also has pool tables and a restaurant.

Palais des Sports Jean Bouin has an Olympic-size skating rink in Nice and welcomes those looking for a little icy adventure (esplanade Maréchal-de-Lattre-de-Tassigny, tel: 04 97 20 20 30).

The Var and Haute Provence

Getting Your Bearings

The Var and Haute-Provence together boast some of the finest and most dramatic scenery in the south of France, most notably in the two mountainous départements of the Alpes-de-Haute-Provence and the Haute-Alpes, where picture-postcard villages and towns, rich in Provençal and Alpine architecture, bear witness to an eventful past. Here, too, is Europe's "Grand Canyon", the Gorges du Verdon, the second deepest gorge in the world after the Grand Canyon, which offers a wealth of sporting activities ranging from climbing and mountain-biking to canoeing and white-water rafting.

The Var is the most wooded region of France, with its forests of chestnuts, cork oaks and conifers, interrupted only by an occasional hidden village. It also claims Provence's longest coastal strip, far less developed than its famous Riviera neighbour.

The wild, rugged landscape of the blood-red Corniche de l'Esterel, with its jagged creeks and tiny rocky coves, contrasts sharply with the sun-bleached sandy beaches of nearby Fréjus and St-Tropez. The coastal resorts have an air of faded glory, with the exception of St-Tropez, which remains almost as glitzy and hedonistic as it was in its "Swinging" Sixties heyday. The picturesque port here remains a favourite mooring for the ostentatious yachts and gin-palaces of the glitterati, but explore beyond the quayside and you will discover a village of great charm. As French writer Colette remarked: "Once you have visited here, you will never want to leave."

D950

★ Don't Miss

At Your Leisure

Previous page: The beach at Miramar on Corniche de l'Esterel
Left: Riding the rapids

0 — 25 km
0 — 15 miles

St-Vincent-les-Forts
Ubaye
D954
D900
Seyne

Le Vernet
2961 ▲ Tête de l'Estrop

2115 ▲ Les Monges
Authon
Bès
D900
La Javie

Colmars
Beauvezer
2580 ▲ Le Petit Coyer
Verdon

Sisteron
1826 ▲ Signal de Lure
Montagne de Lure
Durance
N85

Château-Arnoux
Digne-les-Bains 11
ALPES-DE-HTE-PROVENCE

Peyruis
N96
D4
Bléone
Asse
N85
D955
St-André-les-Alpes

Forcalquier
D12
P l a t e a u
Barrème
N202
Entrevaux 12
N202

La Brillanne
d e
V a l e n s o l e
N100
N96
A51 E712

Manosque
Moustiers-Ste-Marie 10
Riez
1771 ▲ Berberie
Castellane
N85

Parc Naturel Régional du Verdon
Lac de Ste Croix
D952
La Palud-sur-Verdon
Gorges du Verdon 3

D952
Vinon-sur-Verdon
Verdon
D11
D957
Comps-sur-Artuby
D955

D13
Montmeyan
Aups
Fayence
Siagne

Rians
D561
D560
Draguignan
D562
Les Adrets-de-l'Esterel

Barjols
VAR
D562
Carces
Abbaye du Thoronet 9
Le Muy
Corniche de l'Esterel 4

St-Maximin-la-Ste-Baume
E80 A8
Argens
E80 A8
Vidauban
N7
Argens
N7 Fréjus
St-Raphaël
N98

Tourves
N7
Brignoles
Le Luc
Aille
E80 A8
D25
St-Aygulf
N98
Val d'Esquières

N560
D5
N7
D558
Maures
Ste-Maxime

1147 ▲ Signal de la Ste-Baume
Puget-Ville
N97
779 ▲ La Sauvette
La Garde-Freinet
Grimaud 6
St-Tropez 1

Collobrières 8
des
Ramatuelle 5

Le Beausset
Solliès-Pont
D554
Capeau
D12
M a s s i f
N98
D559
Cavalaire-sur-Mer

Bandol
A50
N8
A57
Hyères 2
N98
Bormes-les-Mimosas 7

Six-Fours-les-Plages
D559
N98
TOULON
Île du Levant

La Capte
Giens
Îles d'Hyères 2

Île de Porquerolles
Île de Port-Cros

In Three Days

If you're not quite sure where to begin your travels, this itinerary recommends a practical and enjoyable three-day tour of The Var and Haute-Provence, taking in some of the best places to see using the Getting Your Bearings map on the previous page. For more information see the main entries.

Day One

Morning
Catch a ferry from **2 Hyères** to Port-Cros, one of the three Îles d'Hyères (➤ 72–73) and France's only offshore national park, with its fantastic woodland walks among holm oak, strawberry trees and myrtle. Bring your snorkel, mask and fins and follow the island's unique underwater path to see octopuses, eels, sea peacocks and black-faced blennies amid colourful sponges and sea anemones.

Lunch
The cafés lining the palm-fringed harbour of Port-Cros are ideal for a light lunch before returning by boat to Hyères.

Afternoon
Drive towards St-Tropez via picturesque **7 Bormes-les-Mimosas** (left, ➤ 79), a hilly village of ice-cream coloured houses, celebrated for its mimosa festival in February. You may also have time to detour to the equally delightful hilltop village of **6 Grimaud** (➤ 78–79) or fashionable **5 Ramatuelle** (➤ 78) en route.

Evening
Soak up the atmosphere of St-Tropez's Old Town at La Citadelle restaurant (➤ 86).

Day Two

Morning
Explore the chic boutiques and galleries of **1 St-Tropez** (➤ 68–71), and the bustling Marché Provençal in place des Lices (Tue and Sat am, ➤ 69), before visiting the Vieux Port (right) to watch the world go by.

Lunch

Sénéquier (➤ 86) on quai Jean Jaurès – one of the top celebrity haunts – serves delicious coffee and light lunches alongside the harbour (left).

Afternoon

Spend the afternoon on one of St-Tropez's acclaimed sandy beaches (➤ 71), or explore the wild rocky coastline of the blood-red **4 Corniche de l'Esterel** (➤ 77). En route, visit Fréjus, once a busy Roman town and naval base, with its ancient arena and theatre, and one of the oldest baptisteries in France. Walkers will enjoy the two-hour hike (from the Pointe de l'Observatoire) up Cap Roux, the peak of the Massif de l'Esterel (➤ 77), with its spectacular coastal scenery.

Evening

Return for dinner in one of St Tropez's myriad bistros – La Bouillabaisse (➤ 86) is a popular options. Then rub shoulders with the rich and famous at Les Caves du Roy or the VIP Room (➤ 88).

Day Three

Morning

Head north to the **3 Gorges du Verdon** (➤ 74–76), the longest, wildest canyon in Europe and a paradise for sports lovers.

Lunch

Try some regional specialities at Les Santons (place de l'Église, tel: 04 92 74 66 48) in **10 Moustiers-Ste-Marie** (left, ➤ 80–81), a beautiful village renowned for its faïence de Moustiers.

Afternoon

Visit the Musée de la Préhistoire des Gorges du Verdon (➤ 76) at Quinson, or drive further north into Haute-Provence to visit the spa town of **11 Digne-les Bains** (➤ 81–82), the lavender-growing capital of Provence. From here, the Train des Pignes runs through breathtaking scenery four times a day to Nice.

⓪ St-Tropez

This charming fishing port, which reached the height of international fame in the "Swinging" Sixties, continues to be a playground of the rich and famous. Today, most visitors come to rub shoulders with celebrities from the world of pop music, movies and TV in the waterfront cafés on the picturesque old quayside and to admire the yachts, moored before a backdrop of pink and yellow pastel buildings. These are relatively modern, reconstructed from original designs after the destruction that occurred during World War II.

St-Tropez is based around its picturesque **old quayside**, which is very much the place to see and be seen. Despite the large numbers of visitors and huge luxury yachts moored alongside, it still has a villagey charm. At one end of the quay, which curves along the edge of a beautiful bay, are the remnants of the old fortifications, and the jetty called Môle Jean Réveille. Beyond, the tiny, endearing quarter called La Ponche was once a waterside fishermen's district. Another surviving fragment of the fortifications, Tour Jarlier, stands close by.

At the other end of the quay is the **Musee de l'Annonciade**, a stylish art museum in a former 16th-century religious building. Here you'll find one of the finest collections of French late 19th- and early 20th-century paintings and bronzes. Most of the 100 or so canvases belong to the great movements of pointillism, fauvism and nabism, with many of the paintings depicting local scenes. Look for Paul Signac's *Saint-Tropez, le quai 1899*, Bonnard's *Le Port de St-Tropez* (1899) and Camoin's *La Place des Lices* (1925), along with works by Dufy, Derain, Vuillard and others.

Turning away from the quay, you'll find the Old Town, or *Vieille Ville*, with its narrow streets, small old houses and

Below Sénéquier on quai Jean-Jaurès is a popular café

There are good views from the Citadel

several chic little boutiques. This area, closed to traffic in summer, is relatively uncrowded and a pleasant place to get away from the crowds on the quayside. On the edge of the old quarter is the town's large main square, **place des Lices** (also known as place Carnot). This is the real heart of St-Tropez, and remains very much as it looked in Camoin's *La Place des Lices*, lined with ancient plane trees and bohemian cafés. The best time to visit is on Tuesdays or Saturdays for its colourful market, but come anytime for a game of pétanque and a glass of *pastis* with the locals. From here the town extends into more modern areas.

The **Église St-Tropez** owes its name to a Roman centurion called Torpes, who was martyred for his Christian faith. His head was buried in Pisa and his body put in a boat with a dog and cockerel, who were to devour it. However, when the boat washed up here, his remains were miraculously untouched. For over 400 years the town's most important festival – the Bravade de St-Torpes – has been celebrated in his honour each May. You can see a gilt bust of St Torpes and a model of his boat in the 19th-century baroque-style church, with its distinctive pink and yellow bell-tower.

To the east of town visit the 16th-century hilltop fortress, **La Citadelle**, if only for the view, which embraces the orange curly-tiled roofs of St-Tropez's Old Town, the dark and distant Maures and Esterel hills, and the glittering blue of the bay, flecked with sails. After extensive renovation, the **Citadelle** has reopened with a set of imaginative themed displays pending the scheduled opening there of a maritime museum in 2010.

ST-TROPEZ: INSIDE INFO

Top tips Don't drive to St-Tropez – traffic is terrible, with a long wait to get into town and nowhere to park. Instead, use the large public parking areas at Port Grimaud and take the passenger ferry across the bay.
- Visit in mid-May when the town's bravades **festivals** are held.
- In the summer take a **shuttle bus** from the place des Lices to the beaches.

TAKING A BREAK

La Table du Marché, a smart bistro-cum-deli, offers excellent meals, light snacks, regional specialities, cakes, pastries and wines. It also serves afternoon tea (38 rue Georges Clemenceau, tel: 04 94 97 85 20, open daily all year).

➕ 193 E3

Tourist Information Office
✉ Quai Jean-Jaurès
☎ 04 94 97 45 21
🕓 Jul–Aug daily 9:30–8; Apr–Jun, Sep–Oct daily 9:30–12:30, 2–7; Nov–Mar daily 9.30–12.30, 2–6

La Citadelle
✉ Montée de la Citadelle
☎ 04 94 97 59 43
🕓 Apr–Sep daily 10–6:30; Oct–Mar daily 10–12:30, 1:30–5:30 💷 Inexpensive

Église St-Tropez
✉ Rue de l'Église
🕓 Daily

HISTORY

Founded by Greeks as Athenopolis (City of Athena), the town has long been a popular meeting place for artists. Liszt and Maupassant were its first celebrities in the 1880s, followed by neo-Impressionist painter Signac a decade later. Soon Matisse, Bonnard, Utrillo and Dufy fell under St-Tropez's spell, immortalising the town in paint. Many pictures can be seen in the **Musée de l'Annonciade** (► 68).

Musée de l'Annonciade
✉ Place Georges-Grammont
☎ 04 94 17 84 10
🕓 Jul–Oct Wed–Mon 10–12, 3–8; Dec–Jun Wed–Mon 10–12, 2–6. Closed Nov, 1 Jan, 1 May, Ascension, 25 Dec
💷 Moderate

BEACHES

For sandy beaches you'll have to travel out of town onto the **Cap de St-Tropez**, on the peninsula. Here there are over 6km (4 miles) of enticing golden sand, divided into individual beaches, each with a different character. The classy **Club 55** caters for the Paris set, **Tahiti-Plage** was once the movie stars' favourite, but nowadays star-spotters have more luck at the frivolous **Nikki Beach**. For water sports head for Sun Force and for seafood try **Bora Bora**.

Above: There are plenty of beaches to choose from in St-Tropez

Left: Boats of all sizes fill the harbour at St-Tropez

Below: Pastel-coloured buildings front the harbour

2 Hyères and the Îles d'Hyères

Exotic plants flourish in the southerly resort of Hyères-les-Palmiers, so-called because of its important palm-growing industry. Hyères' main attraction today lies off the Var coast – the three beautiful islands of the Îles d'Hyères.

The Town

A Gothic gateway in the defensive wall in Hyères' **Old Town** leads into an atmospheric residential district of narrow streets lined with tall buildings, which climb to the ruins of a château in a park with wide views. The main square is the place Massillon marketplace, overlooked by the Tour des Templiers, once commanded by the medieval Knights Templar. Other reminders of the Middle Ages include two Romanesque–early Gothic churches: St-Paul and St-Louis. Modern Hyères, below the Old Town, is laid out with wide, busy boulevards edged with palm trees. The Jardins Olbius-Riquier, to the southeast of the old town, are glorious tropical gardens with a small animal enclosure.

Above: The tower of St-Paul's Church rises above the town of Hyères

A double sandbar, 4km (2.5 miles) long, connects Hyères to the **Giens Peninsula**. Here you'll find salt pans which attract numerous wading birds, and the small resort village of Giens. La Tour Fondue, at the eastern tip of the peninsula, is the departure point for ferries to the island of Porquerolles.

The Islands

At around 18sq km (7sq miles), **Porquerolles** is the largest of the Îles d'Hyères. Preserved as a nature reserve, its forest paths are popular with walkers and cyclists. The south coast

HYÈRES AND THE ÎLES D'HYÈRES: INSIDE INFO

Top tips It's **best to park** in the public car park beneath place G Clemenceau as parking in the old town is difficult.

■ You **can't take your car to the islands**; park at the ferry terminal at Giens or near Hyères port.

■ The **best beach** on the islands is Plage de la Palud, at Port-Cros.

■ **Check the time** of the last ferry back before setting off for the islands.

Don't miss You can take **guided snorkelling tours** (bring your own snorkel) from La Palud beach.

of the island has rocky cliffs, while there are sandy beaches on the north coast. Ferries arrive at the little quay of Porquerolles village on the north coast, overlooked by the 19th-century Fort Sainte-Agathe (now an exhibition venue).

Port-Cros, around 10sq km (4sq miles), lies to the east. It is covered with dense Mediterranean woodland and is protected as a national park. Walkers use a network of pretty paths, including a marked trail which leads up to the Fort de l'Estissac and Fort du Moulin, beside the village. The rocky **Île du Levant**, just 8sq km (3sq miles), is the most easterly of the island group. Much of the island has been taken over by the army and is closed to the public, while the remainder is a nudist resort.

Tour des Templiers in Hyères

TAKING A BREAK

Call in for a dish of sea bass and a glass of wine in **La Colombe** in Hyères (663 route de Toulon-La Bayorre, tel: 04 94 35 35 16) or take a picnic to the islands.

🔲 192 B2 (town)
🔲 192 C1 (islands)

Tourist Information Office
✉ Forum du Casino, 3 avenue Ambroise Thomas, Hyères-les-Palmiers ☎ 04 94 01 84 50; www.hyeres-toutisme.com
🕐 Jul–Aug daily 8:30–7:30; Sep–Jun Mon–Fri 9–6, Sat 10–4

Île de Porquerolles
🚢 Daily from La Tour Fondue; timetables at www.tlv-tvm.com

Île de Port-Cros and Île du Levant
🚢 From Port-St-Pierre; timetable at www.tlv-tvm.com

GETTING TO THE ISLANDS

You reach the Îles d'Hyères by **ferry** from two harbours: **Port St-Pierre** near the heart of Hyères town or the **harbour** at La Tour Fondue on the Giens peninsula. The direct ferry from Giens to the Île de Porquerolles takes 20 minutes. Ferries from Port St-Pierre go to Port-Cros (1 hour) and Le Levant (90 minutes).

3 Gorges du Verdon

The Gorges du Verdon, the deepest and most dramatic river gorge in mainland Europe, takes in 21km (13 miles) of steep limestone cliffs and vegetation. Winding, narrow roads, dotted with breathtaking viewpoints giving fabulous vistas of the rocky terrain, line each side of the ravine. At the bottom run the clear waters of the river which gives the chasm its name, and which flow into the vast man-made Lac de Ste-Croix, created in 1970.

Taking in the magnificent view from the Route des Crêtes

The gorge, one of the natural wonders of the world, was formed over millions of years by the River Verdon. It was surveyed for the first time in 1905 by the great speleologist Édouard-Alfred Martel. Yet even today, geology dictates that the winding roads are few and modest in scale as the canyon narrows to 198m (650 feet) across. The steep limestone cliffs rise to 700m (2,300 feet) high on each side, make them accessible only to experienced climbers. The southern route from Moustiers-Ste-Marie, the Corniche Sublime (D71), carved out in the 1940s, gives the most consistent views, with the Balcons de Mescla viewpoint the highlight. Loop north via the ancient hilltop village of Trigance to return along the northern side and the spectacular Route des Crêtes.

ÉDOUARD-ALFRED MARTEL

Martel (1859–1938) is known worldwide as the father of speleology – the science of cave exploration. From an early age, and despite training as a lawyer, Martel began a pioneering exploration of the underground caverns in the limestone landscape of the Causses. His three-day exploration of the Gorges du Verdon, previously believed impenetrable, was undertaken with two companions. Martel's journey was driven partly by curiosity, and partly by the need for research into water supplies, and in the 1950s the government considered blocking the whole valley for a reservoir, but settled instead for the more limited Lac de Ste-Croix.

Exploring in the Gorges

The river powers a hydroelectric plant, and is dammed below Moustiers, offering good opportunities for experienced canoeists and white-water rafters. Short walks lead from many of the viewpoints, such as the zigzag path from the Point Sublime, on the north side. Hardy walkers can tackle the challenging Sentier Martel footpath, which runs along the valley floor between Rougon and Châlet de la Maline and takes at least six hours.

Scaling the heights above Lac de Ste-Croix

TAKING A BREAK

There are plenty of cafés to choose from in the cobbled squares of **Moustiers-Ste-Marie**, though parking may be difficult in high summer. There are also lots of good *belvédères*, or viewpoints, where you can stop for a picnic and enjoy the panoramas.

🔲 187 D1

Tourist Information Office
🔲 186 C2 ✉ Maison de Lucie, place de l'Eglise, Moustiers-Ste-Marie (western edge of canyon)
☎ 04 92 74 67 84; www.ville-moustiers-sainte-marie.fr
🕐 Jul–Aug daily 9:30–12:30, 2–7:15; Jun–Sep 10–12:30, 2–6:30; Apr–May 10–12:30, 2–6; Mar, Oct 10–12:30, 2–5:30; Nov 10–12, 2–5:30; Dec 10–12, 1:30–5

Musée de la Préhistoire des Gorges du Verdon
🔲 192 B5 ✉ Route de Montmeyan, Quinson
☎ 04 92 74 09 59; www.museeprehistoire.com
🕐 Jul–Aug daily 10–8; Feb–Jun, Sep to mid-Dec Wed–Mon 10–6 or 7 💰 Moderate

GORGES DU VERDON: INSIDE INFO

Top tips The **narrow roads** which run along each side of the canyon are in places only just wide enough for two cars to pass – so take extra care if you are in a wider vehicle or towing.
■ Driving just a short stretch of the **Corniche Sublime** will give you a good taste of this natural phenomenon.
■ For a **drive** along the canyon ➤ 172–174.
■ The **Sentier Martel footpath** along the river has collapsed tunnels and is subject to sudden changes in water level. It is best walked with an experienced guide or in a group.
■ **Faïence** is the local decorative earthenware pottery, and you'll see it on sale on the streets and in the little shops of Moustiers-Ste-Marie.

Don't miss The modern, boat-shaped **Musée de la Préhistoire des Gorges du Verdon**, designed by architect Sir Norman Foster, is at Quinson, just southwest of Lac de Ste-Croix. This fabulous museum, dedicated to the people who inhabited the Gorges area around 400,000 years ago, has a re-created cave, interactive displays, and neolithic tools and other items found in the area.

4 Corniche de l'Esterel

The Corniche de l'Esterel is a winding coastal road between St-Raphaël and Théoule-sur-Mer, flanked on one side by the wild red mountains of the Massif de l'Esterel, and on the other by the sparkling blue sea. The road explores the rugged natural landscape and reveals secret coves and deserted bays.

The Corniche de l'Esterel, also known as the Corniche d'Or (Golden Coast Road) or N98, was carved into the impressive seafront cliffs over a century ago. The Touring Club de France was involved in its development, and the route is popular with cyclists. Just as dramatic by car, bus or train, the tortuous road is punctuated by viewpoints overlooking inviting beaches, sheltered yacht harbours, jagged inlets and deserted coves. A small range of hills known as the Massif de l'Esterel rises behind the coast between the little beach resort of Fréjus, with its Roman remains and medieval buildings, and the glitzy resort of Cannes. The hills provide a perfect backdrop, with their harsh, rugged mountains of brilliant red volcanic rock jutting into the sea.

This stretch of wild coast is a ragged shoreline of red cliffs

Covered in green spruce, pine and scrub, and wild flowers in summer, the massif is a conservation area, and two valley zones, the Ravin du Mal Infernet and the Ravin du Perthus, have been designated biological reserves. They are both easily reached by road.

TAKING A BREAK

Café Excelsior, on promenade du President René Coty, St-Raphaël (tel: 04 94 95 02 42) offers fish dishes.

✠ 193 F4
Tourist Information Office
✉ Quai Albert 1er, St-Raphaël ☎ 04 94 19 52 52; www.saint-raphael.com 🕐 Sep–Jun Mon–Sat 9–12:30, 2–6:30

CORNICHE DE L'ESTEREL: INSIDE INFO

Top tips Visit the tourist office at Fréjus or St-Raphaël for a walking map of the massif, published by the Office National des Forêts (price €8.50).
■ Some paths in the massif may be closed in summer because of fire risk.

At Your Leisure

5 Ramatuelle

At the heart of the St-Tropez peninsula, just a short distance inland from the busy, chic resort, lies the pretty village of Ramatuelle. Surrounded by vineyards, which produce the local Côtes de Provence wine, this is one of the most fashionable places in the area to own a second home. Every summer the village hosts popular **jazz and theatre festivals**.

On the road (D89) above Ramatuelle, three ancient windmills, **les Moulins de Paillas**, offer magnificent views of the coast and the countryside. The nearby hilltop village of **Gassin**, built as a look-out point during the time of the Saracen invasions, is a colourful place with smart boutiques and restaurants.

➕ 193 E2
Tourist Information Office
✉ Place de l'Ormeau ☎ 04 98 12 64 00

6 Grimaud

The medieval village of Grimaud stands on the eastern slopes of the Massif des Maures, not far from St-Tropez. One of Provence's most photogenic hilltop villages, it is crowned by an **11th-century château** belonging to the Grimaldi family, after whom the village is

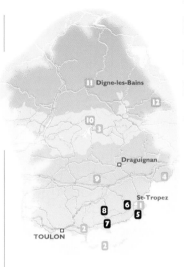

named. The main street, the rue des Templiers, leads to the beautiful Romanesque **church of St-Michel, the Hospice of the Knights Templars** and a restored 12th-century mill.

➕ 193 D3
Tourist Information Office
✉ 1 boulevard des Aliziers ☎ 04 94 55 43 83;

Photogenic Ramatuelle – a typical Provençal hilltop village

www.grimaud-provence.com
🕐 Jul–Aug Mon–Sat 9–12:30, 3–7; Apr–Jun, Sep Mon–Sat 9–12.30, 2:30–6:15; Oct–Mar Mon–Sat 9–12:30, 2:15–5:30

Fragrant lavender fields, for which Provence is famous, are a feature of the countryside

7 Bormes-les-Mimosas

The pretty village of Bormes is perched on a hilltop on the Massif des Maures, just inland from the coast. At its heart is a steep medieval village with ice-cream coloured houses, evocative lanes and passageways climbing up towards the ruins of the Château des Seigners de Fos at the top of the hill.

In February, when the mimosa is in full bloom, the village celebrates with a sensational *corso fleuri* – an extravaganza of floral floats made from thousands of tiny yellow mimosa flowers.

Visit the tourist office for a map of the *circuit touristique* that explores Bormes' steep medieval stairways and alleys, a fine 16th-century chapel dedicated to Bormes' patron saint, the **Église St-Trophyme**, and the ruined 13th- to 14th-century **château** at the top of the hill.

✚ 192 C2
Tourist Information Office
✉ 1 place Gambetta
☎ 04 94 01 38 38;
www.bormeslesmimosas.com
🕐 Apr–Sep daily 9–12:30, 2:30–6:3; Oct–Mar Mon–Sat 9–12:30, 1:30–5:30

8 Collobrières

In the centre of the Massif des Maures, this traditional little village, surrounded by a forest of chestnut trees, is well known for the sweet *marrons glacés* (candied chestnuts) made here. Collobrières holds an annual festival in October celebrating the humble chestnut. Buy chestnuts at the local market, on Sundays, and also Thursdays in summer. The village is also known for its cork, which grows in the forests near by.

Further up the road (off the D14), the **Chartreuse de la Verne**, a beautiful Carthusian monastery, sits isolated among the dense Maures forest, 12km (7 miles) from Collobrières. Founded in 1170 and originally inhabited by Carthusian monks, the complex of cloisters, chapels and cells has been home to a group of Sisters of Bethlehem nuns since the 1980s.

✚ 192 C2
Tourist Information Office
✉ Boulevard Charles Caminat ☎ 04 94 48 08 00 🕐 Tue, Wed, Fri, Sat 10–12, 2–5:30
Chartreuse de la Verne
🕐 Jun–Aug Wed–Mon 11–6; Sep–May Wed–Mon 11–5. Closed religious holidays and Jan

FOR KIDS

- **Cap de St-Tropez** Take your pick of the best beaches (➤ 71).
- **Azur Park** (at Gassin, Golfe de St-Tropez, open early Apr to mid-Sep) has some of the most exhilarating fairground rides in Europe.
- **Village des Tortues** Take a fascinating one-hour tour of this remarkable "village" with its 1,200 turtles and tortoises (at Gonfaron, off Aix–Cannes autoroute, open summer 9–7, winter 9–6).

9 Abbaye du Thoronet

The 12th-century Abbaye du Thoronet, hidden deep in the forest of La Daboussière to the south of Entrecasteaux, is the purest of the three great Cistercian monasteries in Provence and the first to be established (the other two are Sénanque ➤ 150–151 and Silvacane ➤ 103–104). The austere abbey soon became wealthy through substantial donations, but by the 14th century it had gone into decline and it *was* finally abandoned in 1791. Restoration began in the 1850s.

Passing through the gatehouse, you see ahead the low church, built in pink stone, with a square bell-tower and a plain, undecorated interior. Beside the church are attractive cloisters, a chapter house and a tithe barn, which originally

The plain interior of the Romanesque church of the Abbaye du Thoronet, bathed in golden light

stored goods given as tithes, but later became an oil mill. Mass is sung by the Sisters of Bethlehem in the church every Sunday at noon.

✚ 192 C4
☎ 04 94 60 43 90
🕐 Apr–Sep daily 10–6:30 (closed 12–2 Sun); Oct–Mar Mon–Sat 10–1, 2–5, Sun 10–12, 2–5
💷 Moderate

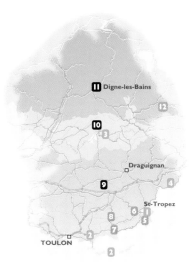

10 Moustiers-Ste-Marie

Perched high on a ridge surrounded by sheer cliffs, Moustiers is one of the main access points for a drive along the great gorges of the Verdon river (➤ 74–76). In the 5th century, monks settled on a rocky ledge above the village, and the present

Smoke drifts from a chimney-pot among the tightly packed rooftops in Moustiers-Ste-Marie

chapel of **Notre-Dame-de-Beauvour** on the site, just a short walk from the village, dates from the 12th and 16th centuries. There are two annual pilgrimages to the chapel. A long chain strung across the gorge

Smoke drifts from a chimney-pot among the tightly packed rooftops in Moustiers-Ste-Marie

suspends a renowned gold star high above the village. The star was presented to the village by a knight called Blacas to celebrate his release from captivity during a crusade.

In the 17th and 18th centuries, white, decorated earthenware pottery from the village became famous throughout the world. Now faïence de Moustiers has been revived and is sold in craft shops in every square.

➕ 186 C2

Tourist Information Office

✉ Maison de Lucie, place de l'Eglise ☎ 04 92 74 67 84; www.ville-moustiers-sainte-marie. fr 🕒 Jul–Aug daily 9:30–12:30, 2–7:15; Jun, Sep 10–12:30, 2–6:30; Apr–May 10–12:30, 2–6; Mar, Oct 10–12:30, 2–5:30; Nov 10–12, 2–5:30; Dec 10–12, 1:30–5

🔟 Digne-les-Bains

Its sheltered location, mild and sunny climate, invigorating air and the thermal springs to the south of town have made Digne-les-Bains a renowned spa centre. It is an excellent base for touring the hills by foot, by car or on the old narrow-gauge "**Pinecone**" line that

The spa at Digne-les-Bains is renowned for its therapeutic benefits

runs through the beautiful mountain valleys to Nice four times a day.

Digne's other major attraction is lavender. This aromatic plant, renowned since the Middle Ages for its therapeutic qualities, has made Digne the lavender-growing capital of Provence. During the spectacular purple processions of the annual **lavender festival**, for five days in early August, even the streets get doused with lavender water! You can buy lavender products at the market on Wednesdays and Saturdays in place du Général-de-Gaulle, and follow a Route de la Lavande, which passes through Digne and takes in all the main lavender producing places in the area.

✚ 186 C3
Tourist Information Office
✉ Rond-Point du 11-Novembre 1918
☎ 04 92 36 62 62;
www.ot-dignelesbains.fr

🔟 Entrevaux

The impressive medieval village of Entrevaux is situated above a narrow gorge in the mountains between Nice and Digne. Once an important border defence between France and Savoy, it was heavily fortified in the 1690s by Vauban, Louis XIV's military architect.

The main access to the town is across a drawbridge, through the Porte Nationale or Porte Royale into a jumble of medieval houses lining the narrow streets. There's plenty to see here, including the fortified cathedral, a restored oil mill and flour mill, a communal bread oven and a collection of historic motorcycles. A remarkable ramp leads up a sheer rock face to Vauban's ruined **Citadel**. There is little to see at the fortress, but it is well worth the climb for the views of the Haut-Var and the mountains beyond. The Porte d'Italie, the town's third gateway, opens onto to a pleasant riverside walk.

🔲 188 B3
Tourist Information Office
✉ Porte Royale ☎ 04 93 05 46 73
🕐 Open summer only Tue–Sun 9:30–12,
1:30–5. Access to citadel by automatic
turnstile
✋ Inexpensive

Above: Vauban's fortified bridge spans
the narrow gorge, providing access to the
village of Entrevaux

Left: The medieval village of Entrevaux
seems to tumble down the hillside to the
River Var below

Where to... Stay

Prices

Expect to pay per night for a double room

€ under €100   €€ €100–€200   €€€ over €200

BORMES-LES-MIMOSAS

Le Bellevue €

This simple family-run hotel has spectacular views over red roofs to the sea, and is good value in this often expensive part of the world. The friendly restaurant serves fresh seafood and local Provençal dishes.

➕ 192 C2 ✉ 12 place Gambetta
☎ 04 94 71 15 15; www.bellevuebormes. com ⏱ Closed mid-Nov to mid-Jan

MOUSTIERS-STE-MARIE

La Ferme Rose €–€€

This two-star inn takes its name from its pink (rose) façade. Inside

you'll find beamed ceilings, a tiled floor and some 1950s-style pieces such as a jukebox. You can enjoy breakfast (extra charge) in the garden in summer. No evening meals are available but you can take the opportunity to visit local restaurants.

➕ 186 C2 ✉ 04360 Moustiers-Ste-Marie
☎ 04 92 75 75 75; www.lafermerose.com
⏱ Apr to mid-Nov, Christmas and New Year

La Bastide de Moustiers €€–€€€

This former cottage, now a four-star inn, houses one of chef Alain Ducasse's restaurants (▶ 86). There are 12 bright bedrooms,

each named after local themes and individually decorated. Some rooms are located in a separate building away from the main hotel, and have a private terrace and direct access to the gardens, from where there are far-reaching views over the surrounding countryside. In the grounds, too, are ponies and deer. There is an elegant dining room, and in good weather lunch and dinner are served on the terrace. The outdoor pool is surrounded by a terrace.

➕ 186 C2 ✉ Chemin de Quinson ☎ 04 92 70 47 47; www.bastide-moustiers.com

RAMATUELLE

Kon Tiki-Riviera Village €

This high-class tent camping ground on the edge of the beautiful Pampelonne beach, is very popular, so reserve ahead. The mobile homes come in different styles, but each has two bedrooms, a kitchenette, lounge area and shower room. Alternatively, bring your

own caravan (trailer) or mobile home, and hook up to water and electricity. Extensive facilities here include currency exchange, safety deposit boxes, watersports, a grocery, restaurant, bar, tennis court and hot showers.

➕ 193 E2 ✉ Plages de Pampelonne
☎ 04 94 55 96 96; www.riviera-villages.com
⏱ Closed Nov to mid-Mar

La Ferme d'Augustin €€–€€€

This three-star hotel, a short walk from Tahiti beach and close to the centre of St-Tropez, combines traditional furnishings with modern amenities – a spa bath in some bathrooms and dressing rooms in the suites, which also have a private terrace and garden. The comfortable lounges have beamed ceilings and stone fireplaces. Outside, the *balneo* pool (heated and with hydro massaging jets) is set in well-maintained gardens.

➕ 193 E2 ✉ Tahiti ☎ 04 94 55 97 00;
www.fermeaugustin.com ⏱ Closed mid-Oct
to early Apr

Where to...
Eat and Drink

Prices
Expect to pay for a three-course meal for one, excluding drinks and service
€ under €25   €€ €25–€50   €€€ over €50

ST-TROPEZ

B Lodge €–€€

This pleasant, boutique-style hotel at the foot of the citadel has 11 stylish, modern double rooms, and one air-conditioned suite. The rooms look onto the harbour or towards the citadel. It's an easy walk downhill to the port. This is a lovely place to stay, without being excessively luxurious and in a relatively quiet location in what is often a noisy resort. The staff are friendly and helpful, and limited parking is available nearby.

➕ 193 E3 ⊠ 23 rue de l'Aïoli
☎ 04 94 97 06 57; www.hotel-b-lodge.com

Hôtel Byblos €€€

This luxurious hotel is a St-Tropez legend, perennially popular with the jet set. Behind an ochre and pink façade, the sophisticated interior is decorated with local materials. Spacious rooms and suites are enhanced by Provençal fabrics and ceramics. It's also home to St-Tropez's best-known nightclub, Les Caves du Roy.

➕ 193 E3 ⊠ Avenue Paul Signac
☎ 04 94 56 68 00; www.byblos.com
🅢 Closed Nov to mid-Apr

Hôtel Lou Cagnard €–€€

This comfortable budget hotel is an excellent option, with rooms that are airy, clean and simple. Enjoy breakfast in the garden on a sunny morning. Parking is available.

➕ 193 E3 ⊠ 18 avenue Paul Roussel
☎ 04 94 97 04 24; www.hotel-lou-cagnard.com 🅢 Closed mid-Oct to early May

Mas de Chastelas €€–€€€

Stay with Depardieu, Belmondo and other French film idols at this beautiful 18th-century *mas* (farmhouse) situated just outside St-Tropez. Set in spacious grounds, the hotel's facilities include two swimming pools, an outdoor Jacuzzi and tennis courts.

➕ 193 E3 ⊠ Quartier Bertaud, Gassin
☎ 04 94 56 71 71; www.chastelas.com
🅢 Closed Nov–Dec, but may vary

BORMES-LES-MIMOSAS

Lou Portaou €€

In a picturesque corner of Bormes, this small restaurant serves a simple menu of fresh Provençal cuisine.

➕ 192 C2 ⊠ 1 rue Cubert-des-Poètes
☎ 04 94 64 86 37 🕐 12–1.30, 7–9.30. Closed Mon and Tue mid-Sep to mid-Jun

COLLOBRIÈRES

La Petite Fontaine €

Try some local delicacies of the Massif des Maures, washed down with wine from the local cooperative on a shady terrace. Peaceful surroundings.

➕ 192 C2 ⊠ 1 place de la République
☎ 04 94 48 00 12 🅢 Closed Sun dinner, Mon

DIGNE-LES-BAINS

Le Grand Paris €€

Holds the reputation as Digne's best restaurant, set in a former 17th-century convent. Try the medallions of monkfish with smoky bacon and an emulsion of baby onions.

➕ 186 C3 ⊠ 19 boulevard Thiers ☎ 04 92 31 11 15 🅢 Closed Dec–Feb

GRIMAUD

Les Santons €€

Top cuisine, fresh local ingredients and impeccable service in elegant Provençal surroundings. Les Santons serves classic French and Mediterranean dishes and is one of the region's top restaurants, so make a reservation to ensure a table at weekends or in summer.

➕ 193 D3 ✉ D558 ☎ 04 94 43 21 02 ⏰ Closed Wed, mid-Nov to mid-Dec

HYÈRES

Le Bistrot de Marius €€

Lyonnais and Provençal specialities are the mainstays of this atmospheric little restaurant in the heart of Hyères' old quarter, with plenty of fish on its reasonably priced set menus. In fine weather, a table outside on the buzzy square in the shadow of the Tour des Templiers is particularly magical.

➕ 192 B2 ✉ 1 place Massillon ☎ 04 94 35 88 38 ⏰ Closed Mon in summer

MOUSTIERS-STE-MARIE

La Bastide de Moustiers €€–€€€

Dine in the country home of the world's top chef, Alain Ducasse. The menu changes daily and features sensational dishes that embrace all the flavours and perfumes of the region, using seasonal produce from the local markets. The restaurant is part of a four-star inn (➤ 84).

➕ 186 C2 ✉ Chemin de Quinson, 04360 Moustiers-Ste-Marie ☎ 04 92 70 47 47 ⏰ Closed Mon–Tue or Wed and 7–31 Jan

ST-TROPEZ

La Bouillabaisse €€

A restaurant that majors on fish, set in a traditional fisherman's cottage on the beach.

➕ 193 E3 ✉ Plage de la Bouillabaisse ☎ 04 94 97 54 00 ⏰ Closed Oct to mid-Feb

Le Café €€

Formerly known as Le Café des Arts, this cosy bar/stylish restaurant has a long history as a centre for intellectual and artistic debate. The archetypal French bar has brown leather couches, wooden fittings and old leather-bound books on the shelves. The terrace is an ideal place to enjoy a bar or a coffee while watching a game of pétanque. Le Café is situated next to the cinema on the place des Lices, and is not to be confused with the newer Café des Arts on the corner.

➕ 193 E3 ✉ 5 place des Lices ☎ 04 94 97 44 69; www.lecafe.fr ⏰ Food daily 10:30am–11pm; café until midnight

Chez Fuchs €€

An unpretentious, family-run bar-tabac, serving hearty bistro fare. Traditional dishes and a lively atmosphere make tiny Chez Fuchs hugely popular. Book ahead.

➕ 193 E3 ✉ 7 rue des Commerçants ☎ 04 94 97 01 25 ⏰ Closed Jun–Sep lunch

La Citadelle €

This tiny atmospheric restaurant has tables that spill out on to the street. Don't miss the delicious tarte tatin.

➕ 193 E3 ✉ 22 bis rue de la Citadelle ☎ 04 94 54 81 19 ⏰ Apr–Oct daily 12–2, 7–10:30

Sénéquier €€

You can't miss the distinctive red awnings and matching tables and chairs on the waterfront, for this is one of the best-known spots in town and a must for breakfast. The coffees are on the pricey side, but this is really the place to be on a sunny morning in St-Tropez (➤ 68).

➕ 193 E3 ✉ Quai Jean-Jaurès ☎ 04 94 97 00 90 ⏰ Daily 8am– 2am, summer; 8am– 8pm, winter. Closed Jan and Feb

La Table du Marché €€

This smart bistro-deli, on a narrow street close to the harbour, offers excellent meals and an array of light snacks, regional specialities, wines, pastries and cakes in a relaxed setting. It also serves afternoon tea.

➕ 193 E3 ✉ 38 rue Georges Clemenceau ☎ 04 94 97 91 91 ⏰ Lunch and dinner all year, 8am–midnight

Where to... Shop

MARKETS

St-Tropez has several markets including the **Marché aux Poissons**, the picturesque fish market (place aux Herbes, open 7–1). This is the best place to get Mediterranean fish such as red mullet, scorpion fish and rainbow wrasse. Even if you are not going to buy, it is worth a visit for the lively atmosphere. At the **Marché Provençal** (place des Lices, Tue, Sat 8–1) you'll find all the typical food of Provence – there's also an antiques corner and traditional local crafts.

Collobrières is surrounded by chestnut groves and its farmers' market, the **Marché Collobriérois** (place de la Libération, open Thu, Sun 8–1), sells chestnut products

ranging from *marrons glacés* and chestnut jam to chestnut-wood wickerwork. Cork products and other regional specialities such as olives and honey are also on offer.

FOOD AND DRINK

In St-Tropez seek out **Tarte Tropézienne** (36 rue Clemenceau, www.tartetropizienne.com, open 8–8 Feb–Oct) for the cake filled with custard that gives this shop its name. The cake was given its name by Brigitte Bardot in 1955. Nearby, at Gassin, **Les Maîtres Vignerons de la Presqu'île de St-Tropez** (Carrefour de la Foux) stocks the wines of the peninsula.

You can pick up the tastes (*saveurs*) and colours of Provence at **Saveurs et Couleurs** in Digne-Les-

Bains (7 boulevard Gassendi, open Tue-Sat 8:30–12:30/2:30–7:15, Sun 9–12:30), selling fine oils, foie gras, vinegars, alcohol, perfumes, Marseille soap, goods made from Provençal fabrics, and items made of olive wood and terracotta.

The small Bandol Appellation Controlée west of Toulon is one of the most renowned wine-growing districts in Provence, with superb reds and sublime roses making good use of the Mourvèdre grape. Conditions in the area surrounding the town are particularly suitable for the grape, as well as white wines using the Clairette and Bourboulenc varieties. **Maison des Vins** on the port in Bandol (22 allées Vivien, open Mon-Sat 10–1, 3–7) has plenty of information about the various *domaines* and a good stock of the wines available to buy.

SOUVENIRS AND GIFTS

Pépinières Cavatore (chemin de Bénat, tel: 04 94 00 40 23) in

Bormes-les-Mimosas is a nursery specialising in mimosa – visit in February to see the trees in full bloom, including rare varieties. It's worth a visit, just to browse. Credit cards are not accepted.

Moustiers-Ste-Marie is known for its decorated faïences, and you can browse the collection of vases, plates and pitchers at the studio of **Atelier Soleil** (chemin de Quinson, open 9–11:30 Mon, Tue, Thu, Fri). The atelier also has a shop close to the church in the centre of Moustiers.

FASHION

Head to St-Tropez for trendy boutiques. **Hermès** (place Grammond) offers the ultimate in French chic, while **Blanc Bleu** (3 rue Allard, open 10–1, 3–7) is good for stylish, sporty fashion for both sexes. **Rondini** (16 rue Clemenceau) is famous for making the Tropézienne, a Roman-style sandal worn by many celebrities, including Picasso.

Where to...
Be Entertained

BARS, CLUBS AND CASINOS

Reputedly the spiciest nightspot in St-Tropez, **Les Caves du Roy** is the haunt of the rich and famous. Admission is free but the drink prices are extortionate (Hôtel Byblos, avenue Paul-Signac, tel: 04 94 56 63 00, open 11pm–5am Easter–Oct). The star-studded **VIP Room** (résidences du Nouveau Port, tel: 04 94 97 14 70, open Apr–Oct daily 9pm to 3am or 5am) is *the* place to see and be seen. For a good choice of draught beers try **Bar Anglais** (Hôtel Sube, 15 quai Suffren 83990, tel: 04 94 97 30 04, from 8am) on the first floor of the prestigious Hôtel Sube. **Le Papagayo Lounge Bar** (Port de Saint-Tropez, tel: 04 94 79 29 50)

is a restaurant-nightclub near the Old Port. It has a terrace with great views, and is a good place for a bit of celebrity-spotting. Clubby music pumping into the small hours makes it popular with the young crowd. Bands perform almost every night during the high season. If clubbing is not your style or you are looking for something laid-back, **Octave Café** (place de la Garonne, St-Tropez, tel: 04 94 97 22 56) is a stylish café with comfortable chairs, low tables, and lounge and live music. You'll find jazz musicians playing in a small back bar area.

Digne-les-Bains' home of culture is **Palais des Expositions** (1 place de la République, tel: 04 92 31 15 21; www.marie-dignelesbains.fr) This modular auditorium holds up

to 3,000 people and hosts concerts, including international singers, and theatre and dance productions.

SPAS

A variety of different treatments are available at the spas at Digne-les-Bains and Gréoux-les-Bains. Options at **Etablissement thermal de Digne-les-Bains** include facials, mud wraps and sessions at the aquagym (Eurothermes, Digne-les-Bains, tel: 04 92 32 32 92, open Mar to early Dec). If you are here in early August, then you can join in the five days of festivities when Digne celebrates its other main industry – lavender.

Hydrotherapy has also been practised at **Etablissement Thermal de Gréoux-les-Bains** for centuries; the waters are considered particularly effective for rheumatism and bronchial complaints (quai des Hautes Plaines, tel: 08 26 46 81 85; www.sante-eau.com, open Mon–Sat, mid-Mar to mid-Dec).

SPORT

The 18-hole golf course, **Golf de Digne les Bains**, nestles between mountains and has a restaurant, two-star hotel, swimming pool and tennis court (57 route du Chalfaut, Digne-les-Bains, tel: 04 92 30 58 00; open 9–6 (8–8 during the summer season).

In Fréjus, you can discover a variety of dive sites, including wrecks, between Dramont and St-Tropez with **Centre International de Plongée de Fréjus** (Aire de Carénage, Port Fréjus, tel: 04 94 52 34 99; www.cip-frejus.com, open all year by appointment).

To experience thrills on the water, **Aqua Viva Est** in Castellane offers guided full- and half-day white-water rafting, canoeing and kayaking trips along the Gorges du Verdon and the Vésubie and Tinée rivers (12 boulevard de la République, tel: 04 92 83 75 74, www.aquavivaest.com, open Easter–late Sep).

The Marseille Area

Getting Your Bearings

There is a surprising amount of diversity in this small region, which embraces Marseille, France's premier port, and Aix-en-Provence, the old capital of Provence.

The city of Marseille has a particularly strong personality – laidback, vibrant and edgy. A world away from the stereotypical cities of the Riviera, this Mediterranean rough diamond lacks the glamorous promenades and glitzy hotels of Nice and Cannes, and the cachet of St-Tropez. It is a traditional, hard-working city, famous for its shipping, its soap, its *pastis*, its *bouillabaisse*, the world's largest annual pétanque competition and *La Marseillaise* (► 94). Its extraordinary blend of history, race and culture led Alexandre Dumas to describe it as the "meeting place of the entire world."

By contrast, few cities are as quintessentially Provençal as Aix-en-Provence, with its beautiful honey-hued *hôtels particuliers* (mansion residences) adorned with ornamental wrought-iron balconies; its sun-baked squares splashed by nearly 100 fountains; and its lively, colourful locals' markets. Aix is the home of the Post-Impressionist artist, Paul Cézanne. It is easy to see why he was so inspired by the surrounding countryside, especially the great Montagne Ste-Victoire, with its limestone peak which reflects every hue of light and shade.

Other celebrated residents are commemorated in their home towns: Nostradamus in Salon-de-Provence, and writer Marcel Pagnol in Aubagne. Here, too, is the Château de Barben with its magnificent Le Nôtre gardens; the Cistercian Abbaye de Silvacane; and the spectacular fjord-like coastline at the Calanques.

N7
D569 Sénas
Eyguières
N538
N113 **Salon-de-Provence** 6
E80 A54
N113
Miramas
St-Chamas
Istres
D5
Étang de Berre
Fos-sur-Mer **Martigues** 5
N568
N568 A55
Carro
Chaîne

Page 89: Notre-Dame de la Garde, Marseille
Left: A fisherman working on his nets

★ Don't Miss

At Your Leisure

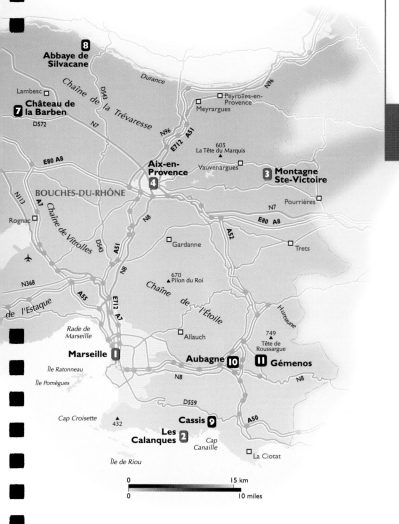

In Two Days

If you're not quite sure where to begin your travels, this itinerary recommends a practical and enjoyable two-day tour of the Marseille area, taking in some of the best places to see using the Getting Your Bearings map on the previous page. For more information see the main entries

Day One

Morning
Start your tour of **❶ Marseille** at the Vieux Port (left, ➤ 94), where the city's heart beats loudest. Try to get up early enough to see the daily fish market on the quai des Belges. Explore the quartier du Panier (➤ 95), the oldest part of the city, where the Greeks built their temples. Today, this atmospheric district is a maze of dark, cobbled, souk-like streets where at times you have to remind yourself which side of the Mediterranean you are on.

Lunch
La Kahéna (2 rue de la République, tel: 04 91 90 61 93) serves couscous and gorgeous sticky pastries.

Afternoon
Admire Marseille's striking coastline on a boat trip from the Vieux Port to the plunging white cliffs of the famous fjord-like **❷ Calanques** (➤ 97). Or take a boat to the offshore fortress of Château d'If (➤ 94), with its extraordinary blend of fact, fiction and legend.

Evening
Return to the Old Port of Marseille to enjoy an aperitif at Bar de la Marine (quai de Rive Neuve) – featured in the novels of Marcel Pagnol and in the film *Love Actually* – followed by a meal to remember in Une Table, au Sud (➤ 108), one of the city's most renowned restaurants. Or catch a performance at the Opéra de Marseille (➤ 110), where the famous National Ballet Company also performs.

Day Two

Morning

Spend the morning exploring the beautiful, ancient town of 4 **Aix-en-Provence** (➤ 100–101). Highlights include the cafés of the the main boulevard, cours Mirabeau (below); the Old Town and its ancient cathedral to the north; and the quartier Mazarin, with fancy mansions to the south. And there's always at least one morning market – either for fruit and vegetables, flowers or books.

Lunch

Try the local game dishes at La Brocherie (➤ 107).

Afternoon

Art lovers in particular will enjoy the circuit Cézanne footpath (➤ 101), which leads to the studio (Atelier Paul-Cézanne, ➤ 101) of the city's most celebrated citizen – a poignant memorial to this great Impressionist artist, which remains just as he left it at his death in 1906.

Cézanne spent much of his life painting the limestone hills surrounding Aix and, in particular, his beloved 3 **Montagne Ste-Victoire** (right, ➤ 98–99), which he painted over 65 times. Drive westwards out of Aix along one of the narrow country lanes and you too will see this inspirational landscape.

Evening

Return to Aix for dinner at L'Aixquis (➤ 107).

❶ Marseille

Marseille, France's premier port on the west coast of Provence, is a lively place with a long history and a distinctive mix of ethnic and cultural influences. The city has plenty to offer, including museums and art galleries and trips to the offshore islands. Start your visit at the vibrant Vieux Port (Old Port), at the heart of the city, where bright fishing boats unload their catches each morning and the surrounding streets are filled with bars and restaurants.

A boat trip to the forbidding Château d'If

Vieux Port

Tourist boats departing from quai des Belges take visitors to the infamous **Château d'If**, a forbidding fortress castle 3km (2 miles) offshore on a barren, rocky island. Built in 1528 by François I to protect the port, it later became a prison, and today guided tours take you to the cells once occupied by aristocratic prisoners. Alexandre Dumas used the château as the setting for his book *The Count of Monte Cristo* (1844).

Close to the port, behind quai de Rive Neuve, is the quartier de l'Arsenal, wher you can taste the local fish soup,

LA MARSEILLAISE

During the French Revolution 500 volunteers were sent from Marseille to Paris. As they marched northwards, they sang a song, composed by Rouget de Lisle in Strasbourg. By the time they reached Paris, it had been adopted as the anthem of the revolution, and was named *La Marseillaise* in honour of the city's "choir".

bouillabaisse (➤ 19).
To the south, perched on a hilltop, is **Notre-Dame de la Garde**, a 19th-century basilica topped with a huge gilded Madonna, which is strikingly lit at night.

North of the Old Port is the colourful **le Panier** district, where stepped alleys and rundown tenements climb up from the docks. Although heavily damaged during World War II, the area is scattered with interesting historic buildings. At the foot of the district is the **Musée des Docks Romains**, which displays a collection of first- to third-century AD Roman objects discovered during post-war rebuilding work. Further up is the former 17th-century hospice, La Vieille Charité. These arcaded galleries now house a cultural centre hosting art exhibitions and a museum. The ostentatious 19th-century neo-Byzantine Cathédrale de la Major, with its domes and striped façade, overlooks the modern docks.

Working and pleasure boats moored side-by-side in the Old Port of Marseille

Leading up from the Old Port and through the heart of the city is **La Canebière**, the main thoroughfare of Marseille, off which lead the main shopping streets. North of here is the fascinating **Musée d'Histoire de Marseille**, which records the city's history and has a third century Roman merchant

Cathèdrale de la Major

ship as its focal point. Alongside is the Jardin des Vestiges, an archaeological site which has been transformed into a pretty garden. A walkway allows an overview of the ruins of the original Greek ramparts, traces of a roadway and parts of the dock as it was in the first century AD. Many of the items excavated here are on display in the museum.

To the south of La Canebière is the **Musée Cantini**, Marseille's most interesting art gallery with a fine collection spanning the Fauvist, Cubist and Surrealist movements, including works by Man Ray, Matisse, Kandinsky, Picasso, Giacometti and Bacon. The museum stands in the centre of Marseille's most chic shopping district.

TAKING A BREAK

Sample the ultimate *bouillabaisse* (➤ 19) beside the Old Port at **Le Miramar** (12 quai du Port, tel: 04 91 91 10 40; closed Sun, Mon).
🕂 191 D2

Tourist Information Office
🕂 198 C2 ✉ 4 La Canebière ☎ 04 91 13 89 00; www.marseille-tourisme. com ⏰ Mon–Sat 9–7, Sun 10–5 🚇 Metro 1: Vieux Port

Château d'If
🕂 198, off A2
☎ 04 91 59 02 30 ⏰ May to mid-Sep daily 9–6; mid-Sep to Mar Tue–Sun 9–5:15; Apr daily 9–5:30 💶 Moderate 🚢 From quai des Belges (☎ 04 91 55 50 09, Apr–Oct)

Musée des Docks Romains
🕂 198 B2
✉ 28 place Vivaux ☎ 04 91 91 24 62 ⏰ Tue–Sun 11–6, Jun–Sep; Tue–Sun 10–5, Oct–May 💶 Inexpensive

Musée d'Histoire de Marseille
🕂 198 C3
✉ Square Belsunce, Centre Bourse ☎ 04 91 90 42 22 ⏰ Mon–Sat 12–7 💶 Inexpensive

Musée Cantini
🕂 198 C1
✉ 19 rue Grignan ☎ 04 91 54 77 75 ⏰ Jun–Sep daily 11–6; Oct–May daily 10–5 💶 Inexpensive

La Canebière runs through the heart of the city from the Old Port

MARSEILLE: INSIDE INFO

Top tips Street parking is difficult so **use the parking areas**. There are several near the Vieux Port.
■ The monthly *César* and *Ventilo* list hundreds of events in the city.
■ Beware of pickpockets in Le Panier district and avoid the area at night. Keep a close eye on your belongings at markets, in seafront areas and in bars.

Hidden gem The **Maison de l'Artisanat et des Metiers des Arts** is always worth a visit for its regularly changing exhibitions of local and international handicrafts and applied arts (21 cours d'Estienne d'Orves, tel: 04 91 54 80 54; open Tue–Sun 1–6; free).

❷ The Calanques

Just outside Cassis, dazzling white cliffs plunge into the crystal waters of spectacular narrow inlets or *calanques* – creating a dramatic coastline of magnificent mini-fjords. The weathered limestone cliffs are popular with climbers and the clear, deep water is ideal for bathing and scuba-diving, making the area a popular excursion from nearby Marseille.

Safe moorings in the sheltered inlets of the calanques

The Calanques can be reached on foot, taking a waymarked path across the high clifftops, followed by a steep scramble down to the beaches, or by boat from Cassis. Picturesque **Port-Miou**, lined with yachts and pleasure craft, is the first and longest *calanque*. **Port-Pin** is the smallest, with a tiny shingle beach shaded by pines, while **En Vau**, the third inlet,

has stark, precipitous cliffs and needle-like rocks rising from the sea. The 1.5-hour walk to reach it, and the steep descent to the sandy beach, keep it free from crowds.

Further west, the Sormiou and Morgiou creeks can be reached by car. When diving at Sormiou in 1991, Henri Cosquer discovered a cave lined with paintings of bison, deer, fish and horses dating from around 25,000 BC. The site was listed as a historical monument in 1992.

TAKING A BREAK

Sur les Quais on the Old Port at La Ciotat is the yacht club's bar and restaurant (tel: 04 42 08 14 14).

➕ 191 E1
Tourist Information Office
✉ Quai des Moulins, Cassis
☎ 08 92 25 98 92; www.ot-cassis.fr
◑ ➤ 104

THE CALANQUES: INSIDE INFO

Top tip Enjoy a different perspective of the calanques on a 45-minute **boat trip** with commentary from the port at Cassis, between 10 and 4:30 daily.

❸ Montagne Ste-Victoire

Artist Paul Cézanne (1839–1906) was fascinated by Mont Ste-Victoire, a huge sunlit wedge of limestone rising in the Provençal countryside east of Aix. He painted it more than 65 times, often portraying it as a blue-grey pyramid rising above red soil and a dense forest of dark green trees, making this great Provençal landmark famous worldwide.

Mont Ste-Victoire lies just east of Aix-en-Provence. Viewed end on, this pale ridge 16km (10 miles) long (running east–west) takes the form of a shapely pyramid. On its lower slopes, the red soil of the Coteaux-d'Aix vineyards give way to thick forest, scrub and fragrant herbs. Above the trees, the limestone peak reflects the light and shadow creating extraordinary designs of blue, grey, white, pink and orange on the landscape.

The mountain was Paul Cézanne's favourite local subject. He would walk from Aix to paint it again and again, from all angles and at all hours, creating some of his greatest canvases, including *La Montagne Sainte-Victoire* (1904) and *Le Paysage d'Aix* (1905). In a letter to his son in 1906, he wrote "I spend every day in this landscape, with its beautiful shapes. Indeed, I cannot imagine a more pleasant way or place to pass my time."

The mountain is encircled by the D10 on the north and the

D17 on the south, which give easy access to its viewpoints and trails. Just off the D10, the Barrage de Bimont (7km/4 miles from Aix) dams the River Infernet to form an artificial lake, the **Lac du Bimont**,

Above and below left: Cézanne's beloved mountain rises up out of the dark green landscape

which provides water to the local towns.

Further along the D10, a marked trail near Les Cabassols farm leads up the steep 3km (2-mile) path to **La Croix de Provence**, the peak (945m/3,100 feet) at the western end of the mountain. Allow several hours for this walk, as the path is difficult in places, requiring sure-footedness. It is worth the effort for the views across the blue and purple hills. **Vauvenargues**, on the D10, is a small, pretty village. The 17th-century château (not open to the public) standing on a rock near by was the home of artist Pablo Picasso.

At the southeastern end of the mountain is the village of **Pourrières**, believed to have been named after a Roman victory over invading Germanic tribes in 102 BC. From here to Puyloubier, south of the mountain on the D17, is vine country, producing rosé wines.

TAKING A BREAK

There are picnic tables and benches by the dam of **Barrage de Bimont**.

🚹 191 F3
Tourist Information Office
✉ 2 place du Général-de-Gaulle, Aix-en-Provence
☎ 04 42 16 11 61; www.aixenprovencetourism.com

MONTAGNE STE-VICTOIRE: INSIDE INFO

Top tips Wear **stout shoes or hiking boots** for the climb to La Croix de Provence.
■ Paths may be closed between July and September because of the risk of fire.
■ **Don't smoke** when walking through forest or scrubland as you may risk starting a forest fire.

Hidden gem The area around the **Barrage de Bimont** and **Lac du Bimont** has been turned into a pleasant park with picnic tables and benches.

❹ Aix-en-Provence

Aix, the historic capital of Provence, is a city of fountains and fine mansions, art and culture. The shaded main street, cours Mirabeau, is lined with pavement cafés and leafy plane trees, and within a short walk is the attractive medieval and Renaissance Old Town with its narrow lanes, markets and pretty squares.

The city started life as Aquae Sextiae, a Roman spa dating from 123 BC. Aix thrived culturally during the Middle Ages under Good King René, an ardent patron of the arts, and prospered during the 17th and 18th centuries when many Renaissance mansions were built.

The **cours Mirabeau** divides Old Aix (*Vieil Aix*) to the north from the quartier Mazarin, with its elegant mansions to the south. Running down the middle of the **cours Mirabeau**

is a series of fountains, including the moss-covered Fontaine d'Eau Thermale, a natural hot spring. This broad boulevard is the place to stroll or sit at a café table under the trees and watch the sauntering crowds go by. Between here and the **Cathédrale St-Sauveur** are some of the most interesting streets, with markets and restaurants, and shops selling bright Provençal handicrafts and designer clothes. This is also where you'll find the town's main square, **place de l'Hôtel de Ville**, with its Italianate town hall. Rising from one corner of the building is a 16th-century belfry, the Tour de l'Horloge, its tower adorned with an astronomical clock. The cathedral, a mix of styles from Romanesque to baroque, has 16th-century Flemish tapestries in the chancel and superb medieval art, notably Nicolas Froment's famous triptych *Le Buisson Ardent* (1475–56), undergoing restoration at the time of writing, depicting a vision of the Virgin and Child

Left: La Rotunde Fountain in place du Général-de-Gaulle

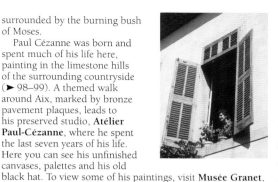

surrounded by the burning bush of Moses.

Paul Cézanne was born and spent much of his life here, painting in the limestone hills of the surrounding countryside (➤ 98–99). A themed walk around Aix, marked by bronze pavement plaques, leads to his preserved studio, **Atélier Paul-Cézanne**, where he spent the last seven years of his life. Here you can see his unfinished canvases, palettes and his old black hat. To view some of his paintings, visit **Musée Granet**, the city's main museum, which has a small collection of his early works. Located in the Gothic priory of the Knights of Malta, the museum displays European paintings collected by 19th-century artist François Granet, along with extensive archaeological finds dating to Roman Aix. The museum has been refurbished.

Below:
An outdoor
restaurant
on cours
Mirabeau

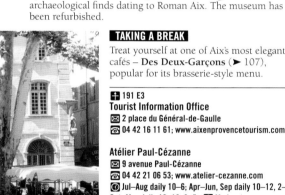

TAKING A BREAK

Treat yourself at one of Aix's most elegant cafés – **Des Deux-Garçons** (➤ 107), popular for its brasserie-style menu.

➕ 191 E3
Tourist Information Office
✉ 2 place du Général-de-Gaulle
☎ 04 42 16 11 61; www.aixenprovencetourism.com

Atélier Paul-Cézanne
✉ 9 avenue Paul-Cézanne
☎ 04 42 21 06 53; www.atelier-cezanne.com
🕐 Jul–Aug daily 10–6; Apr–Jun, Sep daily 10–12, 2–6; Oct–Mar daily 10–12, 2–5 💵 Moderate

Musée Granet
✉ Place St-Jean-de-Malte
☎ 04 42 52 88 32 🕐 Jun–Sep Tue–Sun 11–7; Oct–May Tue–Sun 12–6 💵 Moderate

AIX-EN-PROVENCE: INSIDE INFO

Top tips The **Visa for Aix and its Region** card gives reductions on the entry price to various museums, as well as discounts on bus tickets. Buy it from the tourist office and museums.
■ Visit the **flower market** (Tuesday, Thursday and Saturday morning) at place de l'Hôtel de Ville.
■ Aix has seven annual festivals, including France's élite opera festival, the **Festival International d'Art Lyrique et de la Musique**, lasting for several weeks in late June and July.

At Your Leisure

Pastel-coloured houses line the quai in Martigues

The Chaîne de l'Estaque, a range of low hills, runs along the coast between Martigues and Marseille. Here you can follow woodland walking trails and enjoy sea views.

➕ 190 C3

Tourist Information Centre
✉ Rond Point de l'Hôtel de Ville
☎ 04 42 42 31 10;
www.martigues-tourisme.com
🕐 Mon–Fri 9–12:30, 1:30–5:45, Sat 9–12:30, 2:30–6, Sun 10–12:30

Musée Ziem
✉ Boulevard du 14 Juillet
☎ 04 42 41 39 60
🕐 Jul–Aug Wed–Mon 10–12, 2:30–6:30; Sep–Jun Wed–Sun 2:30–6:30
💰 Free

🔳 Salon-de-Provence

This large industrial town sits between the Crau plain and the hills of western Provence at a junction of roads linking Arles, Avignon, Aix and Marseille.

The Porte de l'Horloge in Salon-de-Provence

🔳 Martigues

Martigues, an excellent base for exploring the Étang de Berre, has picturesque canals that run through its centre between its three "villages".

Jonquières, on the southern side of the main canal, Canal de Caronte, is the busiest and best place to go for a meal or a drink. In the middle is **L'Île**, which has several restored 17th- and 18th-century houses, as well as the splendid Église Ste-Madeleine-de-l'Île. Stand on the bridge at quai Brescon, next to the church, to admire the celebrated view of fishing boats moored on the canal. The scene, known as the *Miroir des Oiseaux* (the birds' mirror), was painted by Felix Ziem (1821–1911). Works by Ziem and other artists are on display in the **Musée Ziem**, in the third village of **Ferrières**.

The astrologer Michel de Nostradame moved here from St-Rémy in 1547 and remained until his death in 1566. It was here he wrote the prophetic tome *Centuries*. His former home, **Maison de Nostradamus**, is today a museum of his life. Near by is the lovely 17th-century gateway, **Porte de l'Horloge**, with a beautiful 16th-century fountain, called the Fontaine Mousse, opposite. Nostradamus's tomb is in the Église St-Laurent, in the north of the town.

The Château de l'Empéri, in place des Centuries, dates from the 10th century and is home to military and local museums.

🚹 190 C4
Tourist Information Office
✉ Cours Gimon ☎ 04 90 56 27 60
◉ Jul–Aug Mon–Sat 9:30–6:30, Sun 9:30–12:30; Sep–Jun Mon–Sat 9:30–12:30, 2–6
Maison de Nostradamus
✉ 11 rue Nostradamus
☎ 04 90 56 64 31
◉ Mon–Fri 9–12, 2–6, Sat–Sun 2–6
❓ 40-minute audioguide in English
Château-Musée de l'Empéri
🚹 190 C4 ✉ Montée de Puech ☎ 04 90 44 72 80 ◉ Wed–Sun 10–12, 2–6 💶 Inexpensive

🄷 Château de la Barben

A magnificent fortified castle on the top of a rocky hill, La Barben was originally a medieval fortress, but it was rebuilt many times over the centuries and today's pile is more like a stately home.

La Barben was acquired by King René in the 15th century. He sold it to the de Forbins, who eventually turned it into a luxurious home. Inside, there are lavish period furnishings and fine craftsmanship, including striking 16th- and 17th-century Flemish and Aubusson tapestries and elegant 18th-century painted ceilings.

The highlight is a spectacular **terraced garden** in formal French style, created by André Le Nôtre, the landscape

The imposing towers of the Château de la Barben seem to be part of the living rock

designer of Versailles. The formality of the flower borders, statuary and basins is emphasised by the surrounding untamed woodland. Other attractions include a reptile collection and a zoo.

🚹 190 C4
✉ 13330 La Barben ☎ 04 90 55 25 41
◉ Apr–Nov daily 10–6; Nov, Feb–Mar Sat–Sun 10–12, 2–5:30 💶 Expensive

🄸 Abbaye de Silvacane

Nestling in a peaceful setting close to the south banks of the Durance, the Abbaye de Silvacane was the last of the three great Cistercian abbeys to be built in Provence, known as the Three Cistercian Sisters (the other two are Sénanque ➤ 150–151 and du Thoronet ➤ 80). Silvacane, considered the loveliest of the three, is a perfect example of the simple, austere elegance promoted by the Cistercians. The name, from Silva

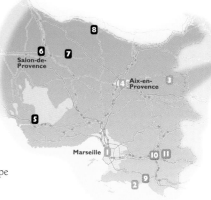

The Abbaye de Silvacane – one of Provence's great Cistercian abbeys

Cana, is Latin for Forest of Reeds, which was all that was here before the monks drained the marshes to create farmland. Founded in the 12th century, the abbey prospered until raids and crop failure in the 14th century ruined it. It was turned into farm buildings before restoration began in the 19th century. The stark beauty of the clean-lined, pale stone church is echoed in a charming cloister with an old fountain. The most striking part of the abbey is the refectory, rebuilt in 1423 in Gothic style. It has a rose window and is less austere than other parts.

🔲 191 D4
✉ La Roque d'Anthéron
☎ 04 42 50 41 69
🕐 Jun–Sep daily 10–6; Oct–May Wed–Mon 10–1, 2–5 🎟 Moderate

🔟 Cassis

This busy little fishing port and modern beach resort basks in a sheltered bay between the white cliffs of the Cap Canaille and the breathtaking *calanques* (fjord-like inlets) to the west (➤ 97). The surrounding hills are cloaked with olives, almonds, figs and the famous terraced vineyards of the region's prestigious *vin de Cassis*. In the village centre, pétanque players meet in dusty squares, while fishermen spread their nets along the quayside, beside waterfront cafés.

There's a small beach of sand and pebbles, and an old castle perched on a hill. An easy clifftop path, linking Cassis with Marseille, gives magnificent views out to sea, but to fully appreciate the dazzling white

cliffs and narrow creeks, take a **boat trip** from the quay.

🔲 191 E2
Tourist Information Office
✉ Quai des Moulins ☎ 08 92 25 98 92;
www.ot-cassis.fr 🕐 Jul–Aug Mon–Fri 9–7, Sat, Sun 9:30–12:30, 3–6; Mar–Jun, Sep–Oct Mon–Fri 9–12.30, 2–6, Sat 9:30–12:30, 2–5:30, Sun 10–12:30; Nov–Feb Mon–Fri 9:30–12:30, 2–5:30, Sat 10–12:30, 2–5, Sun 10–12:30

🔟 Aubagne

Aubagne is a major production centre for traditional Provençal ceramics, which have been made here since the 16th century. Local potters specialise in *santons* (traditional clay figurines)

FOR KIDS
■ **Château de la Barben** The château (➤ 103) has a vivarium (reptile collection) in the vaulted sheep pen, and a zoo with bears, lions and hippos (Jul–Sep daily 9:30–7; Oct–Jun daily 10–6).
■ **Cassis** Spend time on the small pebble and sand beach.

Relaxing on the small beach at Cassis

The elegant town hall at Gémenos

and beautiful decorative items, which can be bought from artisans' shops in the Old Town and at the town's pottery markets and fairs. Aubagne is also the birthplace of playwright and film director Marcel Pagnol (1895–1974), who set many of his works in the town and surrounding countryside. Guided tours take in locations from the films of his novels *Jean de Florette* and *Manon des Sources*.

➕ 191 E2

Tourist Information Office
✉ 8 cours Barthélémy
☎ 04 42 03 49 98

⑪ Gémenos

Gémenos, close to the autoroute and Marseille, is a typical Provençal village, with narrow streets, steps and old houses. While you're in the main square look inside the courtyard of the 17th- to 18th-century Granges du Marquis d'Albertas, a huge building that once housed agricultural workers. Another building of interest is the beautiful 17th-century château, now the town hall.

Outside the village on the D2 are the ruins of the 13th-century **Abbaye de St-Pons**, the setting for religious music concerts in summer.

➕ 191 F2

Tourist Information Office
✉ Cours Pasteur ☎ 04 42 32 18 44;
www.officedetourismegemenos.com
🕐 Oct–Apr Mon–Sat 10–12, 3–6; May–Sep Mon–Sat 10–12, 2–5

Where to... Stay

Prices

Expect to pay per night for a double room

€ under €100   €€ €100–€200   €€€ over €200

AIX-EN-PROVENCE

Des Augustins €€

This hotel offers a blend of history and modernity within a 12th-century former Augustinian convent, in the centre of Old Aix.

✚ 191 E3 ⊠ 3 rue de la Masse
☎ 04 42 27 28 59; www.hotel-augustins.com ⊙ Al year

Le Pigonnet €€€

The four-star Le Pigonnet, at the end of a tree-lined street in the heart of town, is a beautiful family-run *bastide* (country house) hotel furnished with local antiques. Many of the elegant bedrooms look out over the flower-filled gardens, and some have terraces with views of Montagne Ste-Victoire, while others overlook the pool.

✚ 191 E3 ⊠ 5 avenue du Pigonnet
☎ 04 42 59 02 90; www.hotelpigonnet.com

CASSIS

Auberge de Jeunesse de Cassis €

This youth hostel, in the massif of Calanques and one hour on foot from Cassis, is great for those who don't mind roughing it – there are no showers and accommodation is in a 10-bed dormitory. Cooking equipment is available. Waste is recycled and solar energy used.

✚ 191 E2 ⊠ La Fontasse ☎ 04 42 01 02 72; www.fuaj.org ⊙ Closed Jan to mid-Mar

Les Roches Blanches €€

In a commanding clifftop position with gardens leading down to the sea, this four-star hotel has breathtaking views. Most bedrooms have a balcony or terrace, and all have been decorated with fine fabrics. You can enjoy dinner on the terrace or in the dining room. The pool, set on the edge of the terrace, seems to flow into the Mediterranean, which fills the horizon.

✚ 191 E2 ⊠ Route des Calanques
☎ 04 42 01 09 30;
www.roches-blanches-cassis.com
⊙ Closed Nov–Feb

GÉMENOS

Le Relais de la Magdeleine €€

This hotel, situated in a pretty garden, has an attractive 18th-century façade. It is decorated with antiques, and the bedrooms have period furniture, tiled floors and spacious bathrooms. The restaurant serves fine Provençal cuisine, which you can eat on the terrace.

✚ 191 F2 ⊠ Ront point de la Fontaine
☎ 04 42 32 20 16; www.relais-magdeleine.com ⊙ Closed mid-Nov to mid-Mar

MARSEILLE

Le Corbusier €

The hotel is in a block of 300 apartments designed by Le Corbusier in 1952 as part of a design experiment. It was a prototype for "vertical living", combining living space and recreational facilities under one roof. As such, it comes complete with play areas, shops, a cinema, a bar and a library. The bedrooms look to the sea, or the park and terrace. Public parking is available.

✚ 191 D2 ⊠ 280 boulevard Michelet
☎ 04 91 16 78 00;
www.hotellecorbusier.com

Where to...
Eat and Drink

Prices
Expect to pay for a three-course meal for one, excluding drinks and
service
€ under €25   €€ €25–€50   €€€ over €50

Hôtel Hermès €

Situated in the heart of the city by the Vieux Port, this two-star hotel is in a bustling position surrounded by restaurants and cafés. Although lacking the character of older hotels, the 28 bedrooms are light and airy and have a TV, and some have a balcony and harbour views.

➕ 198 B2 ☒ 2 rue Bonneterie
☎ 04 96 11 63 63; www.hotelmarseille.com
⊚ All year

Hotel du Palais €–€€

This smart, refurbished three-star hotel is just a few minutes south of the Old Port and close to Marseille's best shopping district. The 21 rooms are tastefully decorated and have a mini-bar, safe and satellite TV; the hotel also has free WiFi access. Some rooms have king-size beds.

➕ 198 C1 ☒ 26 rue Breteuil ☎ 04 91 37 78 86; www.hotelmarseille.com ⊚ All year

Le Petit Nice Passédat €€€

The contemporary interior of this four-star hotel on the Corniche exudes calm and tranquility. All the bedrooms have air-conditioning, a sea view, satellite TV, mini-bar and safe. The restaurant is Marseille's best best; it was recently awarded its third Michelin star.

➕ 191 D2 ☒ Anse de Maldormé, Corniche J F Kennedy ☎ 04 91 59 25 92; www.petitnice-passedat.com ⊚ All year

Radisson SAS €€–€€€

This stylish modern hotel is in a superb location close to the restaurants and bustle of the Old Port. It boasts a superb outdoor pool with views across the Old Port and 189 smart rooms in Provencal or African style, each with flat screen TV and wireless internet. It's predominantly a business hotel, so the most competitive rates are available at weekends and during holiday periods.

➕ 198 B1 ☒ 38–40 quai du Rive Neuve
☎ 04 88 92 19 50;
www.marseille.radissonsas.com
⊚ All year

AIX-EN-PROVENCE

L'Aixquis €€€

In summer the entrance to this delightful restaurant is bedecked with colourful, flower-filled, hanging baskets. Inside, the subdued lighting, beautifully laid tables and fresh flowers make it the ideal place for a romantic dinner. The menu reflects fine Mediterranean cuisine and features dishes such as grilled lobster with truffle risotto.

➕ 191 E3 ☒ 22 rue Victor Leydet
☎ 04 42 27 76 16; www.aixquis.fr
⊚ Tue–Sat 12–1.30, 7:30–10

La Brocherie €€

Try one of the meat dishes, spit-roasted in the large chimney, or the fish, at this rustic restaurant. Delicious game in season.

➕ 191 E3 ☒ 5 rue Fernand-Dol ☎ 04 42 38 33 21 ⊚ 12–2, 7:30–10. Closed Sat lunch, Sun

Café des Deux-Garçons €€€

"Les 2 G" was the haunt of Cézanne, Picasso, Piaf and Zola. Today, it remains one of Aix's most elegant cafés, popular for its brasserie-style menu.

➕ 191 E3 ☒ 53 cours Mirabeau
☎ 04 42 26 00 51 ⊚ Daily 12–3, 7–11

Chez Féraud €€

There's a distinct Provençal theme to the cooking at this pretty, reasonably priced restaurant, with Coteaux d'Aix, Bandol and Cassis bottles on a very regional wine list.

191 E3 ⊠ 8 rue du Puits Juif
04 42 63 07 27 Tue–Sat 12–1:30, 7–10

Le P'tit Puits €€

Le P'tit Puits refers to the well in the vaulted basement at this restaurant. The dining room is warm and welcoming, with simple cane chairs and rustic stone creating a relaxed atmosphere. The extensive menu includes tartare of tuna and salmon and millfeuille of chicken with tarragon.

191 E3 ⊠ 14 rue Bernardines
04 42 91 42 71 Mon–Fri 12–2, 7–10:30,Sat 7:30–10

Unic Bar €

This is a perfect bar for people-watching as it is opposite Aix's colourful fruit and vegetable market (▲ 109). In summer, fresh fruit juice is the house speciality.

191 E3 ⊠ 40 rue Vauvenargues
04 42 96 38 28 Daily 6am–2am

Chez Gilbert €€€

A member of the Charte de la Bouillabaisse which promotes the correct preparation of this traditional (and expensive) Marseillaise dish, Chez Gilbert is the place to get superb seafood on the harbour in Cassis.

191 E2 ⊠ 19 quai des Baux 04 42 01 71 36; www.restaurant-chez-gilbert.fr
12:15–2:30, 7:15–10:30. Closed Tue eve, Wed & Jan

Le Clos des Arômes €€

Stuffed sardines with aniseed flavours and tomato jus or fillet of daurade with pink grapefruit jus are typical of the menu items at this pleasant small hotel/restaurant, where you can eat in the pretty garden in fine weather

191 E2 ⊠ 10 rue Abbé Paul Mouton

04 42 01 71 84; www.le-clos-des-aromes. com 12–2, 7:15–9.30. Closed all day Mon, Tue & Wed lunch

Les Arcenaulx €€

Numerous books line the walls of Marseille's former arsenal. Diners sit at long red banquettes to enjoy the regional cuisine, which includes tagine of wild daurade with caramelised onion and artichoke.

198 B2 ⊠ 25 cours Estienne d'Orves
04 91 59 80 30; www.jeanne-laffitte.com
Mon–Sat 12–2, 8–11

Chez Fonfon €€€

The lively fishing port is the place to try bouillabaisse, the superb fish soup for which Marseille's restaurants are especially famous. Chez Fonfon has been run by the same family for more than 50 years and is an institution in the town.

191 D2 ⊠ 140 Vallon des Auffes
04 91 52 14 38 Mon 7:30–9,45, Tue–Sat 12–2, 7:30–9:45

La Trilogie des Cépages €€

Food takes second place to the vast selection of wines at this discreet, softly lit restaurant near the Old Port, where the helpful staff will find something offbeat and interesting to complement your salmon tartare with vanilla or fillet of duck with foie gras.

198 B3 ⊠ 35 rue de la Paix Marcel Paul
C04 91 33 96 03; www.trilogiedescepages. com Mon–Wed 12–2, 7:30–10, Thu–Fri 12–2, 7:30–11, Sat 7:30–11

Une Table, au Sud €€–€€€

Lionel Lévy's smart restaurant overlooking the Old Port is one of Marseille's most talked-about, thanks to his innovative dishes like scallops with yoghurt and herring caviar or milkshake of bouillabaisse. Lévy – who trained with celebrity chef Alain Ducasse – has opened a fashionable but more affordable brasserie, La Virgule, nearby.

198 B2 ⊠ 2 quai du Port
04 91 90 63 53; www.unetableausud.com
Tue–Sat 12–2, 7:30–10. Closed August

Where to... Shop

MARKETS

Aix-en-Provence has several interesting markets, including the **Marché aux antiquaires**, which is the place to browse for period furniture, old books and decorative items (place du Palais de Justice, open Tue, Thu, Sat 7–1). For fresh produce visit the **Marché des Producteurs**, also in Aix, where local farmers display their cheeses, fruit and vegetables under the shade of plane trees (place Richelme, open daily 7–1). In Marseille, at the **Marché des Capucins**, you'll find spices, fruit and vegetables from all over the world and some household goods (place des Capucins, open Mon–Sat 8–7), and the **Marché aux Poissons** has fresh fish, which is gutted and scaled on the spot (quai del Belges, daily 8–1).

SOUVENIRS AND GIFTS

For traditional faïence (high-quality glazed ceramics) and santons clay figurines dressed or painted in regional costumes), visit **L'Atelier d'Art** in Aubagne, the pottery capital of France (2 boulevard Émile-Combes, tel: 04 42 70 12 92). Santons are also produced at **Santons Marcel Carbonel**, which sells 700 different figures (6 promenade du Jeune Anacharsis, tel: 04 42 13 17 45, open Tue–Sat 9:30–12:30, 2:30–6:30).

Marseille is known all over the world for its soap. You can buy it enriched with clay, essential oils and honey at one of the city's few remaining specialist soap stores, **La Compagnie de Provence**, close to the Old Port (1 rue Caisserie, tel: 04 91 56 20 94, open Mon–Sat 10–7).

FOOD AND DRINK

Confiserie Entrecasteaux, in Aix, is one of the best places to buy calissons (a local speciality), glacé fruit, nougat and chocolate (2 rue Entrecasteaux, tel: 04 42 27 15 02, open Mon–Sat 8–12:15, 2–7). **Maison Béchard** is also well known for its calissons (12 cours Mirabeau, tel: 04 42 26 06 78). Puyricard's handmade chocolates are considered the finest in France; you can visit their factory, **Chocolaterie Puyricard**, in a northern suburb of Aix (420 route du Puy-Ste-Réparade, quartier Beaufort, Puyricard, tel: 04 42 96 11 21).

At **Le Four des Navettes**, Marseille's oldest bakery, try the famous orange-flower navettes – boat-shaped biscuits (136 rue Sainte, tel: 04 91 33 32 12). **Torrefaction Noailles** is a sweetshop-cum-tea salon, and another local favourite (56 La Canebière, tel: 04 91 55 60 66, open Mon–Sun 7am–7.30pm).

FASHION

Madame Zaza of Marseille is the place to go for leading designs which show a distinct Mediterranean influence. Inside the pleasant store you'll find shirts and skirts, which are sometimes embroidered with gold (73 cours Julien, tel: 04 91 48 05 57, open Mon–Sat 10–1:30, 2–7).

Petit Boy in Aix sells fashions for children aged from 6 months to 16 years (6 rue Aude, tel: 04 42 93 13 05).

ART, ANTIQUES AND BOOKS

In Aix, you can browse the shelves at **Librairie de Provence**, a large bookshop with an excellent choice of regional travel, literature and culinary titles (31 cours Mirabeau, tel: 04 42 26 07 23). **Yves Ungaro** is an aladdin's cave of pictures and objets d'art at the heart of Aix's antiques quarter (1 rue Jaubert, tel: 04 42 63 22 94).

Where to...
Be Entertained

BARS, CLUBS AND CASINOS

In Aix-en-Provence, the **Casino de Aix**, housed in a strikingly modern building, has slot machines by the hundreds, a games room, four restaurants and a concert hall (avenue de l'Europe, tel: 04 42 59 69 00, open 10am–3am, until 4am Fri–Sun). For over-18s only.

Hot Brass, an established haunt for jazz lovers, is the place to go for traditional jazz (quartier Celony, route d'Eguilles, tel: 04 42 21 05 57, open Fri–Sat 11:30pm–5am), or try **Le Scat**, a traditional club with live jazz, soul, R&B and reggae (11 rue de la Verrerie, tel: 04 23 00 23, open Tue–Sat 11pm–5am).

In Marseille, **Le Pelle-Mêle** is a classy little jazz and piano bar

just off the Old Port (8, place aux Huiles, tel: 04 91 54 85 26, open Tue–Sat 5–2), while across the harbour **La Caravelle** is a famous cabaret bar dating back to pre-war years, with live music at weekends and free Marseillaise tapas in the early evening (34 quai du Port, tel: 04 91 90 36 64, open daily 8–2).

From May to mid-September you can dance under the stars at **La Maronaise** (route de la Maronaise, La Goude, tel: 04 91 72 79 39, open weekends 11–5 in May, daily from June). **Trolleybus**, Marseille's number-one rock venue, also has bars and bowling alleys (24 quai de Rive-Neuve, tel: 04 91 54 30 45, open Tue–Sat 11:30pm–5am, until 6am Sat–Sun; Tue–Wed, bar only, open until midnight).

THEATRE, OPERA AND CINEMA

In Aix, the striking modern **Pavillon Noir** (530 avenue Mozart, tel: 04 42 93 48 00; www.preljocaj. org) is the permanent home for the contemporary Ballet Preljocaj. The nine-screen cinema complex **Le Cézanne** screens the latest Hollywood blockbusters and major French films, although Hollywood films are rarely shown in their original language (1 rue Marcel-Guillaume, tel: 08 92 68 72 70; www.lescinemasaixois.com).

Marseille has several theatre venues. **Théâtre National de Marseille la Criée**, the city's leading theatre, gives acclaimed performances (30 quai de Rive-Neuve, tel: 04 96 17 80 00).

Language is no barrier at **Massalia Théâtre**, a marionette theatre (41 rue Jobin, tel: 04 95 04 95 70).

Rebuilt in 1924, **L'Opéra de Marseille** is the stately home of the Philharmonic Orchestra of Marseille and also hosts operas throughout

the year (2 rue Molière, tel: 04 91 55 11 10; www.marseille.fr).

SPORTS AND ACTIVITIES

In Aix, test your skills on the indoor karting track at **Kart'In Aix** (Zone d'Activité des Milles, 820 rue André Ampère, tel: 04 42 97 79 99, open Tue–Thu 6:30pm–12:30am, Fri 6:30pm–1:30am, Sat 3:30pm–1:30am, Sun 3:30pm–8:30pm).

At **Bowling du Bras d'Or**, there's bowling and a large screen showing sport (23 boulevard Charrier, tel: 04 42 27 69 92, open 2pm–2:30am).

The region's top spectator sport is *le foot* (football) and its top team is **Olympique de Marseille** (www.om.net for tickets).

You can go diving with **Centre de Loisirs des Goudes**, in the Bay of Marseille, around the Rioux archipelago, and explore caves and wrecks (2 boulevard Alexandre Delabre, tel: 04 91 25 13 16; www.goudes-plongee.com, open 8am–10pm).

The Camargue Area

Getting Your Bearings

The Camargue area is centred round the Bouches-du-Rhône – a beautiful region of timeless medieval villages and honey-coloured farmsteads, smothered in bougainvillaea and oleander, their pink-tiled roofs and trellised vines sharply defined against cloudless blue skies. It is a traditional, romantic region, once home of the troubadours, where courtly love first developed. Before that, it was the most important part of the Roman Empire outside Italy.

Ancient monuments abound, including the remarkable ruins of Glanum, a Greco-Roman town; and the Roman arena, theatre, chariot-race course and necropolis of Arles – magnificent ancient treasures which have made this city, the former Roman capital of Provence, a UNESCO site. Arles today is a lively, popular city, which has successfully preserved many local customs, costumes and traditions.

Just beyond the official borders of Provence in the nearby Languedoc region, the medieval ramparted town of Aigues-Mortes, the dazzling Roman bridge – the Pont du Gard – and the extensive Roman remains of Nîmes are worth a visit.

Back in Provence, the Bouches-du-Rhône area boasts some of the region's most beautiful and varied countryside – from the lacy limestone peaks of the Alpilles and the nodding sunflower fields of Arles' resident artist, Vincent Van Gogh, to the sandy marshes of the Camargue. This untamed region is famous for its gypsies and unique nature reserve, where pink flamingos, young bulls and white horses splash through the marshes – surely one of the most evocative images of the whole of Provence.

Above: The Roman amphitheatre in Nîmes
Page 111: The Pont du Gard

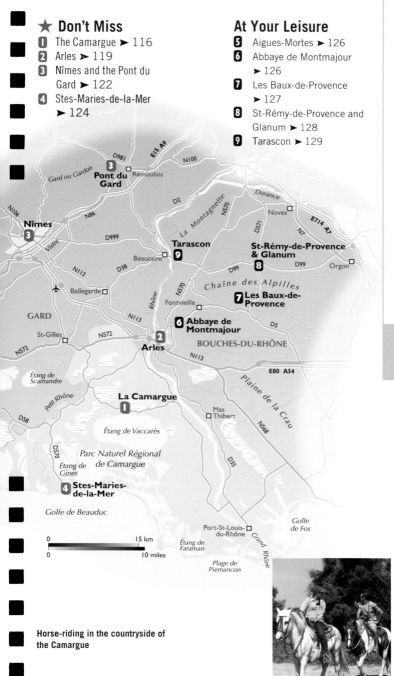

★ Don't Miss

At Your Leisure

Horse-riding in the countryside of the Camargue

In Three Days

If you're not quite sure where to begin your travels, this itinerary recommends a practical and enjoyable three-day tour of the Camargue area, taking in some of the best places to see using the Getting Your Bearings map on the previous page. For more information see the main entries.

Day One

Morning
Spend the morning exploring the ancient monuments of **2 Arles** (➤ 119–121). Make the Musée de l'Arles et de la Provence Antiques (➤ 121) your first port of call for a grasp of the town's history. The ruins of the Théâtre Antique (below) suggest it was even more lavish than the theatre in Orange in its heyday, while the beautifully preserved Les Arènes today stages frequent *Cours Camarguais* (Provençal bullfights).

Lunch
Enjoy a lunch of regional specialities at the popular locals' restaurant, L'Escaladou (➤ 131), or a snack at the lively Café la Nuit (11 place du Forum, tel: 04 9096 44 56), subject of a famous Van Gogh painting.

Afternoon
Head out into Van Gogh country, past the **6 Abbaye de Montmajour** (➤ 126–127), one of the most elaborate Romanesque churches in Provence, through the picturesque villages of Fontvieille and Maussane-les-Alpilles to the ancient ruined citadel of **7 Les Baux-de-Provence** (➤ 127–128) – once called the Pompeii of Provence – set in a landscape of crumpled white limestone crags known as the Chaîne des Alpilles. From here it is a stone's throw to the chic market town of **8 St-Rémy-de-Provence** and the ruins of **Glanum** (➤ 128–129), the nation's oldest classical buildings.

Evening
Enjoy simple Provençal flavours and local wines al fresco at Café des Arènes (right, ➤ 132) in St-Rémy-de-Provence.

Day Two

Morning
Visit the magnificent medieval château and the Souleïado museum of Provençal fabrics at **9 Tarascon** (► 129).

Lunch
Tuck into regional cuisine in Tarascon's atmospheric restaurant, Abbaye St-Michel de Frigolet (► 132).

Afternoon
Marvel at the nearby **8 Port du Gard** (above, ► 122–123), a remarkable feat of Roman engineering in the Languedoc region. Then drive to **8 Nîmes** (► 122–123) to see the extraordinary oval-shaped Arènes, the best preserved Roman amphitheatre in the world.

Evening
Le Bouchon et l'Assiette (► 132) offers excellent-value set menus of regional specialities.

Day Three

Spend the day in the **1 Camargue** (► 116–118), a land of salty marshes, rice fields, brackish lagoons and coastal dunes, renowned for its passionate people, its silver-cream horses, black bulls and salmon-pink flamingoes. Join a pony trek (below) at one of the ranches, or while away the hours spotting exotic water birds. The quaint fishing village of **Stes-Maries-de-la-Mer** (► 124–125) is steeped in the tradition and folklore of the region, and Brûleur de Loups (► 132), with its fish dishes, is a good lunch venue.

❶ The Camargue

The natural wilderness of the Camargue, the marshy flatland of the Rhône delta, is famous for its exotic wildlife, its semi-wild white horses, its little black bulls bred for fighting and its annual gypsy festival. Thousands of pink flamingos come to feed in the shallow waters here, and evaporating sea water leaves vast crystalline saltpans. Roads are few, so extend your exploration on foot or, better, by guided boat trip.

No area in France matches the Camargue for its landscape: brackish lagoons, flat rice fields and salty marshes, sand spits and coastal dunes, tufted with coarse, spiky grass and interlaced with shallow streams and canals. Even its boundaries – the Grand Rhône and Petit Rhône deltas and the sea – are forever shifting. This extraordinary landscape harbours an outstanding variety of wildlife and the unique lifestyle of the Camarguais cowboys.

Preserving traditions
The people of the Camargue are hardy folk. They live in low, thatched, whitewashed cottages with bulls' horns over the door to ward off evil spirits. They proudly guard the Camarguais heritage, by wearing traditional costume and raising horses and cattle on ranches, or *manades*. Contrary to popular belief the famous white horses are not wild. They are actually owned by a *manadier* or breeder, but are left to roam semi-free. Some are also used for trekking expeditions. The small, black local bulls with their distinctive lyre-shaped horns, are bred for the ring (➤ 119). Watching a mounted *gardian* drive his herd through the marshes is a truly unforgettable sight!

Reed beds fringe the waters of the Camargue

Elegant pink flamingoes

Wildlife

The Camargue also offers sanctuary to some of Europe's most exotic water birds, including purple herons and stone curlews. The nature reserve centres on the shallow **Étang de Vaccarès**. The reserve of the Étang de Vaccarès itself is open only to visitors with a special permit, but there are vantage places off the surrounding roads (especially the D37) from where you can watch bird life. The reserve's headquarters is on the eastern side of the *étang*, where the superb **Centre d'Information La Capelière** has one of the best displays on the Camargue, with marked nature trails and information about the birds and plants of the area. There are four hides and two observation platforms within a few minutes of here, and a walking trail, 1.5km (1 mile) long.

On the west side of the *étang* is the Maison du Parc Naturel Régional de Camargue, 4km (2.5 miles) north of Stes-Maries-de-la-Mer, with displays and large viewing windows. To get closer to the bird life, go to the adjacent **Parc Ornithologique du Pont de Gau**, where there are half-hour trails around the Étang de Pont de Gau, or the Étang de Ginès sanctuary, where bulls graze in the summer. Large aviaries near the entrance to the park house birds of prey.

South of here, the salt marshes give way to sand dunes and ponds. It's great for birding: look for flamingoes, avocets and egrets feeding in the shallows; bitterns and herons in the reedbeds; and ducks, geese and waders on the shore.

TAKING A BREAK

The **Domaine Paul Ricard** on the D37 at Méjanes rents out bicycles and ponies, and a large restaurant serves meals based on fresh local produce (tel: 04 90 97 10 51).

⊞ 194 C2
Réserve Nationale de Camargue
⊠ Centre d'Information La Capelière, Arles
☎ 04 90 97 00 97; www.reserve-camargue.org
🕐 Apr–Sep daily 9–1, 2–6; Oct–Mar Wed–Mon 9–1, 2–5 🖐 Inexpensive

Maison du Parc Naturel Régional de Camargue
⊠ Pont de Gau ☎ 04 90 97 86 32
🕐 Apr–Sep daily 10–6; Oct–Mar Sat–Thu 9.30–5

Parc Ornithologique du Pont-de-Gau
⊠ D570 from Arles or Stes-Maries-de-la-Mer
☎ 04 90 97 82 62; www.parcornithologique. com 🕐 Apr–Sep daily 9 to sunset; Oct–Mar daily 10–sunset 🖐 Moderate

The Étang de Vaccarès

Manade Jacques Bon, Camargue
⊠ Le Mas de Peint, Le Sambuc ☎ 04 90 97 20 62 ❓ Professional ranch with rodeos and tours on horseback

Musée Camarguais
⊠ Mas du Pont de Rousty ☎ 04 90 97 10 82
🕐 Apr–Sep daily 9–6; Oct–Mar Wed–Mon 10–5. Closed 1 Jan, 1 May, 25 Dec
🖐 Moderate

Sailing the blue waters of the Mediterranean

THE CAMARGUE: INSIDE INFO

Top tips Take precautions against **mosquitoes**, which breed prolifically in the marshes.
■ Always take plenty of **drinking water** with you when you set out to explore the area.
■ The best months for **birding** vary according to location and species; consult the tables detailing what you can see where at www.reserve-camargue.org
■ For a **drive** in the Camargue ➤ 168–169.

② Arles

Arles, at one time the Roman capital of Provence, then a medieval ecclesiastical centre, is today a lively, popular city, largely due to a variety of cultural events and influences. These include an internationally renowned photographic fair, and the influence of local fashion designer, Christian Lacroix, whose imaginative creations reflect the colourful traditional Arlésian costumes (► 8).

The Roman arena at Arles is used today for bullfights and performances

Arles has many historical places, most of which are in the largely traffic-free old quarter and can be reached on foot. Especially notable are the Roman arena and, next to it, the Roman theatre, but there are medieval sights too. The boulevard des Lices, the busy main street, runs alongside the old quarter and it is here that you'll find many shops, bars, hotels and restaurants, as well as the tourist office.

Arles' Highlights

Built during the first century ad, **Les Arènes** was the largest amphitheatre in Gaul (136m/149 yards long and 107m/117 yards wide), and scene of blood-thirsty contests between gladiators and wild animals. Originally, it had three storeys, but during the Middle Ages the stones from the third level were used to build churches and houses inside the arena to shelter the poor. These were demolished in 1825, leaving the amphitheatre once again free for bullfights. Near the arena is the **Théâtre Antique**. Much of the stonework of this Roman theatre was also dismantled to build houses and churches. The remaining rows of seats and two columns of the stage wall are, today, the setting for concerts, drama and the July Les Suds music festival.

According to custom, the Roman necropolis of **Les Alyscamps** (from the Latin *elisii campi*, elysian fields) was built outside the city walls along the Via Aurelia. Christians took over the cemetery and several miracles are said to have taken place here, including the appearance of Christ. The necropolis had 19 chapels and several thousand tombs – all that remains is a poplar-lined alleyway dotted with moss-covered tombs.

The city's **Cathédral St-Trophime**, on place de la République, is a masterpiece of Provençal Romanesque architecture. The original church was built in the 5th century, then rebuilt at the end of the 11th century, and the ornate tympanum, depicting the Last Judgement, was added in the next century. The cloister of St-Trophime, with rich carvings and sensitively

VINCENT VAN GOGH

In 1888, the artist Vincent Van Gogh (1853–90) left Paris and came to Arles, where he fell under the spell of the Provençal light and landscapes. He lived in a modest cottage – the little yellow house which featured in his paintings – which was destroyed by bombing in 1944. It was at this productive time that he painted masterpieces, including the famous *Sunflowers* series. The following year, after a row with his friend Paul Gauguin over the founding of an artists' colony at Arles, and cutting off part of his own left ear, Van Gogh was committed to hospital, which has now become the Espace Van Gogh (above). It stands opposite the Muséon Arlaten, and still has the garden seen in his painting *Jardin de l'Hôpital à Arles*. In 1889, Van Gogh was moved to the mental hospital out of town at St-Paul-de-Mausole (► 129). A year later he returned north, and in 1890 he committed suicide at Auvers-sur-Oise, near Paris.

Left: Visitors exploring a corner of the Roman necropolis Les Alycamps

illuminated chapels hung with Aubusson tapestries, is among the treasures of Provence. The **Muséon Arlaten**, on rue de la République, was founded by poet Frédéric Mistral in 1896. Displays cover aspects of everyday life in the region during the 17th to the 19th centuries and include a fascinating exhibition of Arlésian costume.

Musée de l'Arles et de la Provence Antique, beside the Rhône about 2km (1.2 miles) from the centre of Arles, is an absolute must see. It is built over the Cirque Romaine, an enormous second century chariot racecourse, which has been excavated. It is a modern museum covering the history of the area from Roman rule to the Christian era. On display are numerous Classical items found in the city, including Roman mosaics, sculptures of Augustus and Venus of Arles, and a fine collection of carved marble sarcophagi.

The Thermes de Constantin in Arles is one of the largest bathhouses in Provence

TAKING A BREAK

The rustic **La Mamma** near the arenas (20 rue de l'Amphithéâtre, tel: 04 90 96 11 60) serves tasty Italian and regional cuisine.

➕ 194 C3
Tourist Information Office
✉ Esplanade Charles de Gaulle, boulevard des Lices ☎ 04 90 18 41 20; www.arlestourisme.com ⏰ Apr–Sep daily 9–6:45; Oct–Mar Mon–Sat 9–4:45, Sun 10–1

Les Arènes
✉ Rond-Point des Arènes ☎ 04 90 49 38 20
⏰ May–Sep daily 9–6:30; Mar, Apr, Oct daily 9–6; Nov–Feb daily 10–5. Closed some public hols and during bullfights 💷 Moderate

Musée de l'Arles et de la Provence Antiques
✉ Presqu'île du Cirque-Romain ☎ 04 90 18 88 88; www.arles-antique.cg13.fr ⏰ Apr–Oct daily 9–7; Nov–Mar 10–5. Closed some public hols 💷 Moderate

ARLES: INSIDE INFO

Top tips The **Pass Monuments**, available from the tourist office, covers nine sights in Arles.
■ Browse around the town's huge **Saturday morning market** on boulevard des Lices. The second-hand market, on the same street, is on the first Wednesday of every month.
One to miss You won't see paintings by Van Gogh in Arles's **Fondation Van Gogh**, near the amphitheatre. However, the gallery has some interesting art by other modern painters, including Francis Bacon, which takes its inspiration from Van Gogh's works.

3 Nîmes and the Pont du Gard

Just 20km (12.5 miles) apart, the town of Nîmes, a vital part of Roman Provence, and the spectacular aqueduct that was built to channel water to its citizens, combine to form one of the great sights of France.

Around Nîmes

Pont du Gard

There are interesting buildings in the city's old quarter, but what makes this a must-see site is the 2,000-year-old amphitheatre, **Les Arènes**. It's the best preserved Roman amphitheatre in the world, and it's still in regular use. Inside, the three tiers of stone seats are designed for around 20,000 spectators – note that there's no safety rail on the top tier.

Nîmes's 1st-century BC Roman temple, the **Maison Carrée**, is less spectacular in scale, but amazingly well preserved, with some exquisite small mosaics in the interior. The temple is next door to the contemporary art gallery, known as the **Carrée d'Art**. This light and spacious modern building, designed by English architect Sir Norman Foster in 1984, displays a collection of modern art and temporary exhibitions.

LA GARRIGUE

The low-growing vegetation around the Pont du Gard is called *la garrigue*. In these tough, dry conditions, the plants that thrive are often tough and dry themselves, like box and holm oak, or with spiny leaves, such as thistles and gorse. Growing among these are the herbs that create the scents and flavours of Provence – thyme, marjoram, rosemary, sage and lavender.

The Pont du Gard

This huge, honey-coloured marvel of engineering strides across the River Gardon in three imposing tiers. Close examination from the bridge beside it shows that there's no mortar holding it up, just the skill of the Romans who constructed it around 19 BC, using 6-tonne stone blocks. The water channel is the top tier, part of an ambitious but successful scheme to transport water from the spring near Uzès 50km (31 miles) to the Roman settlement at Nîmes. You can learn more about the context of its building and 19th-century restoration in the excellent exhibition centre on the left bank.

TAKING A BREAK

Drop in for a light meal and a glass of wine at the art-filled **Vintage Restaurant** in Nîmes, on a tiny square between the arena and Maison Carée (7 rue de Bernis, tel: 04 66 21 04 45).

🚹 194 B4
Tourist Information Office
✉ 6 rue Auguste ☎ 04 66 58 38 00; www.ot-nimes.fr ⏱ Jul–Aug Mon–Fri 8:20–8, Sat 9–7, Sun 10–6; Apr–May, Sep Mon–Fri 8:30–7, Sat 9–7, Sun 10–6; Oct–Mar Mon–Fri 8:30–6:30, Sat 9–6:30, Sun 10–5. Closed 1 Jan, 25 Dec

Les Arènes
✉ Place des Arènes ☎ 04 66 21 82 56 ⏱ Jun–Aug daily 9–7; Apr, May, Sep daily 9–6:30; Mar, Oct daily 9–6; Nov–Feb 9:30–5 💰 Moderate

Maison Carrée
✉ Place de la Comédie ☎ 04 66 21 82 56 ⏱ Jun–Aug daily 10–7:30; Apr, May, Sep daily 10–7; Mar, Oct daily 10–6:30; Nov–Feb daily 10–1, 2–5 💰 Inexpensive

Musée d'Art Contemporain (Carrée d'Art)
✉ Place de la Maison Carré ☎ 04 66 76 35 70 ⏱ Tue–Sun 10–6 💰 Moderate

Pont du Gard
🚹 194 C4 ✉ Exhibition Centre, Pont du Gard ☎ 08 20 90 33 30; www.pontdugard.fr ⏱ Site open all year 6am–1am; exhibition hall open daily 9:30–7, Easter–Sep; 10–5:30, Oct–Easter. Closed Mon am all year and 2 weeks in Jan 💰 Exhibition hall: moderate

NÎMES AND THE PONT DU GARD: INSIDE INFO

Top tips In midsummer the **heat can be intense**, so it pays to plan your visit around a shady lunch stop in Nîmes, visiting the Pont du Gard either early in the morning or later in the afternoon, when the sun is not so fierce.

■ For a great **overview of Nîmes**, head straight for the **Magne tower**, in the Jardin de la Fontaine.

■ At the **Pont du Gard**, the car park fee (moderate) also pays for access to the aqueduct. Entry to the exhibition centre costs more, and there's also the option of an informative 25-minute video. **Ludo** is a discovery zone for kids.

4 Stes-Maries-de-la-Mer

The picture-postcard resort of Stes-Maries-de-la-Mer, steeped
in the tradition and the folklore of the Camargue, makes a
perfect base for visits into the heart of the region.

With sandy beaches to the east, the town is a good base for
activities including bicycle rental, horse-back riding and
watersports, while the nearby marshy flatlands and lagoons
are famous for their bird life and white horses.

According to legend, the Virgin Mary's half-sisters Maria
Jacobé and Maria Salome landed here in AD 40 with their
black serving maid Sarah, patroness of gypsies. When they
died, a chapel was built over their graves (later replaced by
Notre-Dame-de-la-Mer) and the village has been a place
of pilgrimage ever since. The main pilgrimage takes place

**Looking out
over the
gently sloping
rooftops of
Stes-Maries-
de-la-Mer**

A GYPSY CAPITAL

Although they come from all over Europe, most of the gypsies who attend the
annual pilgrimage are Spanish. Colourful gypsy caravans are a permanent
feature of the area around the town, as is the Spanish entertainment such as
flamenco, which is put on for visitors.

A forest of masts in the busy marina of Stes-Maries-de-la-Mer

on 24–25 May. Gypsies, dressed in brilliant skirts and shawls, ribbons and flowers, carry statues of the Marias and the bejewelled black Sarah in a small blue boat into the sea to be blessed, led by handsome mounted *gardians* in full Camargue cowboy dress. This is followed by a festival of bullfighting, rodeos, flamenco and fireworks.

A tower, in rue Victor Hugo next to the church, houses the **Musée Baroncelli** (irregular hours), which displays local historical finds. Both the museum tower and the church tower give views of the town and the Camargue.

TAKING A BREAK

Enjoy fresh seafood at **Les Embruns**, 11 avenue de la Plage (► 132).

✚ 194 B1
Tourist Information Office
✉ 5 avenue Van-Gogh ☎ 04 90 97 82 55;
www.saintesmaries.com

Musée Baroncelli
✉ Rue Victor Hugo ☎ 04 90 97 87 60
🕐 Irregular hours

STES-MARIES-DE-LA-MER: INSIDE INFO

Top tips Get close to the pastures and the manade (herds of bulls and horses) of the Camargue on a 90-minute **boat trip** on the Petit Rhône river. Contact A.C.T. Tiki III, Le Grau d'Orgon–D38, 13460 Stes-Maries-de-la-Mer (tel: 04 90 97 81 68/04 90 97 81 22; www.tiki3.fr).
■ The best place to find **somewhere to park** is the area beside the beach.

At Your Leisure

5 Aigues-Mortes

The impressive medieval town of Aigues-Mortes stands in the flat Camargue landscape, enclosed within its perfectly preserved powerful **ramparts**, built in the 13th century at the command of Philip III. The ramparts, which include 15 towers and 10 gateways, stretch for more than 1.5km (1 mile) around the town.

Park outside the walls beside the Porte de la Gardette, enter the town through the gate and you'll find a simple grid system of streets leading to the busy main square, the place St-Louis, dominated by a statue of Louis IX. This is the heart of the

The impressive Tour de Constance, part of Aigues-Mortes' remarkable fortifications

town where the Tourist Information Office and many of the cafés and restaurants are located. **The Tour de Constance**, built as part of the town's defences, is the most impressive of the towers. It became a prison, and in the 17th century hundreds of Protestant women were locked up here in appalling conditions. The

tower can be reached only via the Logis du Gouverneur, starting point for the official tour of the ramparts.

From Easter to September, trips by boat, horse-and-carriage or *petit train* leave from outside the town's main gate and take you into the Camargue's salt marshes. Wednesday and Sunday are market days.

🔒 194 A2
Tourist Information Office
✉ Place St-Louis
☎ 04 66 53 73 00; www.ot-aiguesmortes.fr
🕐 Jul–Aug Mon–Fri 9–8, Sat–Sun 10–8;
Sep–Jun Mon–Fri 9–1, 2–6, Sat–Sun 10–12, 2–6

6 Abbaye de Montmajour

Set on a small hill 3km (2 miles) northeast of Arles, Montmajour was among the most powerful monasteries in medieval Provence and, even in ruins, it's still an impressive sight.

St Trophimus, an early Christian saint, fled here from Arles to hide in a cave, which became a holy place. Later, a group of hermits took up residence to safeguard the site where he had lived. The community grew, which led to the founding of the monastery in the 10th century. Under Benedictine rule, the abbey prospered, establishing priories and reclaiming the surrounding marshlands, and became an important site of pilgrimage. The abbey became very wealthy – and corrupt. In 1639, the Benedictines sent a group to rectify matters, but the monks in residence, reluctant to leave, sacked the abbey. The community was disbanded in 1786. Restoration began in 1907.

Today you can explore the extensive ruins and marvel at the sheer scale of the buildings. The impressive, incomplete 12th-century Upper Church is austere. The crypt, to the right of the nave, is partly built into the hillside, and has finely

detailed carvings of wild beasts and
demons on the colonnades. Look
out for masons' marks in the church
vaulting and the graffiti dating back
to medieval times in the cloister.

The **keep**, 26m (85 feet) high, is
an impressive fortified structure built
in 1369. The reward for climbing
the 124 steps is the panoramic views
across to the Alpilles, Arles, Tarascon
and the Plaine de la Crau. From here,
go down the hill to see the 11th-
century **Ermitage St-Pierre**, in the
hillside caves where St Trophimus
sought refuge.

➕ 194 C3
✉ Route de Fontvieille, Arles
☎ 04 90 54 64 17
🕐 Apr–Sep daily 10–6:30;
Oct–Mar Tue–Sun 10–5
💶 Moderate, under 18 free

The Abbaye de Montmajor

🔢 Les Baux-de-Provence

The ancient ruined **citadel** of les
Baux-de-Provence is sited on a
stony plateau on one of the highest
ridges of the Chaîne des Alpilles.
Les Baux is divided into two: the
bustling inhabited lower village,
where elegant Renaissance houses
line the shiny cobbled streets, and
the deserted Ville Morte (Dead
City) perched above, its ruined
buildings hardly distinguishable
from the surrounding limestone
crags.

During the Middle Ages, this
was the seat of the **seigneurs
de Baux**, one of southern France's

Place Louis Jou in Les Baux-de-Provence

most powerful families. Their Cour
d'Amour – a society of lords, ladies
and wandering troubadours – was
renowned throughout the Midi
and, ever since, Les Baux has been
a pilgrimage centre for poets and
painters.

A map directs you around
the site of the Ville Morte, to the
13th-century keep and other
medieval towers, a film show and
reconstructions of medieval siege

Pathways meander through the ruins of the citadel in Les Baux-de-Provence

machines. But it is the views from this high cliff-edge location that are the main attraction, taking in a landscape of wild, rocky terrain broken up with vineyards and woods.

Alongside the ruins of the Dead City is the handsome, busy **"modern" Les Baux**, which dates mainly from the 16th to 17th centuries. This area outside the original fortress contains shops, houses, art galleries, a folksy *santons* (traditional clay figurines) museum and a 16th-century town hall.

The **Val d'Enfer** (the Valley of Hell), a spectacular gorge to the north of the village, is also worth a visit. Here, an underground cavern, **Cathédrale des Images**, offers an amazing sound and light experience.

⊞ 190 A5
Tourist Information Office
⊠ Maison du Roy ☎ 04 90 54 34 39;

www.lesbauxdeprovence.com
Les-Baux-de-Provence Citadelle
⊠ Ville Morte ☎ 04 90 54 55 56
⊙ Spring daily, 9–6:30; summer 9–7:30; autumn 9:30–6; winter 9–5
⚑ Moderate

⑧ St-Rémy-de-Provence and Glanum

In St-Rémy you will find the true flavour of Provence – the warm peaches-and-cream coloured buildings, the maze of lanes, the fountains, quiet shaded squares and the tree-lined boulevards. There are few sights of importance within the town itself, but many fine 16th- to 18th-century mansions can be seen

in the old quarter, and there are some small art galleries and museums.

Nostradamus was born here in 1503, but today St-Rémy owes its popularity to Van Gogh, who convalesced in an asylum just south of town after his quarrel with Gauguin and the ear-cutting incident in Arles. He produced 150 canvases and more than 100 drawings during his one year's stay here, including *Starry Night*, *The Sower* and his famous *Irises*. From April to October the tourist office runs a 90-minute **guided tour** visiting sights that he painted (Tue, Thu, Fri at 10am). The tour also gives reduced entry fees for **St-Paul-de-Mausole** (the sanitorium where Van Gogh committed himself for treatment and rest in 1898) and the **Musée Estrine**. Alternatively, get a map from the tourist office for a self-guided tour.

Near the sanitorium lie the extensive remains of the wealthy Greco-Roman town of **Glanum**, the oldest classical buildings in France. The area was first settled in 6 BC and the city was abandoned in the third century when it was overrun

Tarascon's red-tiled rooftops

by barbarians. Buildings near by, called Les Antiques, were also part of the Roman town. They include the oldest and smallest triumphal arch in France, dating from 20 BC and the best-preserved mausoleum of the Roman world, erected as a memorial to Caesar and Augustus.

➕ 190 A5
Tourist Information Office
✉ Place Jean-Jaurès
☎ 04 90 92 05 22;
www.saintremy-de-provence.com
Glanum
✉ Avenue Vincent van Gogh, Route des Baux

FOR KIDS

■ **Tarascon** The château was used as a prison up until the 1920s – look for graffiti by 18th-century English prisoners.

☎ 04 90 92 23 79 ⏰ Apr–Aug daily 10–6:30; Sep–Mar Tue–Sun 10:30–5. Closed 1 Jan, 1 May, 1 Nov, 11 Nov, 25 Dec 💰 Expensive

9 Tarascon

Most people visit Tarascon, former frontier town of the kingdom of Provence, to see the fortress of Good King René. Built between 1400 and 1449 on the banks of the Rhône, with a moat and turreted towers and an elegantly styled interior, it is now one of the finest **medieval châteaux** in France. The town is also famous for its dreaded **Tarasque**, a man-eating monster who, according to legend, was vanquished by the town's patron, Ste Marthe. On the last Sunday in June the green, dragon-like, papier-mâché Tarasque parades around town, starting four days of fun with festivities, fireworks, bonfires and bullfights. Tarascon also has several markets and fairs during the year, including an Orchid Festival in February, a medieval fête in August and a market in November dedicated to *santons* (traditional clay figurines).

The **Musée Souleïado**, at 39 rue Proudhon, in the old quarter (Jul–Aug Tue–Sat 10–5; Sep–Jun Tue–Sat 10–1, 2–6) is worth a look to find out about the town's traditional cloth-making industry, using vivid colours in the Provençal style.

➕ 194 C3
Tourist Information Office
✉ 16 boulevard Itam
☎ 04 90 91 03 52; www.tarascon.org
Château de Tarascon
✉ Boulevard de Roi-René
☎ 04 90 91 01 93
⏰ Apr–Aug daily 10–6.30; Oct–Mar daily 10:30–5
💰 Moderate

Where to... Stay

Prices
Expect to pay per night for a double room

€ under €100   €€ €100–€200   €€€ over €200

Arlatan €€–€€€

This charming 16th-century residence of the comtes d'Arlatan is one of the region's most beautiful historic hotels, and has 30 rooms individually decorated with Provençal antiques. You can take breakfast in the peaceful walled garden. There is private parking.

🚇 194 C3 ⊠ 26 rue Sauvage ☎ 04 90 93 56 66; www.hotel-arlatan.fr ⓒ Closed early Jan–early Feb

Hôtel Calendal €–€€

A two-star hotel located close to the arenas in Arles, the Calendal makes a comfortable and inexpensive base for exploring the town and the wider area. There are 38 air-conditioned bedrooms, with views to the arenas or over a garden courtyard. Inside, you'll find the tiled floors and wrought iron typical of Provence. Breakfast can be eaten in the garden.

🚇 194 C3 ⊠ 5 rue Porte-de-Laure ☎ 04 90 96 11 89; www.lecalendal.com

Nord-Pinus €€–€€€

This hotel, in the centre of the Old Town, is a classified national monument. It has strong literary connections as it was once a favourite haunt of the Félibres poets and other *literati*, including Stendhal, Mistral, Cocteau and Henry James. Today it is popular with Christian Lacroix, top matadors and other wealthy *aficionados*, and is decorated accordingly with bullfighting posters and trophies alongside antique furniture and various *objets d'arts*. For people who want to feel truly Arlésian!

🚇 194 C3 ⊠ Place du Forum ☎ 04 90 93 44 44; www.nord-pinus.com ⓒ Closed Jan

Le Mas d'Aigret €–€€€

If you want to see the dawn rise over Les Baux, then you'll need to stay in the village, and this unusual hotel carved into the rocky hillside is a great place to be, with wonderful views. There are 16 mostly air-conditioned rooms, many recently refurbished and with terraces and lovely views. Facilities include a lounge, bar and outdoor pool.

🚇 190 A5 ⊠ 13520 Les Baux-de-Provence ☎ 04 90 54 20 00; www.masdaigret.com ⓒ Closed two weeks in Nov

Le Mas de Peint €€€

This was the house of 17th-century Lyon draper, Antoine Peint. It became a farm in the 19th century – rice is still grown on the estate and cattle are bred here. There are eight bedrooms and three suites, some with beamed ceilings and others with a Victorian bathroom. Enjoy farm-grown food in the evenings.

🚇 190 A3 ⊠ Le Sambuc ☎ 04 90 97 20 62; www.masdepeint.com ⓒ Closed Jan to mid-Mar, mid-Nov to mid-Dec

Hôtel Imperator Concorde
€€€

Proud, opulent and a little old-fashioned, this historic, centrally located hotel is the traditional favourite of visiting bullfighters. The surroundings, on the quai de la Fontaine close to the gardens of the same name are stately, if busy; the 62 air-conditioned rooms are soundproofed and have mini bar, satellite TV and floral decor, and there's a pleasant garden at the back.

🔢 194 B4 ⌗ Quai de la Fontaine ☎ 04 66 21 90 30; www.concorde-hotels.com
🕐 All year

ST-RÉMY-DE-PROVENCE

Chateau des Alpilles €€–€€€

Set in a 4ha park outside St Rémy with magnolias, gingkos and a magnificent avenue of plane trees, this pretty 18th-century mansion mixes grandly traditional interior with a few more contemporary touches. There are just 14 high-ceilinged rooms and three suites, plus a family-sized apartment in an annexe. The hotel has its own restaurant and bar, and there's an outdoor pool.

🔢 190 A5 ⌗ Départmentale 31, 13210 St Rémy de Provence ☎ 04 90 92 03 33;
www.chateaudesalpilles.com 🕐 Closed Nov & Jan to mid-Mar

Hotel Les Ateliers de L'Image €€–€€€

This four-star hotel is an oasis of sophisticated minimalism at the heart of the town. It has 25 bedrooms and 6 suites, all with every modern amenity. There is a garden, an outdoor pool and the choice of Provençal and Japanese restaurants.

🔢 190 A5 ⌗ 36 boulevard Victor Hugo
☎ 04 90 92 51 50 🕐 Closed mid-Dec–Feb

STES-MARIES-DE-LA-MER

Hotel de Cacharel €€

A former *gardian* ranch in the heart of the marshes, with 16 comfortable bedrooms, each with bath or shower. Facilities include a swimming pool, and there is accompanied horse-back riding to explore the wetlands of the Camargue and to see the local black bulls.

🔢 194 B1 ⌗ Route de Cacharel
☎ 04 90 97 95 44; www.hotel-cacharel.com
🕐 All year

Where to...
Eat and Drink

Prices

Expect to pay for a three-course meal for one, excluding drinks and service

€ under €25   €€ €25–€50   €€€ over €50

ARLES

L'Escaladou €

This authentic, down-to-earth, Arlésian restaurant in the centre of Arles is usually packed with locals, who enjoy hearty helpings of tasty Arles sausages and *boeuf gardian* (a spicy beef stew with olives, served with Camarguais rice).

🔢 194 C3 ⌗ 23 rue Porte-de-Laure
☎ 04 90 96 70 43 🕐 12–2:30, 6:30–11
🕐 Closed Wed

Corazon €€

This delightful restaurant is situated in a 16th-century town house complete with a courtyard and fountain. A calm and intimate atmosphere is created in a number of small dining rooms, which are hung with artworks for sale. The menu is Provençal but creative, with an emphasis on fish in dishes such as *choucroute de la mer* with three types of fish and crème de champagne, or the brochette of prawns and scallops with spiced vegetables. A bottle of house wine will cost around €16; there's also a *salon de thé*.

🔢 194 C3 ⌗ 1 bis rue Réattu
☎ 04 90 96 32 53 🕐 Tue–Sat 12–2:30, 7–10. Closed Sun and Mon

La Mamma €–€€

This restaurant, near the amphitheatre, has a tiled floor, wicker chairs and a pizza oven. The menu lists Italian and regional dishes such as *saltimbocca à la romana*, with ham, mushrooms and cream, plus pasta.

194 C3 ⊠ 20 rue de l'Amphithéâtre
☎ 04 90 96 11 60; www.lamammaarles.com
⏱ Tue–Sat 12–2:30, 7–10:30, Sun 12–2:30.
Closed Mon

LES BAUX-DE-PROVENCE

La Reine Jeanne €€

The large windows of this small restaurant give fine views of the valley. The regional cuisine includes peppers marinated in olive oil, leg of lamb with confit garlic, and a Provençal platter with olive tapenade. A cod and poached vegetable *aïoli* is served every Friday.

190 A5 ⊠ Rue Porte Mage ☎ 04 90 54 32 06; www.la-reinejeanne.com ⏱ Daily 12–3, 7–9:30

NÎMES

Le Bouchon et l'Assiette €–€€

Situated in an attractive old building near the Fontaine gardens, this restaurant offers great value *prix-fixe* menus. The furnishings in the dining room may be simple, but the cooking is richly flavoured and beautifully presented – try the *foie gras*, served grilled with peppers and grape caramel.

194 B4 ⊠ 5 bis rue de Sauve
☎ 04 66 62 02 93; www.bouchon-assiette. com ⏱ Thu–Mon noon–1:30, 7:45–9:15. Closed 1–15 Jan mid-Jul to mid-Aug

Le Vintage Restaurant €–€€

Situated between the arena and La Maison Carrée, in a tiny square with a fountain, this delightful bistro has a dining room which is also used as a gallery for local artists, or sit in the courtyard in warmer weather.

194 B4 ⊠ 7 rue de Bernis ☎ 04 66 21 04 45 ⏱ Tue–Fri 11–2:30, 7–11, Sat 7–11. Closed 2 weeks in Aug

STES-MARIES-DE-LA-MER

Brûleur de Loups €€

The tempting menu at this seafront restaurant includes *bourride* (a creamy, garlicky fish soup), fresh grilled "catch of the day" and even *carpaccio* of bull (thinly sliced and raw).

194 B1 ⊠ 1 avenue Gilbert-Leroy
☎ 04 90 97 83 31
⏱ 12–1:45, 7–9:30. Closed Tue eve, Wed and mid-Nov to Dec

Les Embruns €€

Enjoy the best local ingredients at this restaurant, with its rustic yet refined interior. Fresh seafood is served in a variety of guises, including in paella, one of the specialities. *Prix-fixe* menus are available, including a *menu gourmand*. Around €12.50 for a bottle of house wine.

194 B1 ⊠ 11 avenue de la Plage
☎ 04 90 97 92 40; ⏱ Daily 12–3, 7–10:30 in season; lunch only low season. Closed Jan

ST-RÉMY-DE-PROVENCE

Café des Arènes €

This small bar-cum-restaurant serves tasty local cuisine. Try a bull steak followed by crème brûlée with thyme. The pavement terrace offers shade from the sun most of the year.

190 A5 ⊠ 9 boulevard Gambetta
☎ 04 32 60 13 43 ⏱ Closed Sun eve, Mon Nov–Mar

TARASCON

Abbaye St-Michel de Frigolet €–€€

This restaurant is situated at the heart of a 12th-century abbey. The dining rooms are Provençal in style, and in fine weather you can dine out on the terrace. The cuisine has a regional flavour: try the red mullet with basil mayonnaise, and Frigolet liqueur crème brûlée.

184 A2 ⊠ Communauté des Prémontrés, Abbaye St-Michel de Frigolet ☎ 04 90 90 52 70; www.frigolet.com ⏱ Daily 12–1:30, 7–8:45. Hotel guests only Mon–Tue

Where to... Shop

SOUVENIRS AND GIFTS

Quality reproductions of original Provençal jewellery can be found at **Bijoux Dumont** in Arles (3 rue du Palais, tel: 04 90 96 05 66, open Tue–Sat 9–12, 2:30–7), where they use mostly 18-carat gold, silver or semiprecious stones and incorporate the emblems of the region into their designs. Choose from Provençal crosses, Stes-Maries-de-la-Mer cross pendants and cicada brooches.

In St-Rémy-de-Provence, **Les Olivades** (28 rue Lafayette, tel: 04 90 92 00 80) is the place to go for colourful printed fabrics, traditional Provençal clothing and gift ideas.

FASHION

Christian Lacroix, the celebrated *haute-couture* designer, was born in Arles and his vibrant collections capture the spirit of Provence. The the fashions, jewellery, hats and handbags of his boutique at the heart of Arles' pedestrian zone are a major draw for the rich and fashionable (52 rue de la République, tel: 04 90 96 11 16, open Mon 2:30–7, Tue–Sat 9–12, 2–7). **L'Arlésienne** (12 rue du Président-Wilson, tel: 04 90 93 28 05) is the place to go to kit yourself out in *Camarguais* costume.

Maria Maria, in Stes-Maries-de-la-Mer, is a boutique with an ochre-walled and Spanish blue-tiled interior, and a *feria* (festival) atmosphere. It specialises in Andalucian costumes, embroidered shirts and *gardian* clothes. You'll find some big names (Christian Lacroix, Tomar Artesania) alongside the work of local designers (7 place des Remparts, tel: 04 90 97 71 60, open daily 10–12, 2–7, and 9–9 in summer and during special events).

At **Boutique Le Gardian**, also in Stes-Maries-de-la-Mer, you'll find the clothes to get outfitted like a *gardian*: felt hat, broad belt and tall boots made of soft leather. You'll also find a range of well-known outdoor brands (9 rue Victor Hugo, tel: 04 90 97 85 34, summer daily 9–10pm, winter 9:30–12, 2–6).

FOOD AND DRINK

In Arles, the family firm of **Conserverie Tomasella** (12 rue Jouvene, tel: 04 90 93 17 95) manufactures and sells all manner of wonderful gourmet foods, from foie gras and pâté to confit duck, cassoulet and wine, much of it attractively packaged to take home from its small shop. Chocolate-maker **Joël Durand** in St-Rémy-de-Provence combines chocolate with the region's local produce; one option is chocolate with lavender (3 boulevard Victor Hugo, tel: 04 90 92 38 25, open Mon–Sat 9:30–12:30, 2:30–7:30, Sun 10–1, 2:30–7:30). Glacé fruit has been the speciality at **Lilamand**, also in St-Rémy, since 1866. Try the glacé chestnuts or glacé fruit jam (5 avenue Albert Schweitzer, tel: 04 90 92 11 08, open Tue–Sat 10–12:30, 2:30–7). For traditional pottery, including hand-painted plates, carafes and dishes, drop into **Terre è Provence** (1 rue Lafayette, tel: 04 90 92 28 52, open 9:30–1, 2–7, closed Sun–Mon and 15–31 Jan).

ART, ANTIQUITIES AND BOOKS

In Arles, **Antiquités Maurin** is a treasure trove of regional furniture, paintings and ceramics dating from the 17th to the 20th centuries (4 rue de Grille, tel: 04 90 96 51 57, closed Sun, and Mon morning).

Browse framed pictures and cards of Provence at **Galerie du Pharos** in St-Rémy-de-Provence (2 rue Jaume Roux, tel: 04 90 90 63 42).

Where to...
Be Entertained

Most of the nightlife in the region centres around Arles. **Théâtre d'Arles** presents a mixture of contemporary drama and balle. There are also regular children's shows (boulevard Clemenceau, tel: 04 90 52 51 55; ticket line: 04 90 52 51 51. Ticket office open Mon–Fri 11–1, 3–6:30; on performance days, Mon–Fri 11–3 and from 5, Sat and Sun from 3). At **El Patio**, on the banks of the Rhône, you'll be entertained by Chico, leader of the celebrated band the Gypsy Kings. Here you can enjoy gypsy evenings with flamenco and rumba. Reservations are essential (Le Patio de Camargue, tel: 04 90 49 51 76, open Sat 8pm).

La Café la Nuit is a popular meeting place in central Arles, and the subject of a Van Gogh painting (11 place du Forum, tel: 04 90 96 44 56, open 9am– midnight).

Le Krystal, with its modern steel and pink décor and blue neon lights, hosts various theme nights. The choice includes retro, house and Latin. Or on non-theme occasions you can dance to an orchestra every Sunday and Monday (Hameau de Moulès, tel: 04 90 98 32 40, open Tue 7pm–2am, Fri–Sat 11pm–6am).

Discothèque La Haute Galine, in St-Rémy-de-Provence, is one of the few late-night options for partying in this part of Provence. It offers a variety of music styles (chemin Cante Perdrix et Galine, tel: 04 90 92 00 03, open Fri–Sat from 11pm).

SPORTS AND ACTIVITIES

At Arles you can get off the beaten track and discover the region's wildlife on an exciting four-wheel-drive tour, with **Camargue Safaris Gallon**. You'll go to the inland waterways and see the white horses, small black bulls and pink flamingos for which the area is famous. Some deals include biking and horse-back riding (36 avenue Edouard Herriot, tel: 04 90 93 60 31, open all year by appointment).

Horses and bulls are bred at **La Cabano dis Ego**, and the owners organise various activities, including traditional horse-back riding, French cowboy games and even hot-air balloon flights (Le Sambuc, tel: 04 90 97 20 62, open all year).

The village of Stes-Maries-de-la-Mer is a good base for activities. With **A.C.T. Tiki III** you can go on a 90-minute boat excursion on the Petit Rhône river to discover a landscape typical of the Camargue and get close to the herds of bulls and horses. Reservations are advised (Le Grau d'Orgon–D38, tel: 04 90 97 81 68/04 90 97 81 22; www. tiki3.fr, open Mar–Nov).

If you prefer to be on horse-back then you can discover the scenery of the Camargue's inland waters, beaches and wildlife, including flamingoes, on 2-hour or full day excursions with **Promenade des Rièges**. The stables have the white horses for which the Camargue is so well known (route de Cacharel, tel: 04 90 97 91 38; www.promenadedesrieges.com, by appointment).

For a complete change, try the wide range of treatments on offer at **Thalacap Camargue**. At this thalassotherapy spa you can benefit from the therapeutic values of sea water, including seaweed and mud wrap, and hydromassage. Facilities include a gym, Turkish bath and sauna (avenue Jacques-Yves Cousteau, tel: 04 90 99 22 22; www.thalacap.fr; hours variable closed early to mid-Dec).

The Vaucluse

Getting Your Bearings

The Vaucluse is one of France's smallest départements, but also among its most popular, due to its wealth of ancient history and variety of scenery, from the delicate lacy silver crags of the Dentelles de Montmirail and the bleak, awesome massif of Mont Ventoux to the rolling, verdant hills of the Lubéron. The timeless quality of the Rhône valley's sun-bleached landscape is reinforced by some of the finest Roman remains, at Orange and Vaison-la-Romaine, and the entire region is saturated in medieval buildings, from the remotest hilltop village to the papal grandeur of historic Avignon – the other Rome – enriched by art and architecture over the centuries, and papal property up until the French Revolution.

For many, the Lubéron region epitomises the real magic of Provence, with its sleepy, medieval villages, hidden in a lush, green landscape. Peter Mayle's celebrated books present life here as idyllic and, despite the region's popularity, it is still possible to escape the tourist hordes and discover your own delights – a dusty game of *pétanque* in a fountain-splashed square; a stroll through olive groves and vineyards; coffee and croissants in a café; romantic, crumbling castle ruins; and pastis in the local bar are all a part of life here.

Vaucluse's colourful markets offer the opportunity to taste the specialities of this region (Cavaillon melons, Carpentras truffles, crystallised fruits in Apt) and no visit is complete without trying some of France's finest wines, in the villages of Châteauneuf-du-Pape, Gigondas and Beaumes-de-Venise.

A basket of lavender for sale

Page 135: The village of Brantes,
in the foothills of Mont Ventoux

In Four Days

If you're not quite sure where to begin your travels, this itinerary recommends a practical and enjoyable four-day tour of the Vaucluse, taking in some of the best places to see using the Getting Your Bearings map on the previous page. For more information see the main entries

Day One

Morning

Spend a day in the medieval, walled city of **1** Avignon (➤ 140–143). Start at the UNESCO-listed Palais des Papes (➤ 140), the jewel in Avignon's crown. From here, it is a short stroll to the river and the celebrated Pont St-Bénézet (right, ➤ 141).

Lunch

Enjoy a classy Mediterranean lunch at No 75 (75 rue Guillaume Puy, tel: 04 90 27 16 00) in the picturesque ancient quarter of the city.

Afternoon

Soak up the atmosphere of Avignon's lively, main square – place de l'Horloge – abuzz with cafés, artists and buskers, or spend time window-shopping in rue Joseph Vernet, named after Avignon's most famous painter (whose seascapes can be seen in the Musée Calvet here, ➤ 141).

Evening

Dine in style at Hiély-Lucullus (5 rue de la République, tel: 04 90 86 17 07), one of Avignon's top gourmet temples.

Day Two

Morning

Spend the morning admiring two of the finest Roman monuments in Europe – the Arc de Triomphe, a grand three-arched monument, (➤ 146) and the massive Théâtre Antique, built into the slope of Colline St-Eutrope, (➤ 146) – in the historic town of **3** Orange.

Lunch

Restaurant des Princes (➤ 147) is a reliable lunch stop.

Afternoon

Tour the pretty wine villages of Haut Vaucluse – Beaumes-de-Venise, Vacqueyras, Gigondas – on the slopes of the Dentelles de Montmirail, en route to ❹ **Vaison-la-Romaine** (left, ➤ 148–149), to visit the former city of Vaisio Vocontiorum, one of the best-preserved Roman sites of Provence.

Evening

Enjoy an evening of Provençal cuisine and top-notch wines at La Fontaine (➤ 162) in Vaison-la-Romaine.

Day Three

Morning

Visit the photogenic hilltop village of ❺ **Gordes** (➤ 150–151). Hunt out the extraordinary stone bories (prehistoric settlements) on the outskirts of the village, and visit the ❺ **Abbaye de Sénanque** (right, ➤ 150–151), set in a field of lavender.

Lunch

Hostellerie Le Phebus (➤ 162) is a delightful place for an al fresco lunch.

Afternoon

Head to ❽ **Roussillon** (➤ 155–156), with its celebrated ochre quarries and follow the 1km (half-mile) Sentier des Ocres (Ochre Trail).

Evening

Enjoy an elegant meal overlooking the brilliant red ochre cliffs at David (place de la Poste, tel: 04 90 05 60 13).

Day Four

Morning

Explore the picturesque hilltop villages of the ❻ **Lubéron** (➤ 152–153). Start at Oppède-le-Vieux, with its ruined château, and progress through Ménerbes and Lacoste to Bonnieux.

Lunch

Try Le Galoubet (➤ 162) in Ménerbes, or Le Pont Julien (➤ 161) in Bonnieux, for robust regional cuisine.

Afternoon

Leave your car and ramble through the lavender fields, pine woods and vineyards of the beautiful Parc Naturel Régional du Lubéron.

Evening

There are plenty of choices for dinner in Lourmarin. Le Moulin de Lourmarin (➤ 162) is especially well rated.

❶ Avignon

The historic quarter of Avignon, enclosed within its impressive medieval walls and dominated by a huge papal palace, is a cheerful and lively tourist area. The town's famous bridge, immortalised in a popular children's song, is an essential stop.

Avignon has been the scene of countless conflicts since Roman times, and for over a century it was the seat of the popes and centre of a religious and political power struggle. It was a French pope, Clement V, who first moved his residence from the Vatican to Avignon in 1309. From then on, a succession of French popes and cardinals built up a powerful base here, and the enduring legacy of this exciting period, when culture and scholarship flourished, is the magnificent fortified palace, the **Palais des Papes**. When the popes eventually returned to

Taking a break beneath the magnificent Palais des Papes

The view across the Rhône from the gardens of Rocher des Doms

Rome in 1403, they took many of their treasures with them, and today there is a bleak emptiness about it. The entire complex is so vast that it has been described as "a city within a city", and takes as much as half a day to visit. Don't miss the fanciful Audience Hall, the frescoes of the Stag Room, the princely papal bedroom, St Martial's Chapel and the Hall of the Consistory.

A walk on the **riverside ramparts** reveals the two sides of Avignon today – the village-like atmosphere of the historic walled Old Town, its skyline adorned with steeples and monuments; and the sprawling factories and bustling modern suburbs beyond, accommodating the city's 100,000 inhabitants. It is a busy place, especially in July when the narrow lanes and pedestrian zones resound with buskers, street theatre and café cabarets taking place during the renowned arts festival.

Trompe-l'oeil in the place de l'Horloge

Around the town, you'll find the best shopping along rue de la République, while the cafés of the **place de l'Horloge**, a lively square abuzz with artists and buskers, offer the chance to relax with a coffee and watch the world go by. There are several museums to explore, including the beautifully restored 14th-century **Petit Palais**, an art museum with a remarkable collection of medieval works, as well as Romanesque and Gothic sculpture and frescoes. The **Musée Calvet** is Avignon's main museum, with collections of French, Italian, Flemish and Duch paintings, sculpture and porcelain from the last five centuries. Be sure to make time for the **Pont St-Bénézet** – the Pont d'Avignon immortalised in song. It was originally a wooden structure, built in 1177 by the

SUR LE PONT D'AVIGNON

The cheerful **children's song** about dancing on the bridge dates back to the 15th century, but its composer is unknown. It came to wider attention in 1853, when Adolphe Adam (better remembered for his ballet, *Giselle*) included it in an operetta, *Le Sourd ou l'Auberge Pleine*. The song proved so popular that it became the focus of its own operetta in 1876. Crooner Jean Sablon recorded a famous swing version of the song in 1939, and it is said that BBC radio played it 14 times in one day as a coded message before the D-Day landings. Recorded hundreds of times in different ways, it has even inspired classical piano variations. Today it is used widely around the world to teach children the French language.

young shepherd St Bénézet, and was rebuilt in stone after a siege in 1226. It was buffeted by the strong flow of the Rhône, and in the mid-17th century, most was washed away. Now just four picturesque arches remain.

The surviving arches of Pont St-Bénézet

One of the best vantage points to appreciate Avignon's medieval grandeur is the 13th-century **Fort St-André at Villeneuve-lès-Avignon**, on the other side of the river. The view is especially good at sunset, as the golden southern light bathes the town, and it is a popular place for an evening out.

TAKING A BREAK

Enjoy tea and cakes, or perhaps a light lunch at **Le Simple Simon**, an eccentric English-style tea room and restaurant in the heart of the Old Town (26 rue Petite-Fusterie, tel: 04 90 86 62 70, open Tue–Sat noon–7).

🚩 184 B3

Tourist Information Office
🚩 195 B1 ✉ 41 cours Jean-Jaurès
☎ 04 32 74 32 74;
www.avignon-tourisme.com
🕐 Apr–Oct Mon–Sat 9–6 (7 Jul), Sun 10–5;
Nov–Mar Mon–Fri 9–6, Sat 9–5, Sun 10–12

Palais des Papes
🚩 195 off C3 ✉ Place du Palais
☎ 04 90 27 50 00;
www.palais-des-papes.com
🕐 Mid-Mar to Oct daily 9–7, 8 or 9; Nov to mid-Mar 9:30–5:45 💶 Expensive mid-Mar to Oct; moderate Nov to mid-Mar

Musée Calvet
➕ 195 B3 ✉ 65 rue Joseph Vernet ☎ 04 90 86 33 84 ⏰ Jun–Sep Wed–Mon 10–6; Oct–May 10–1, 2–6 💰 Moderate

Petit Palais
➕ 195 off C3 ☎ 04 90 86 44 58 ⏰ Jun–Sep Wed–Mon 10–1, 2–6; Oct–May Wed–Mon 9:30–1, 2–5:30 💰 Moderate

AVIGNON: INSIDE INFO

Top tips The **Avignon Passport**, available from the tourist office or at participating sights, gives reduced price entry to the main sights.
■ The **Palais des Papes** offers guided tours in English (for groups on request but audioguides are available for individuals).
■ For a relaxing way to see the town take one of the little **sightseeing land trains** which set off frequently from place du Palais (mid-Mar to Oct).
■ The **Festival d'Avignon** (Avignon International Festival of Theatre) offers top-name entertainment, plus many fringe shows for three weeks in July (www.festival-avignon.com).

Hidden gem The **Fondation Angladon Dubrujeaud**, in an elegant city mansion on rue Laboureur, includes paintings by Sisley, Manet, Cézanne and Picasso, and Provence's only original Van Gogh (tel: 04 90 82 29 03, www.angladon.com; open Wed–Sun 1–6; also Tue, May–Nov).

❷ Châteauneuf-du-Pape

Set amid the stony, sun-baked, red soil of the southern Rhône, the picturesque, old fortified village of Châteauneuf-du-Pape, surrounded by its famous vineyards, is dedicated to the production of the world-famous red wines which bear its name.

Châteauneuf-du-Pape is a popular visitor destination, with people coming to see the village and more importantly, to taste the wines. At the bottom of the village in Cave Brotte, the **Musée Père Anselme** is dedicated to the history of local viticulture, and visitors can indulge in wine tastings

Vineyards surround Châteauneuf-du-Pape

CHÂTEAUNEUF-DU-PAPE: INSIDE INFO

Top tip You can taste high-quality chocolate in Chateauneuf free of charge at the family-run chocolatier Bernard Castelain (tel: 04 90 83 54 71, open Mon–Sat 9–12, 2–6).

WINE ROUTES

Numerous wine routes in the region lead you through charming yellow-stone villages with shady squares, old fountains and red-tiled roofs, hidden in a sea of vineyards and largely given over to restaurants and cellars offering free wine tasting.

and are offered the chance to buy. Among the best-known vineyards in the town are Château Le Nerthe, Château Rayas, Château de la Gardine, Château de Beaucastel and the Château des Fines Roches. The **Fête de la Véraison** (Grape-ripening Festival) in early August celebrates the maturing of the grapes with medieval pageantry, troubadours, jousting and juggling. Wine producers set up their stalls in the village and offer the chance to try their wines.

Séguret, one of the pretty villages on the wine routes

The wines of Châteauneuf-du-Pape are world renowned, largely thanks to 14th-century Pope Jean XXII of Avignon. It was he who built the now-ruined château, with its splendid views of the Rhône valley, as a summer residence, and then went on to plant the first vineyards.

🔲 184 B3
Tourist Information Office
✉ Place du Portail ☎ 04 90 83 71 08
🕐 Jul–Aug Mon–Sat 9:30–7; Oct–May Mon–Sat 9:30–12:30, 2–6

Musée Père Anselme
✉ Cave Brotte ☎ 04 90 83 70 07
🕐 Apr–Sep daily 9–1, 2–7; Oct–Mar daily 9–12, 2–6 🎟 Free

WINEMAKING

Many Côtes du Rhône wines are made from just one grape variety, but vintners here blend up to 13 different grapes to produce their distinctive wines of unique complexity. The vines are widely spaced, and the soil is covered with pebbles to magnify the heat of the sun during the day and release it at night. This results in a wine with a high alcohol content (12.5 per cent or higher). Most of the 13 million bottles of wine made here are a full-bodied red, although it's worth trying one of the 700,000 bottles of white. Look out for the crossed keys of the château embossed on the bottle, as this signifies that it is an authentic bottle of Châteauneuf-du-Pape.

3 Orange

Historic Orange, the "Gateway to Provence", lies in the fertile plain of the Rhône river. Its main claims to fame are two of the finest Roman monuments in Europe – the great triumphal arch and the massive theatre. Today, Orange is an important centre for Côtes du Rhône wines and produce such as olives, honey and truffles. The heart of the town dates from medieval times and is lively and bustling, with picturesque lanes and squares. It is small and easily explored on foot.

The Théâtre Antique

One of the best surviving theatres from the ancient world, the Théâtre Antique was built over 2,000 years ago, with seating for up to 10,000 spectators. Although all that remains of the theatre is a mere shadow of its former splendour, it is nevertheless easy to imagine the theatre in its heyday. The monumental stage wall (*frons scanae*), made from red sandstone and measuring 103m (113 yards) long, 37m (40 yards) high and nearly 2m (6.5 feet) thick, is the only one in the world to survive completely from ancient times. Originally the theatre was used for meetings and lectures, and staged anything from circus acts to Greek tragedies. Its excellent acoustics are demonstrated every July and August in the **Chorégies**, a world-famous festival of opera, drama and ballet, held here since 1869. Classical, jazz and pop concerts are also held here throughout the summer.

Above: The Roman Arc de Triomphe stands in the middle of modern Orange

The Arc de Triomphe

The massive 22m (71-foot) Arc de Triomphe was constructed as a symbol of Roman power following Caesar's conquest of

**Below left:
The view
from Colline
St-Eutrope**

the Gauls and victory over the Greek fleet. Its three archways are covered with intricate carvings and nautical symbols portraying maritime supremacy. The arc is on a roundabout surrounded by traffic from the busy N7.

The first-rate **Municipal Museum** gives a detailed insight into life in Roman Gaul. The most remarkable exhibit is a huge marble slab depicting the Romans' remarkable land survey of the region, which detailed boundaries, land owners and tax rates. There is also a full history of the city, and some interesting portraits of the royal House of Orange. The museum is a splendid introduction to the Théâtre Antique.

TAKING A BREAK

Restaurant des Princes at the Amarys Hotel (86 avenue de l'Arc de Triomphe, tel: 04 90 51 87 87) is a reliable pit-stop for lunch, with a vibrant modern dining room, hors d'oeuvres and dessert buffets and good value set-lunch menus. .

➕ 184 A4
Tourist Information Office
✉ 5 cours Aristide-Briand ☎ 04 90 34 70 88; www.otorange.fr
🕐 Apr–Jun, Sep Mon–Sat 9–6:30, Sun 10–1, 2–6:30; Jul–Aug Mon–Sat 9–7:30, Sun 10–1, 2–7; Oct–Mar Mon–Sat 10–1, 2–5

**Today the
Théâtre Antique
is the venue for
festivals and
concerts**

Théâtre Antique
✉ Place des Frères-Mounet ☎ 04 90 51 17 60
🕐 Jun–Aug daily 9–7; Apr–May, Sep daily 9–6; Mar, Oct daily 9:30–5:30; Nov–Feb daily 9:30–4:30 💵 Moderate, also valid for Musée Municipal

Arc de Triomphe
✉ Avenue de l'Arc-de-Triomphe/N7

Municipal Museum
✉ Rue Madeleine-Roch
☎ 04 90 51 17 60
🕐 Jun–Aug daily 9:15–7; Apr–May, Sep daily 9:15–6; Mar, Oct daily 9:45–12:30, 1:30–5:30; Nov–Feb daily 9:45–12:30, 1:30–4:30 💵 Expensive

---

ORANGE: INSIDE INFO

Top tips There is **parking** alongside cours Aristide Briand and in cours Pourtoules near the Théâtre Antique.
■ Telephone **Théâtre Antique** for details of guided tours (for groups), and concert and theatre information.
■ To the west of the theatre, **Colline St-Eutrope** is well worth the climb to reach its cool, shady park with magnificent views over Orange, the theatre and the Rhône plain beyond.

4 Vaison-la-Romaine

Undisputedly one of Provence's best-preserved Roman sites, Vaison is an extraordinary blend of modern town, medieval village and former Roman city – Vaisio Vocontiorum – now the town's greatest attraction.

Soaking up the atmosphere at the restored Roman theatre

Archaeological sites

The two Roman sites, Villasse and Puymin, are separated by a modern road. The **Puymin quarter,** the higher and larger of the two sites, has a visible street layout, some surviving walls and remains of frescoes and mosaic floors. The highlight is the 1st-century AD **Roman theatre**, which was restored in the 20th century and is now the venue for a range of events. Its tiered rows of seating, joined by stairs and topped with a portico, could accommodate 6,000 spectators. Other points of interest on this site include the extensive House of Apollon Lauré; the even larger Tonnelle House; the public space known as the Sanctuary; and an area of smaller houses and workshops.

The smaller, lower site, called **quartier de la Villasse,** has an important street of small shops, workshops and villas with mosaic floors. One notable structure is the ruins of the House of the Silver Bust, the largest house excavated in Vaison. The archaeology museum fee is included in the entry ticket for Villasse.

The medieval quarter

Once you've explored the Roman sites, walk down the main

street, Grande Rue, and cross the Roman bridge over the Ouvèze River to the **medieval quarter**. Clinging to a lofty jagged rock, the houses of Vaison's medieval village have been lovingly restored by artists and craftspeople. It is a steep climb to the ruined 13th-century château through a maze of twisting cobbled streets, rewarded by sweeping views across Ouvèze Valley and the Côtes du Rhône vineyards as far as the snow-topped Alps.

TAKING A BREAK

Sit on the terrace at **Vieux Vaison** (8 place du Poids, in the medieval quarter, tel 04 90 36 19 45) and tuck into pizzas from the wood-fired oven, pasta dishes and grills.

Above: Pont Romain spans the Ouvèze River

Right: Old houses overlook the Roman ruins

➕ 184 C5
Tourist Information Office
✉ Place du Chanoine-Sautel
☎ 04 90 36 02 11;
www.vaison-la-romaine.com

Roman sites
✉ Avenue Général-de-Gaulle
☎ 04 90 36 02 11
🕐 Puymin & Musée: Jun–Sep daily 9:30–6:30; Apr–May daily 9:30–6. La Villasse: Jun–Sep daily 10–12:30, 2:30–6:30; Apr–May daily 10–12:30, 2:30–6; Museum and both sites Oct–Mar daily 10–12:30, 2–5/5:30. Closed Jan–5 Feb 💷 Moderate, covers both sites

VAISON-LA-ROMAINE: INSIDE INFO

Top tips The Roman sites, archaeological museum and other sights may be visited on the **Billet Pass**. Buy from the ticket office adjacent to the Roman sites.
■ There are **large parking areas** next to the Roman sites.
■ A large, lively **street market** takes place every Tuesday morning.
■ A **summer festival** of drama, music and dance is held at the Roman theatre in July. Every three years, there is also a **Festival of Choral Music** in August.

Hidden gem The Romanesque cathedral, **Notre-Dame de Nazareth**, on avenue Général-de-Gaulle, has lovely 12th-century cloisters. It is about 10 minutes' walk from the quartier de la Villasse site.

5 Gordes and the Abbaye de Sénanque

Famous for its artists' colony, magnificent Cistercian abbey and ancient borie village, Gordes makes an ideal centre for touring the Lubéron.

Gordes is justifiably rated one of the most beautiful villages in France. Its grandiose church and Renaissance château rise from a golden plinth on a spur of Mont Ventoux, surrounded by narrow cobbled streets and tiers of sandstone houses that spill down the steep, stony slopes. During World War II, the village fell into decline, but in the 1960s artists brought new life to the village, restoring the delightful Renaissance houses and setting up attractive galleries, studios and boutiques. Now considered a chic place to have a second home, it is well served with shops and restaurants. The château currently contains the tourist office, on the first floor, along with the **Museum of Pol Mara**, a Flemish contemporary artist and honorary citizen of Gordes.

Above: Abbaye de Sénanque nestles peacefully in an attractive wooded valley Right: Exploring the narrrow cobbled streets in Gordes

Abbaye de Sénanque

In a secluded valley north of Gordes, bathed in a sea of lavender, is one of the great symbols of Provence, the Cistercian abbey of Sénanque. The honeyed stone abbey was built in the 12th century by the Cistercian Order, as the third – and last – of their monasteries in Provence. The three monasteries were known as the "Three Cistercian Sisters of Provence" (the other two are Silvacane ➤ 103–104 and du Thoronet ➤ 80). The monks here still follow a secret medieval recipe to concoct a pungent, herb-flavoured yellow liqueur called Sénancole. Notices advise that Sénanque abbey is not a tourist site but a place of monastic life, with a pious atmosphere and a rule of silence which visitors are requested to respect. At present, all visitors must join a guided tour (available in French only).

BORIES

Southwest of Gordes, the most famous collection of *bories* in France lies in dusty scrubland. These beehive-shaped, dry-stone huts sheltered the earliest farmers and semi-nomadic shepherds as early as the 3rd century BC.

**Above:
Intriguing
stone huts at
Village des
Bories**

TAKING A BREAK

La Pause, a tiny, café-teashop in the village centre, serves light meals and snacks (Route Neuve, tel: 04 90 72 11 53; closed Sun evening).

🔼 184 C3
Tourist Information Office
✉ Le Château, Gordes ☎ 04 90 72 02 75; www.gordes-village.com 🕐 Mon–Sat 9–12, 2–6, Sun 10–12, 2–6

Château de Gordes
☎ 04 90 72 02 75 🕐 Daily 10–12, 2–6. Closed 1 Jan, 25 Dec 🖐 Inexpensive

Village des Bories
✉ D2 from Gordes ☎ 04 90 72 03 48 🕐 Daily 9–sunset
🖐 Moderate

Abbaye de Sénanque
✉ Gordes ☎ 04 90 72 05 72; www.senanque.fr
🕐 Guided tours start at around 10am. Up to 11 tours per day Jul–Aug, 2 in winter. Closed Sun am and public hols
🖐 Moderate. Groups by advance reservation only

GORDES AND THE ABBAYE DE SÉNANQUE: INSIDE INFO

Top tips Gordes has a lively two-week music festival in August.
■ All visitors to the abbey must join a guided tour (in French). Dress modestly. Closure at 12 and 5 or 6 is very prompt.
■ After your visit, take the opportunity to **buy lavender oils and soaps**, handmade by the monks.

6 The Lubéron

The Parc Naturel Régional du Lubéron is a protected region of cedar and pine countryside interspersed with lavender fields, almond and olive groves, fragrant herbs, garrigue scrub and vineyards, draped across a compact range of small mountains that stretch from Cavaillon to Manosque.

The dramatic wooded gorge of the Combe de Lourmarin (road D943) splits the region in two. The high, wild Grand Lubéron mountains lie to the east. Walkers tackling the strenuous climb from Auribeau to the uppermost peak of Mourre Nègre (1,100m/3,609 feet) will be well rewarded with dizzy views from the Basse-Alpes to the Mediterranean. To the west, many of the pretty hilltop villages of the Petit Lubéron have been restored and are now fashionable second homes.

The busy old market town of **Apt**, north of the Lubéron mountains, makes an ideal centre for touring the area. The best place to start is at the **Maison du Parc Naturel Régional du Lubéron**, which details walks and other outdoor activities, together with a small local natural history museum. The town itself is renowned for its jams and crystallised fruit – try some at the bustling Saturday market. Apt is also well known for its lavender essence and handmade pottery, and is an important centre for the truffle trade in winter.

Above:
Old town houses in the village of Lourmarin, at the foot of the Montagne du Luberon
Left: Wines produced in the Lubéron

The Lubéron Villages

The neighbouring villages of Bonnieux, Lacoste, Ménerbes and Oppède-le-Vieux vie for the title of prettiest Lubéron village.

Bonnieux, overlooking the vineyards, cherry trees and lavender fields of the Coulon valley, has many fine monuments, including the Town Hall, a bakery museum and some notable Renaissance paintings in its two churches.

Lacoste is rich, exclusive and crowned by an 11th-century fortress, which in its heyday was one of the region's grandest.

The Lubéron's highest-profile village, **Ménerbes**, has long attracted celebrities, including Picasso's mistress Dora Maar and, more recently, François Mitterand and British writer Peter Mayle. The village, the setting for Peter Mayle's bestseller, *A Year in Provence* (1989), is a lively place with a vibrant weekly market, 13th-century fortress and 14th-century church.

At first glimpse **Oppède-le-Vieux** appears a typical hilltop village, but on closer inspection you will see that many of the houses are in ruins, overrun with weeds. Some of the old cottages and the Romanesque church have been restored by resident artists, and Oppède is returning to its former glory.

To the South

The imposing Renaissance château, medieval houses, tiny fountain-filled squares and inviting restaurants of **Lourmarin** create a picturesque ensemble on the southern slopes of the Lubéron. French novelist and philosopher Albert Camus bought a house here after winning the Nobel Prize for literature in 1957. His simple grave can be visited in the village cemetery.

The pretty village of **Ansouis**, on a rocky crest, is dominated by the keep of its great château, home of the Sabran family for the last 800 years. The 12th-century fortress was modernised during the Renaissance, and is today more of a large country house than a castle. On the ground floor there are displays of weapons and armour, while upstairs you'll find Flemish tapestries and elegant pieces of Italian-Renaissance furniture.

Left: Bonnieux, one of the pretty Lubéron villages

TAKING A BREAK

When visiting the village of **Lacoste** stop at the cheap and cheerful Café de France, where you can enjoy a light lunch such as salade Niçoise or omelette and fries (Le Village, lunch only, except Jul and Aug).

Maison du Parc Naturel Régional du Lubéron
🚩 185 D2
✉ 60 place Jean Jaurès, Apt ☎ 04 90 04 42 00; www.parcduluberon.com 🕐 Apr–Sep Mon–Sat 8:30–12, 1:30–7; Oct–Mar Mon–Fri 8:30–12, 1:30–6 💶 Free

Tourist Information Office
🚩 185 D2
✉ 20 avenue Philippe-de-Girard, Apt
☎ 04 90 74 03 18; www.ot-apt.fr
🕐 Jul–Aug Mon–Sat 9–7, Sun 9:30–12.30; May–Jun, Sep Mon–Sat 9–12, 2–6, Sun 9.30–12:30; Oct–Apr Mon–Fri 9–12, 2–6

Tourist Information Office
🚩 185 D2
✉ 7 place Carnot, Bonnieux ☎ 04 90 75 91 90;

Top: Vineyards in the Lubéron hills
Above: An archway frames a narrow street in Apt

www.btourisme-en-luberon.com
🕐 Mon–Fri 9:30–12:30, 2–6:30, Sat 2–6:30

Tourist Information Office
🚩 185 E2
✉ Place du Château, Ansouis
☎ 04 90 09 86 98; www.tourisme-ansouis.com
🕐 Daily 10–12, 2–6

THE LUBÉRON: INSIDE INFO

Top tips Drop into the Maison du Parc Naturel Régional du Lubéron for information on walks and other activities in the park.
■ Pause at the terrace near the 12th-century church in **Bonnieux** and enjoy the stunning views of the valley and nearby hilltop villages.
■ In **Oppède-le-Vieux** you can walk the overgrown pathways in the upper part of the village to the summit, but take care as there are many unprotected drops.

One to miss Don't expect to find Peter Mayle in Ménerbes – he lived near by until he was driven away by visiting fans.

At Your Leisure

🔢 Cavaillon

Cavaillon is France's greatest market garden – its very name synonymous with those delicious, sweet, pink-fleshed melons – and boasts one of Europe's largest wholesale fruit and vegetable markets. The vast, mouth-watering **market** for the general public every Monday morning is considered the most important market in the Vaucluse.

The town's agricultural wealth stems from its location in the fertile Durance valley. From the Colline St-Jacques, a one-time neolithic site at the top of the town, there are spectacular views across the valley to the distant highlands of the Lubéron and the Alpilles.

In the town centre, numerous Roman finds have been assembled in the **Musée Archéologique**. The former cathedral is also worth visiting, as is the beautifully preserved 18th-century synagogue, with its small museum

illustrating the region's traditional protection of Jewish communities.

➕ 184 C2
Tourist Information Office
✉ Place François-Tourel
☎ 04 90 71 32 01; www.cavaillon-luberon.com
🕐 Mid-Mar to mid-Oct Mon–Sat 9–12:30, 2–6:30; Jul–Aug Sun 9–12:30; mid-Oct to mid-Mar Mon–Fri 9–12, 2–6, Sat 9–12

🔢 Roussillon

Once known worldwide for its ochre dyes, Roussillon is now considered one of France's most beautiful villages. Perched on a platform of rich rust-coloured rock called Mont Rouge, the village is hidden amid dark pine forests and scrub, and surrounded by jagged cliffs

Above: The town of Cavaillon, viewed here from the neolithic site of Colline St-Jaques, is known as the melon capital of France

Roussillon is a jumble of ochre buildings of various hues

houses, built by the ochre miners over the centuries, present a full palette of ochre shades, which create a special glow in the streets. The hub of the village is the small, lively square beside the Mairie (town hall), where the Roussillonais gather in the outdoor cafés. Narrow lanes and winding stairways lead up to a Romanesque church, offering a sweeping panorama of the ochreous Vaucluse scenery, with its hill villages and distant mountains.

🔁 185 D3
Tourist Information Office
✉ Place de la Poste ☎ 04 90 05 60 25; www.roussillon-provence.com
🕐 Tue–Fri 9:30–12, 1:30–6, Mon, Sat 9:30–12, 1:30–5:30

and hollows of every shade of ochre imaginable, from blood red, gold, orange and pale yellow to white, pink and violet. For here lie the richest deposits of ochre in all France.

The ochre industry began here at the end of the 18th century, bringing prosperity to the villagers until 1958, and although today very few quarries are worked, Roussillon still holds its merry Ochre Festival at Ascensiontide. Visitors can explore the old opencast quarries along the 1km (0.5-mile) **Sentier des Ocres** (Ochre Trail, open Jul–Aug daily 9–7:30; Sep–Jun daily 9–5; inexpensive), which has information signboards along the way. To make the most of the trail, you'll need to be able to walk well in difficult terrain.

The picturesque

9 Fontaine-de-Vaucluse

Tucked away at the end of the narrow *vallis clausa* (enclosed valley), Fontaine-de-Vaucluse is famous for its emerald-green spring, a 15-minute walk along the traffic-free Chemin de la Fontaine, beside the Sorgue river. The spring gushes from a huge cave-like abyss at the foot of a sheer cliff into a strange, still and very deep pool, surrounded by rocks and vegetation and often by a dense,

The swift waters of Fontaine-de-Vaucluse

dripping spray. Research has proved that this is one of the world's largest and most powerful natural springs. It consists of a vast underground labyrinth of rivers and is able to produce up to 630 million cubic metres (22,260 million cubic feet) of water each year, flowing down the narrow valley to become the Sorgue. For maximum effect, come in March or April.

Fontaine's other main tourist attractions include a **paper mill**, and a small **museum** dedicated to the famous 14th-century Italian poet Petrarch. He wrote most of his poetry here, inspired by the solitude and wilderness he found in the valley.

🕂 184 C3
Tourist Information Office
✉ Chemin de la Fontaine
☎ 04 90 20 32 22
🕐 Tue–Sat 9:30–12:30, 1:30–5:30
Moulin à Papier Vallis Clausa
✉ Chemin de Gouffre
☎ 04 90 20 34 14
🕐 Hours vary. Closed 1 Jan, 25 Dec
Musée Pétrarque
✉ Left bank of the Sorgue

☎ 04 90 20 37 20
🕐 Apr–Oct Wed–Mon 10–12, 2–6
💰 Inexpensive

🔟 Mont Ventoux

The awesome, isolated massif of Mont Ventoux – the "Giant of Provence" – rises 1,909m (6,261 feet) above the Plateau de Vaucluse, making it the highest peak between the Alps and the Pyrénées. Italian poet Francesco Petrarch was the first recorded man to reach its summit, in 1336. It is a good 5-hour hike (for organised walks including

Above: The village of Bedoin, near Mont Ventoux

FOR KIDS

- **Roussillon** Older children might enjoy scrambling over the rough terrain of the quarries, but this may be more difficult for young children. Make sure they wear something that you don't mind being stained with ochre.
- **Fontaine-de-Vaucluse** On the way to see the spring, **Ecomusée du Gouffre** (tel: 04 90 20 34 13, hours vary) displays collections of rocks and minerals, but also deals vividly with efforts to discover the source of the water flowing from the Fontaine.

a nocturnal hike contact Bedoin Tourist Office, tel: 04 90 65 63 95, or Malaucène Tourist Office, tel: 04 90 65 22 59), but most people drive to the summit of the mountain, where high-tech observation and communications equipment is installed. From here the vista takes in the Alps, the Rhône Valley, the Vaucluse Plateau, the Cévennes and the Mediterranean. Wrap up warm, even in summer. Its bleak limestone peak, totally devoid of vegetation, has been blasted white by icy mistral winds of up to 160km/h (100mph). For much of the year the summit is snow-clad and popular with skiers.

➕ 185 D4

Mont Ventoux Information
✉ Chalet d'Accueil du Mont Ventoux
☎ 04 90 63 42 02

🔟 Dentelles de Montmirail

The higher part of the slopes of this small range of hills in northern Vaucluse is wild wooded country, but most of the lower slopes are covered with vines producing Côtes du Rhône red wines. Among the prettiest and most evocative wine villages are Séguret and Gigondas. The ochre cottages of **Séguret** house crafts-people renowned for their dried flowers and *santons* (traditional clay figurines). The wines of the small, unspoiled village of **Gigondas**, set against the jagged backdrop of the Dentelles, are reputed to be the best in the area, notably the intense red Grenache wines. Others wine villages worth a visit include Vacqueyras and Beaumes-de-Venise. Majestically framed by the lacy silver crags of the Dentelles, **Beaumes** is known for its sweet, golden Muscat wines. Taste them at the Cave des Vignerons or during the region's annual wine festivals, accompanied by goat's cheese, *foie gras* and melons in Muscat. Wine tasting is available in all the villages.

➕ 184 C4

Tourist Information Office
✉ Rue du Portail, Gigondas
☎ 04 90 65 85 46

Tourist Information Office
✉ Maison des Dentelles, place du Marché, Beaumes-de-Venise
☎ 04 90 62 94 39;
www.ot-beaumesdevenise.com
🕐 Mon–Sat 9–12, 2–6 or 7

Where to... Stay

Prices
Expect to pay per night for a double room
€ under €100   €€ €100–€200   €€€ over €200

APT

Le Couvent €–€€
Tucked into a quiet corner of the old town in Apt, this handsome maison d'hôtes in a 17th-century former convent is a peaceful, comfortable base from which to explore the Lubéron, complete with a sunny terrace and outdoor pool. The rooms are spacious and airy, elegantly furnished in modern style, with high ceilings and good bathrooms, and include a vast three-bed room on the top floor and a family room for four.

🏠 185 D2 ⊠ 36 rue Louis Rousset ☎ 04 90 04 55 36; www.loucouvent.com ⓒ All year

AVIGNON

Auberge de Cassagne €€€
This delightful four-star hotel, just five minutes outside Avignon, is tastefully decorated and offers a high standard of comfort. The spacious bedrooms are furnished with Provençal antiques and fabrics, and have luxurious bathrooms. All rooms have satellite TV and a minibar. The hotel is set in beautiful gardens, with an outdoor and an indoor pool. There is a restaurant of international renown, and you can chose to dine on the terrace.

🏠 184 B3 ⊠ 450 allée de Cassagne, le Pontet ☎ 04 90 31 04 18; www.aubergede-cassagne.com ⓒ Closed Jan

Camping de Bagatelle €
Situated on the île de la Barthelasse, an island on the Rhône connected to Avignon by a bridge, this large camping ground can accommodate tents or caravans (trailers), and is surrounded by greenery. Facilities include a grocery store, bars, a restaurant, pool, bicycle rental and kids' playgrounds. There's also a youth hostel. It's €14.62 to pitch a two-man tent, €18.62 for a caravan.

🏠 184 B3 ⊠ île de la Barthelasse ☎ 04 90 86 30 35; www.campingbagatelle.com ⓒ All year

La Ferme €
This old farmhouse is on the île de la Barthelasse – once a hunting reserve and then a fashionable place to promenade and picnic.

🏠 184 B3 ⊠ Chemin des Bois, île de la Barthelasse ☎ 04 90 82 57 53; www.hotel-laferme.com ⓒ Closed Nov to mid-Mar

Hôtel d'Europe €€–€€€
Follow in the steps of Napoleon Bonaparte, Pablo Picasso and Salvador Dalí, and stay at the Marquis of Graveson's former house, which was built in 1580 and turned into a hotel in 1799. The hotel is furnished with antiques, candelabra, paintings and Persian carpets. There are 44 bedrooms, and the 3 suites have a terrace with wonderful views over Avignon. There's a restaurant and parking.

🏠 184 B3 ⊠ 12 place Crillon ☎ 04 90 14 76 76; www.heurope.com ⓒ All year

La Mirande €€€
This is an elegant four-star hotel in a medieval cardinal's palace, on a quiet cobbled square at the foot of the Palais des Papes, within the walled city of Avignon. The hotel has been carefully restored and is furnished with antiques and paintings. The bedrooms are luxurious, with beautiful marble bathrooms, and most overlook the square or the garden with the Palais des Papes in the background. There is a candlelit bar, an excellent restaurant (you have the option of

dining on the terrace in summer), a tea room and a garden.

184 B3 ⌂ **4 place de la Mirande** ☎ **04 90 14 20 20; www.la-mirande.fr** ⏱ **All year**

BONNIEUX

De l'Aiguebrun €€

A beautiful old, stone farmhouse just a few kilometres east of the village of Bonnieux, in the peaceful heart of the Lubéron National Park. Seven bedrooms decorated in authentic Provençal style, and a restaurant.

185 D2 ⌂ **RD 493** ☎ **04 90 04 47 00** ⏱ **Closed Jan–Feb**

GORDES

Le Mas de la Beaume €€

This beautiful stone mas (farmhouse) overlooks the village. Inside you'll find baskets of flowers hanging from the old beams, embroidered lampshades and lots of polished wood. There are five bedrooms, all traditionally furnished with consummate taste. The picturesque garden has a swimming pool and a terrace where a fantastic farmhouse-style breakfast is served with home-made jams.

184 C3 ⌂ **84220 Gordes Village** ☎ **04 90 72 02 96; www.labeaume.com**

LOURMARIN

Hostellerie le Paradou €€

A small stream runs through the wooded gardens of this small, sleepy hotel beneath the gorges of Lourmarin on the road to Apt. Le Paradou is a friendly place decorated in contemporary Thai style; the restaurant serves Thai and French cuisine.

185 D2 ⌂ **Combe de Lourmarin (0943)** ☎ **04 90 68 04 05**

ORANGE

Arène Klum €–€€

This small, three-star hotel, in a quiet traffic-free square in the historic centre of Orange, offers 30 good-value bedrooms, each with a safe, air-conditioning and a mini-bar. There is a small breakfast room and a separate restaurant. There is a private garage (parking fee).

184 A4 ⌂ **8 place de Langes** ☎ **04 90 11 40 40; www.bestwestern-hotel-arene.com**

ROUSSILLON

Le Clos de la Glycine €€

Pale colours, limed beams and Provençal furniture create a sophisticated, elegantly summery ambiance at this beautiful small hotel in the heart of Roussillon. There are superb views of Roussillon's ochre cliffs from the Michelin-starred restaurant. The rooms have either village, cliff or valley views, and there's one apartment with a terrace and sweeping views.

185 D3 ⌂ **Place de la Poste** ☎ **04 90 05 60 13; www.luberon-hotel.com**

VAISON-LA-ROMAINE

Hostellerie Le Beffroi €–€€

Set in a 16th-century mansion and an adjoining building that dates from the 18th century, this three-star hotel is full of local character. There are beamed ceilings, tiled floors and fine furniture. The 22 comfortable bedrooms have private bath or shower, satellite TV and a mini-bar. Some of the rooms have panoramic views of the medieval town of Vaison-la-Romaine, while others overlook the terraced gardens (where breakfast is served in good weather). The restaurant creates original dishes prepared from seasonal local produce, which can be accompanied by a choice of wines, including Côtes du Ventoux and Côtes du Rhône. There is a swimming pool in the gardens and a private garage (there is a parking fee).

184 C5 ⌂ **Rue de l'Évêché, Cité Médiévale** ☎ **04 90 36 04 71; www.le-beffroi.com** ⏱ **Closed Feb–Mar**

Where to...
Eat and Drink

Prices

Expect to pay for a three-course meal for one, excluding drinks and service

€ under €25   €€ €25–€50   €€€ over €50

APT

Les Délices de Léa €–€€

With a woman chef at the helm, this modest, pretty little restaurant in Apt's old town has quickly developed a local following for its sweet-savoury flavour combinations, such as foie gras with crème glacée of figs or duck breast with poached yellow fruits, vanilla, honey and sesame. The short, affordable wine list majors on Luberon and Ventoux bottles.

🔒 185 D2 ✉ 87 rue de la République
📞 04 90 74 32 77 🕐 Lunch 12–1:30, dinner 7–9. Closed Sun, Mon lunch

AVIGNON

Christian Étienne €€€

The food does not come cheap at this Avignon restaurant, but the quality is excellent and the setting superb. It's housed in a 14th-century palace, complete with frescoes, and with a view out from the terrace over the fabulous Palais des Papes. Truffles are a significant feature of the cooking, and there's also a lobster-based menu.

🔒 184 B3 ✉ 10 rue de Mons
📞 04 90 86 16 50;
www.christian-etienne.fr
🕐 Tue–Sat noon–1:15, 7:30–9:15

D'Ici et d'Ailleurs €€

You can choose from Provençal or Asian- and Mexican-influenced menus at this delightfully informal, friendly restaurant. Either way the portions are generous, and the interior is simple but attractive with exposed stonework and glass display cabinets, and the service is friendly. The food is pretty healthy, too.

🔒 185 D2 ✉ 4 rue Galante
📞 04 90 14 63 65
🕐 Tue–Sat 11–2, 6–12

BONNIEUX

Le Pont Julien €€

In a traditional Provençal house, with lamps and paintings decorating the unpretentious interior, at the heart of the Luberon's regional park. There are two dining rooms and a terrace for the warmer weather. The menu offers the likes of snail brochettes with garlic butter, confit duck on sauerkraut with cider and lamb pot au feu with ravioli, using regional produce wherever possible.

It is advisable to book at least 48 hours in advance.

🔒 185 D2 ✉ N100
📞 04 90 74 48 44; www.lepontjulien.com
🕐 12–1:45, 7:45–8:45. Closed Mon eve, Tue all day.

CAVAILLON

Prévot €€€

Chef Jean-Jaques Prévot's lavish dining room is matched by the equally rich cuisine. Try his jugged hare in wine and foie gras sauce and his succulent Cavaillon melon desserts, or his Flavours of Luberon menu.

🔒 184 C2 ✉ 353 avenue Verdun
📞 04 90 71 32 43;
www.restaurant-prevot.com
🕐 Closed Sun–Mon

CHÂTEAUNEUF-DU-PAPE

La Mère Germaine €–€€

This is one of the the village's most popular restaurants, with views of the vineyard from the traditional dining room. The wine list includes the best crus of the *appellation*.

☎ 184 B3 **✉** Avenue du Commandant-Lemaître **☎** 04 90 83 54 37; www.lameregermaine.com **⏰** Lunch and dinner daily

GORDES

Hostellerie Le Phebus €€€

Le Phebus is both a restaurant and a four-star hotel. Chef Xavier Mathieu's sophisticated regional cuisine includes dishes such as fillet of sole pan-fried in salt butter with tangy jasmine and vanilla, and farmhouse duck *foie gras*. You can choose to eat in the elegant dining room, which has beamed ceilings, or, weather permitting, you may prefer the terrace with its fabulous views. You can expect to pay around €28 for a bottle of the house wine.

☎ 185 D3 **✉** Route de Murs, 84220 Joucas-Gordes **☎** 04 90 05 78 83; www.lephebus.com **⏰** Closed lunch Tue, Wed, Thu and late Apr to mid-Oct

Le Mas Tourteron €€

Elisabeth Bourgeois' stunningly pretty restaurant is set in a delightful garden just outside Les Imberts, southwest of Gordes. The cooking has a Provençal stamp, with ingredients such as lamb, rabbit, honey and tapenade supplemented by home-grown vegetables to create fresh, seasonal set menus.

☎ 184 C3 **✉** Chemin de Sainte Blaise les Imberts, 84220 Gordes **☎** 04 90 72 00 16; www.mastourteron.com **⏰** Closed lunch Mon–Sat and Jan–Feb

La Pause €

This friendly café-cum-teashop in the village centre is an ideal place to stop for a tasty snack or light meal.

☎ 184 C3 **✉** Route Neuve **☎** 04 90 72 11 53 **⏰** Closed Sun pm

LOURMARIN

Le Moulin de Lourmarin €€€

This restaurant is set in a beautiful converted 18th-century oil mill. Under an impressive vaulted stone roof, the candlelit tables are dressed with blue and yellow fabric. Chef Edouard Loubet uses vegetables from the restaurant's garden, along with herbs and spices typical of the Lubéron, in dishes such as wheat and clam risotto, and pigeon from the Alpilles with a reduction of rocket (*arugula*). The three menus are a feast for the senses.

☎ 185 D2 **✉** Rue du Temple, 84160 Lourmarin **☎** 04 90 68 06 69; www.moulindelourmarin.com **⏰** Easter–end Sep daily; Oct–Mar Thu–Mon

MÉNERBES

Le Galoubet €€

Exquisite regional cuisine served in a small, cheerful dining room or *al fresco* under the olive trees.

☎ 185 D2 **✉** 104 avenue Marcellin Poncet **☎** 04 90 72 36 08 **⏰** Closed Wed

ORANGE

Le Yaca €

Locals pile in to this animated, jolly restaurant for its robustly traditional virtues. The stone arches and wood beams in the modest-sized dining room provide a rustic setting for the likes of chicken liver pâté with onion jam, sole meunière or snails à la Provençale, and there are several good-value, *prix-fixe* menus to choose from.

☎ 184 A4 **✉** 24 place Sylvain **☎** 04 90 34 70 03 **⏰** Closed Tue, Wed

VAISON-LA-ROMAINE

La Fontaine Restaurant €€

This hotel/restaurant, situated in a 18th-century building in the old part of town, has an ornate dining room. The menu concentrates on traditional Provencal dishes, and the wine cellar stocks predominantly local Côtes du Rhône and Ventoux labels.

☎ 184 C5 **✉** Le Beffroi, rue de l'Evêché, Cité Médiévale **☎** 04 90 36 04 71; www.le-beffroi.com **⏰** Easter–Oct Wed–Mon 12–2, 7.30–9

Where to ... Shop

MARKETS

The markets of Avignon are ideal for buying picnic supplies. At the **Marché des Halles** (place Pie, open Tue–Sun 6am–1:30pm) you can purchase a wide range of local produce, or try the **Marché Forain** (boulevard Limbert, place des Maraichers, St-Chamand, open Sun). This is Avignon's biggest market for exotic North African spices, vegetables and fruit.

Antiques dealers mix with locals who sell the contents of their cellars at the **Marché aux Puces**, also in Avignon. Arrive early for the pick of the best bargains at this large bazaar (place des Carmes, open Sun 7–1).

SOUVENIRS AND GIFTS

Look for individual shops selling beautiful printed fabrics of the region, including tableware and clothing. In Vaison-la-Romaine try **Souléiado** (2 cours Henri Fabre, tel: 04 90 36 38 33, open Tue–Sat 10–12, 3–7).

Drop into **Cannelle** in Roussillon, a small shop full of fun gift ideas, regional produce (olive oils, liqueurs) wines and perfumes (place de la Poste, tel: 04 90 05 71 27).

In Avignon, visit **Scènes Intérieures** (41 rue d'Amphoux, tel: 04 90 86 46 31), a beautiful interior design and gift shop.

FOOD AND DRINK

If you're shopping for edible treats try crystallised fruits in Apt. **Apt Union** (quartier Salignan, BP 137, tel: 04 90 76 31 31, open Mon–Sat 9–12, 2–6) is a world leader when it comes to the glacé cherry. In the centre of Apt, **La Bonbonnière** (57 rue de la Sous-Préfecture, tel: 04 90 74 12 92, open 8:30–12:30, 2:30–7:30) sells mouth-watering jellies, Florentines and lemon calissons, as well as jams and honey.

In Avignon, **Les Délices du Luberon** (20 place du Change, tel: 04 90 84 03 58, open Mon–Sat 10–1, 2–7) is an Aladdin's cave for foodies, with a vast, tempting range of olive oils, tapenade, olives and Provençal rouille. **La Tropézienne** (22 rue St-Agricole; tel: 0 490 86 24 72, www.la-tropezienne.fr.st; open Tue–Sun, daily in Jul) is famous for its *papalines* (black chocolates) filled with liquor scented with 60 regional spices. They also sell glacé fruits, jams and the speciality – *tropézienne* – a delicious cake filled with cream.

Au Goût du Jour in Roussillon is a smart deli specialising in regional honeys, oils, wines, cheeses, tea and champagne (5 rue Richard Casteau, tel: 06 70 10 31 84).

Lou Canestéou is considered Vaison-la-Romaine's best cheese shop. It offers a choice of local goat's cheese, including *banon* (in chatigne leaves), *picadon* and *cachat* (10 rue Raspail, tel: 04 90 36 31 30).

ART, ANTIQUES AND BOOKS

Stop off at **Shakespeare Librairie**, in Avignon, for a book and a cup of tea. This is a discount English bookshop and tea shop (155 rue Carreterie, tel: 04 90 27 38 50, open Tue–Sat 9:30–12:30, 2–6:30). **Hervé Baum**, also in Avignon, sells all sorts of objects for the home and garden (19 rue Petite Fusterie, tel: 04 90 86 37 66).

In L'Isle-sur-la-Sorgue, **L'Isle aux Brocantes** has more than 35 dealers trading in an "antiques village" (passage du Pont, 7 avenue des 4-Otages, tel: 04 90 20 69 93).

Gifts and paints in every i shade of ochre can be found at **Galerie des Ocres** in Roussillon (Le Castrum, tel: 04 90 05 62 99).

Where to...
Be Entertained

BARS, CLUBS AND CASINOS

In Avignon, **Opéra Café**, a contemporary chic bar-restaurant, on the city's busiest square, is a hit with the hip crowd. There is a DJ every evening (24 place de l'Horloge, tel: 04 90 86 17 43, open 10am–1.30am, 3am Jul). Choose from two bars and two dance floors at **Le Blues**, which hosts karaoke nights, disco, live rock, jazz and blues (25 rue Carnot, tel: 04 90 85 79 71, open 11pm–4:30/5am). **Cadillac Café** is decorated with 1950s Americana. There are frescoes of Marilyn and Elvis, pool tables, video games, as well as theme nights and summer barbecues (11 bis route de Lyon, tel: 04 90 86 99 57, open daily 2pm–1am). A huge mural of a

tropical beach decorates the walls at **Cubanito's Café**, where you can try a free salsa class any evening at 9pm (51 rue Carnot, tel: 04 90 86 98 04, open Mon–Fri 11am–1am, Sat–Sun 5pm–1am).

THEATRE AND MUSIC

Orange's Roman **Théâtre Antique** is the spectacular setting for concerts, opera and theatre (rue Madeleine Roch, tel: 04 90 51 17 60).

Opéra Théâtre d'Avignon is the venue for concerts by the Orchestra Lyrique de Région Avignon-Provence and ballet productions (place de l'Horloge; enquiries 11–6, tel: 04 90 82 42 42; tickets tel: 04 90 82 81 40 or book online at www.operatheatredavignon.fr

If you are in Avignon during the festival, as well as the official events you can enjoy performances at nearly 100 venues for the Off Festival, with around 700 companies taking part (www. avignonlestivaletcompagnies.com). The official festival is presented in a range of venues.

The Chorégies in Orange present well-known operas in the unforgettable setting of the **Théâtre Antique** for several weeks from mid-July (tel: 04 90 34 24 24; www.choregies.com).

In Cavaillon, **Le Grenier à Sons**, a 350-seat concert hall, stages jazz, rock, blues, reggae and more by established musicians and budding talents (157 avenue du Général-de-Gaulle, tel: 04 90 06 44 20; www. grenier-a-sons.org).

SPORTS AND ACTVITIES

You can swim on the île de la Barthelasse in Avignon in the Olympic-sized open-air **Piscine des**

Arènes (île de la Barthelasse; www.piscinedesarenes.com, open mid-Jun to mid-Sep).

There are 16 computerised lanes at **Bowling**; snacks are available (avenue Paul-Claudel, tel: 04 90 88 50 11, open 3pm–2am (4am Fri–Sat). You can rent skates at **Patinoire d'Avignon** ice rink, where the *Castors* (Beavers) ice-hockey team are based (2483 chemin de l'Amandier, tel: 04 90 88 54 32; www.patinoire-avignon.com; open early Sep to mid-May Mon–Fri 9:30–12, 2:30–5.30, also Fri 9pm–11:30pm, Sat 2:30–5.30, 9–11:30, Sun 3–6).

Montgolfières Provence, in Gordes take you on balloon flights that last between 40 and 80 minutes (Le Mas Fourmiguère Joucas, tel: 04 90 05 79 21; www.montgolfiere-provence-ballooning.com).

Vélo Loisir en Lubéron cycling club organises tours in the Parc Naturel Régional du Lubéron tel: 04 90 76 48 05; www. veloloisirluberon.com).

Walks and Tours

THE HEART OF PROVENCE

Drive

DISTANCE 135km (88 miles) **TIME** Allow a full day

START/END POINT Aix-en-Provence ⊞ 191 E3

From Aix-en-Provence this tour heads into Montagne Ste-Victoire before turning south towards the Massif de la Ste-Baume. The roads are narrow in places and hilly in others, which makes the drive interesting rather than arduous.

1–2

Leave **Aix-en-Provence** on the **D10**, towards St-Marc-Jaumegarde and Vauvenargues, to reach the **Barrage de Bimont** after about 7km (4 miles). The lake behind the Barrage de Bimont dam provides water for local towns.

2–3

Continue on the **D10** to the pretty village of **Vauvenargues**, famous for its Renaissance **château**, inherited by Pablo Picasso in 1958. The artist died here in 1973 and is buried in the grounds. The park and château are not open to the public. Rejoin the **D10** by driving through the village (there is only one road).

The **D10**, now signed **Jouques and Rians**, runs along the northern flank of the Montagne Ste-Victoire, which inspired artist Paul Cézanne.

3–4

Bear right shortly, following the **D10** signed Rians. The road narrows, climbs and offers good views all the way. At the next intersection, turn left (signposted Rians D23). This is the **D23** towards Rians, which ends at a T-junction with the D3. Turn right, signed **Ollières and St-Maximin-la-Ste-Baume.** Approaching **St-Maximin**, turn left at the traffic lights, then right and left again as you cross St-Maximin. The **basilica** here is the best example of Gothic architecture in Provence.

4–5

Go over a roundabout to take the **N560** signed **Nans-les-Pins.** Continue for 100m (110 yards), turn left at traffic lights. Go over at the next traffic lights onto the **D64** signed **Mazaugues.** Follow the **D64** to the **D1** and turn right towards **Rougiers.** Turn left off the D1 into the

village at the sign for **Rougiers centre**, and left again at the café/tabac up rue Ste-Anne. Go uphill towards a **ruin and a church** on top of the hill ahead. Bear sharp left and go through a barrier (closed during periods of high fire risk), before continuing up the valley. Go over a crest and down to an intersection. Turn right onto the **D95** (only the back of the sign is visible, to check that you are on the right road make sure the wrong side indicates Plan-d'Aups).

Then, at a T-junction, turn left onto the D80 (signposted Plan d'Aups) and continue to the **Hôtellerie at La Ste-Baume**, a 19th-century restoration of a Dominican friars' pilgrim hostel, dating from medieval times, now a base for spiritual studies. Continue on the **D80** through **Plan-d'Aups**, after which the road widens. At the next intersection, bear right onto a road signed Auriol, which joins the D45a to make a long, twisting descent around hairpin bends. When you reach the D560 at a roundabout, take the first exit signed **St-Zacharie.**

5–6

At the village, continue until a road on the left, the **D85**, is signed **Trets and Col du Petit Galibier**. Stay on this road, later the **D12**, which climbs providing fine views, to reach **Trets**. Here are the remains of medieval walls, as well as square 14th-century towers and a 15th-century castle and church.

6–7

Approaching **Trets**, turn left at a roundabout, go straight over a mini-roundabout, and bear left at the next intersection to approach a roundabout with olive trees. Bear left here onto the **D908** signed **Peynier**, a village with a pleasant Romanesque church.

7–8

Pass **Peynier** to the south and climb through wooded hills. After 4km (2.5 miles) take the **D46C** to the right, signed for **Belcodène**, and go through the village following signs for **Fuveau**. At a fork in the road, keep right, go over the *autoroute* and enter **Fuveau**. Turn left and right into the main square, then, almost immediately, take the first street on the left,

the road to **Aix-en-Provence and Gardanne**. At a roundabout with a central fountain, take the D46 exit signed for **Aix**. Turn right and follow this road and the **N7** to Aix.

Taking a break

There are many restaurants and brasseries to choose from in St-Maximin-la-Ste-Baume.

THE CAMARGUE
2 Drive

The Camargue, Provence's best-known wildlife location and one of Europe's most important wetlands, is famous for its hardy white horses, black bulls, pink flamingoes and some of Europe's most exotic birds.

DISTANCE 95km (59 miles) **TIME** Allow a full day
START/END POINT Arles ✚ 194 C3

1–2
Head west from Arles and cross the Grand Rhône. Take the **D570** (signed for Stes-Maries-de-la-Mer) to Albaron, once a powerful stronghold but now fighting off the sea with pumping stations rather then repelling human invaders. From here take the **D37** to Méjanes.

2–3
Méjanes is a small lakeside resort with a narrow-gauge

railway, a bullring and ponies and horses for hire. From here, follow the **D37** as it runs past the Étang de Vaccarès, the largest of the Camargue's lagoons.

Taking a Break
Restaurant de Méjanes
⊠ Domaine de Méjanes, on the D37, 4km (2.5 miles) south of Albaron ☎ 04 90 97 10 51 ⑥ Lunch daily, dinner by reservation

3–4
The **Étang de Vaccarès** (▶ 117) is part of a nature reserve called the Réserve Nationale de Camargue, which has its visitor office and headquarters at La Capelière. On this stretch, stop the car at any of the laybys (turnouts) and the distinctive smell of marsh immediately becomes apparent – a combination of

Plane trees line the route near **Arles**

Golfe de Beauduc

0 ————— 10 km

0 ————— 5 miles

Salin-
de-Giraud □
④

*Étang de
Faraman*

WILDLIFE OF THE CAMARGUE

The Camargue is home to countless birds, including ducks, waders and geese. The shallow lagoons provide excellent feeding grounds for swans, avocets and egrets, while the freshwater marshes, with their extensive reed beds, are used as nesting sites by herons, moorhens, coots and mallards. Among the most spectacular sights are the colonies of resident pink flamingoes.

salt, rotting vegetation and growing plants. At Villeneuve, turn south towards **La Capelière**. It's easy to miss the excellent **visitor centre** – keep a lookout for the sign and be ready to turn off the road on the left. There are marked nature trails, and the 1.5km (1-mile) path around the building has signs giving details about the area's plants and animals. Continue south past Salin-de-Badon, noted for its birds, to Salin-de-Giraud.

4–5

Salin-de-Giraud is the best known of the region's salt-producing towns. The tree-lined avenues are dominated by the Solvay refinery, where glittering piles of salt can be glimpsed through the railings. Now take the **D36** north as it slices through the marshy land to the west of the sluggish Grand Rhône. Eventually it joins the **D570**, and continue which leads northeast back to Arles.

3 VAISON-LA-ROMAINE

Walk

The town of Vaison-la-Romaine (▶ 148–149), which straddles the River Ouvèze, is a mixture of Roman city, medieval village and modern town. This walk, which has some steep climbs, takes you past the town's Roman bridge, the medieval gateway and the 12th-century cathedral.

DISTANCE 3.5km (2 miles) **TIME** 1.5 hours
START/END POINT Main parking area, avenue Général-de-Gaulle ✚ 184 C5

1–2

Start from the main parking area, next to the **Roman sites** on **avenue Général-de-Gaulle**. Walk through the heart of town down to the ancient **Pont Romain**, a Roman bridge 17m (56ft) long. Note the level of the Ouvèze River below the bridge; in the floods of September 1992 the river flowed over the top of the Pont Romain.

2–3

Take the road opposite the bridge, which leads up to the **Haute Ville**. Go through the **arched gateway**, a remnant of the medieval

ramparts. Upper Vaison is an almost complete medieval town, with attractive alleys of houses dating from the 13th and 14th centuries. Turn sharply left, backtracking a little, up the narrow **rue de l'Horloge**. Continue climbing, looking towards the **clock tower** that gives the

road its name. Follow the road around to the right, and turn left at a T-junction onto **rue de l'Église**, following signs for the château. There

The medieval town of upper Vaison rises on a hill above the River Ouvèze

Taking a break

You will find plenty of cafés and restaurants on and around the Grande Rue and place Chanoine-Sautel, near the Roman sites

is a viewpoint to the left, near the **church**. Pass the church and continue uphill to Plan Pascal and on again, up some steps, to the **rue de la Charité**. This road narrows into a rough track. At the end of the stone wall on the left, turn left and climb to the ruins of the **château**.

3–4

The château (closed to the public) gives you wonderful views of the Roman ruins and the lower town. Return to the stone wall. Turn right and then left under an arch, go down the rough-hewn steps on the left to a beautiful

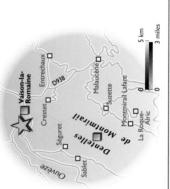

A statue of Empress Sabina excavated from Vaison's Roman ruins

square with a fountain and the **Hôtel de Prévôt**. Leave the square to the left and go down **rue des Fours**, one of the prettiest streets in old Vaison. When a road leads off to the right, keep straight ahead. Turn right at the next rue Soubeiranne junction to reach a T-junction. Turn left, then take the next turn on the right into Promenade des Consuls. Descend the steps on the left to reach **rue du Château**. Turn left and follow the road to a main road junction. Bear right and cross the River Ouvèze by the **Pont Neuf**. Take the first right into avenue Jules Ferry and then go left to reach the **cathedral**.

4–5

Inside the 12th-century Romanesque **Cathédrale Notre-Dame de Nazareth**, the old bishop's throne sits behind the altar and on the north side of the cathedral there are lovely cloisters. Return to **avenue Jules Ferry** and walk 500m (545 yards) to **avenue Général-de-Gaulle** and the entrance to the **quartier du Puymin**.

5–6

The quartier du Puymin has some fascinating **Roman ruins**, including several villas and a theatre that held around 6,000 people. After visiting this extensive Roman site, cross the road to enter the other major area, the **quartier de la Villasse**, where you'll find the Roman baths. The parking area is near by.

TOP TIP

You can do this walk at any time of year. On clear days there are good views of Mont Ventoux (▶ 157–158) from the château ruins.

4 GORGES DU VERDON

Drive with walks

This drive offers spectacular views of the Gorges du Verdon (▶ 74–76) as you follow the river west from Castellane to the Lac de Ste-Croix. After stopping in Moustiers-Ste-Marie for refreshment, you follow the Verdon's south bank, a slightly easier drive, with equally dramatic views.

1–2

Leave **Castellane**, a popular base for walkers and climbers, from the roundabout by the

BE PREPARED

If you intend to do any walking, ask for the walking routes from the tourist office at Castellane or Moustiers-Ste-Marie before you set out. Always check the weather conditions and take a torch (flashlight), water and food.

DISTANCE 137km (85 miles) **TIME** One day (excluding walks)
START/END POINT Castellane ✚ 187 E2

Grand Hôtel du Levant, on the **D952** signed **Moustiers-Ste-Marie.** The road splits at the **Pont de Soleils;** this is the bridge you'll reach on the return route to Castellane. Bear right to stay on the **D952** signed **Moustiers;** soon you'll enter a short tunnel. Immediately at the tunnel exit a sign on the left indicates the **D23B** to the **Belvédère du Couloir Samson.** A short, dead-end road takes you to this **viewpoint** with parking spaces, at the bottom of the Verdon valley.

2–3

From Belvédère du Couloir Samson you can follow part of a seven-hour **walk** to a summit called **La Maline** at 1,460m (4,788 feet). Noticeboards emphasise the need for careful preparation, professional equipment and proper attention to the rapidly changing water level of the river. Back in your car, return to the **D952** and turn left. Bear left in the village

of **Rougon** and 1km (less than a mile) before reaching the village of **La Palud-sur-Verdon,** a sign left indicates the **Route des Crêtes.**

3–4

The Route des Crêtes offers dramatic views of the canyon as it climbs to the highest points of the north bank of the river, with numerous *belvédères* (viewpoints) where you can stop. A sign indicates whether the Route des Crêtes is *ouvert* (open) or *fermé* (closed) because of snow. If it is closed, skip to point 4–5. Otherwise, turn off onto the dramatic road. When you reach the **Pas de la Baou** (1,285m/ 4,215 feet), the river is 715m (2,345 feet) below. From these heights, the road descends and there are views to the west. Take care as there are few safety barriers or walls around these hair-pinned descents and you are likely to encounter walkers until the road returns to **La Palud-sur-Verdon.**

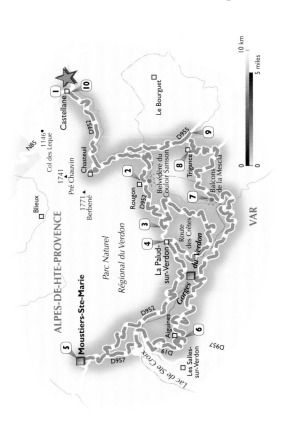

ALPES-DE-HTE-PROVENCE

Parc Naturel
Régional du Verdon

Moustiers-Ste-Marie

La Palud-
sur-Verdon

Aiguines

Les Salles-
sur-Verdon

Lac de Ste Croix

Rougon

Chasteuil

Castellane

Le Bourguet

Belvédère du
Couloir Samson

Trigance

Balcons
de la Mescla

VAR

Col des Leque

Pré Chauvin

Berbené

Blieux

Route
des Crêtes

Gorges du Verdon

N85

D952

D952

D952

D955

D952

D957

D957

D19

D957

10 km

5 miles

4–5

At La Palud-sur-Verdon you can **rent mountain bicycles** or find a **guided walk** or **climb**.

The town hall, in a small **château**, has an exhibition explaining the geology, flora and fauna of the area. Turn left on the **D952**, signed for Moustiers. As the road reaches the end of the Grand Canyon, there are views to the **Lac de Ste-Croix**. At a roundabout, bear right to **Moustiers-Ste-Marie**, an ideal place to eat lunch.

5–6

Moustiers-Ste-Marie (➤ 80–81) is known for its **faïence** (fine glazed ceramics) and for a silver star suspended on a chain between two rock faces. Legend tells that it was first erected by a knight grateful for his return to the village after being held prisoner by the Saracens. Leave Moustiers by retracing your route back to the roundabout, going straight over on the **D957** and following the sign for Aiguines. The road crosses a bridge where the Verdon River flows into the lake; here you can rent kayaks and electric boats. Shortly, take a left turn onto the **D19** to **Aiguines**.

6–7

Park on the road in the heart of Aiguines and

Left: The attractive hillside village of Trigance

go down steps on the right to a small arcade of artisanal shops. One of these specialises in wood-turning, once the village's single but prosperous industry. Take the **D71** as it climbs out of Aiguines and stop at the **orientation table** about 1km (less than a mile) further on. The river and views are now mainly on your left, with numerous stopping places and viewing points. Care should be taken on these sometimes narrow corners, and especially at a short series of mini-tunnels cut into the rock face, the **Tunnel de Fayet.** The last of the viewing opportunities is at the **Balcons de la Mescla.**

7–8

The Balcons de la Mescla has a **bar-restaurant** where you can stop for refreshments and enjoy more superb views. After several kilometres, watch for signs to **Trigance and a Maison de l'Information.** Turn left to descend to the village.

8–9

Trigance has small shops, a well, an art gallery and the last working water-powered **flour mill** in Provence, all dominated by a sombre château (closed to the public). The **tourist office** is a further 5km (3 miles) out of the heart of the village. Follow the road as it skirts Trigance to the south. At a T-junction with the **D955**, turn right; the tourist office is on the right after 500m (545 yards).

9–10

The tourist office has excellent displays about local geology and you can also buy local produce there, including wonderful Provençal soap. Head back along the **D955** until you reach the Pont de Soleils; turn right on the **D952** to return to Castellane.

Taking a break

Ma Petite Auberge
✉ Boulevard de la République, Castellane ☎ 04 92 83 62 06 🕐 Sat–Wed 12–2, daily 7–9.30.

La Treille Muscate
✉ Place de l'Église, Moustiers-Ste-Marie ☎ 04 92 74 64 31 🕐 Mid-Feb to mid-Nov. Closed Wed Jul–Aug, also Wed pm and Thu rest of year.

Practicalities

BEFORE YOU GO

WHAT YOU NEED

● Required ○ Suggested ▲ Not required	Some countries require a passport to remain valid for a minimum period (usually at least six months) beyond the date of entry – check before booking	UK	Germany	USA	Canada	Australia	Ireland	Netherlands	Spain
Passport/National Identity Card		●	●	●	●	●	●	●	▲
Visa (regulations can change – check before booking)		▲	▲	▲	▲	▲	▲	▲	▲
Onward or Round-Trip Ticket		▲	▲	▲	▲	▲	▲	▲	▲
Health Inoculations (tetanus and polio)		▲	▲	▲	▲	▲	▲	▲	▲
Health Documentation (▶ 180, Health)		●	●	●	●	●	●	●	●
Travel Insurance		○	○	○	○	○	○	○	○
Driver's License (national)		●	●	●	●	●	●	●	●
Car Insurance Certificate		○	○	n/a	n/a	n/a	○	○	○
Car Registration Document		●	●	n/a	n/a	n/a	●	●	●

WHEN TO GO

Peak season · Off-season

	JAN	FEB	MAR	APR	MAY	JUN	JUL	AUG	SEP	OCT	NOV	DEC
°C	12°C	12°C	14°C	18°C	21°C	27°C	28°C	28°C	25°C	22°C	17°C	14°C
°F	54°F	54°F	57°F	64°F	70°F	81°F	82°F	82°F	77°F	72°F	63°F	57°F

Very wet · Wet · Cloud · Sun · Sun/Showers

Temperatures are the **average daily maximum** for each month, although they can rise to 35°C (95°F) in July and August. Spring starts in March when the mimosa and almonds come into bloom on the coast, and it is usually warm enough to sit outside on the terrace in April. Mountain melt-water in spring brings the possibility of flash floods in the Rhône valley. Summers are hot and dry, and the coastal areas are very crowded. The autumn months (September and October) can be very pleasant, although there may be occasional thunderstorms. Colder weather arrives in November, with snow settling on high ground in December. The *mistral* wind blows down the Rhône valley during the winter months, but you can avoid it by heading east to the Côte d'Azur.

GETTING ADVANCE INFORMATION

Tourist Information
● Alpes-Maritimes: www.guideriviera.com
● Marseille and Carmargue (Bouches du Rhône) area: www.visitprovence.com

● Var: www.tourismevar.com
● Haute Provence: www.alpes-haute-provence.com
● Vaucluse: www.provenceguide.com

In the UK
Maison de la France
Lincoln House
300 High Holborn
London WC1V 7JH
☎ 09068 244 123

GETTING THERE

By Air Nice-Côte d'Azur and Marseille-Provence are the main airports in the region, but there are also international flights from within Europe to the smaller airports: Toulon, Nîmes-Arles-Camargue and Montpellier.

From the UK carriers include France's international airline, Air France (tel: 0870 1424343 in UK; 0802 320820 in France; www.airfrance.com), British Airways (tel: 0844 4930787; www.ba.com), easyJet (tel: 0871 750 0100; www.easyjet.com) and Ryanair (tel: 0871 246000; www.ryanair.com). The flight time from London to Provence is around 2 hours.

From the US and Canada Delta Air Lines operates a few direct flights between New York and Nice-Côte d'Azur, but passengers from most US cities will usually have to change at Paris or London (Heathrow, Gatwick and Stansted). Delta Air Lines (tel: 1 800 241 4141 in US; www.delta.com), From May to October, Canadian charter airline Air Transat (tel: 1-866 847 1112, www.airtransat.ca) flies direct to Nice from Montréal and Toronto, and to Marseille from Montréal. The flying time direct from New York to Provence is around 8 hours.

By Rail Paris is the main railway hub, with six major railway stations. SNCF, the national carrier, operates high-speed train (TGV) services from the Gare de Lyon in Paris to Provence. The Eurostar passenger train service (tel: 08705 186186 in UK) from London St Pancras via the Eurotunnel to Paris Gare du Nord takes 3 hours, there are direct Eurostar services from London to Avignon in summer (Jul–Sep; six hours).

By Sea Several ferry companies operate regular services from England and Ireland to north and northwest France. Crossing times from England vary from 35 minutes to 9 hours, and from Ireland around 14 to 18 hours.

TIME

France is on Central European Time, one hour ahead of Greenwich Mean Time (GMT +1). From late March, when clocks are put forward one hour, until late October, French summer time (GMT +2) operates.

CURRENCY AND FOREIGN EXCHANGE

Currency The euro (€) is the official currency of France and Monaco. Notes (bills) are issued in denominations of €5, €10, €20, €50, €100, €200 and €500 and coins are in denominations of 1, 2, 5, 10, 20 and 50 cents, and €1 and €2.

Exchange You can exchange travellers' cheques at some banks and at bureaux de change at airports, main railway stations or in some department stores, and exchange booths. All transactions are subject to a commission charge, so you may prefer to rely on cash and credit cards. Travellers' cheques issued by American Express and VISA may also be changed at many post offices.

Credit cards are widely accepted in shops, restaurants and hotels. VISA (Carte Bleue), MasterCard (Eurocard) and Diners Club cards with four-digit PINs can be used in most ATM cash dispensers. Some smaller shops and hotels may not accept credit cards – and some petrol stations do not accept foreign cards.

In the US	In Australia	In Canada
Maison de la France	Maison de la France	Maison de la France
825 Third Avenue, 29th floor	Level 13, 25 Bligh Street	1800 Avenue McGill College,
New York, NY 10022	Sydney, NSW 2000	Suite 1010,
☎ 514/288-1904	☎ (02) 9231 5244	Montreal H3A 3J6
		☎ 514/288-2026

WHEN YOU ARE THERE

CLOTHING SIZES

U.K.	Rest of Europe	U.S.A.		
36	46	36		
38	48	38		
40	50	40		
42	52	42		Suits
44	54	44		
46	56	46		
7	41	8		
7.5	42	8.5		
8.5	43	9.5		
9.5	44	10.5		Shoes
10.5	45	11.5		
11	46	12		
14.5	37	14.5		
15	38	15		
15.5	39/40	15.5		
16	41	16		Shirts
16.5	42	16.5		
17	43	17		
8	34	6		
10	36	8		
12	38	10		
14	40	12		Dresses
16	42	14		
18	44	16		
4.5	38	6		
5	38	6.5		
5.5	39	7		
6	39	7.5		Shoes
6.5	40	8		
7	41	8.5		

NATIONAL HOLIDAYS

1 Jan	New Year's Day
27 Jan	St Devote's Day (Monaco only)
Mar/Apr	Easter Sunday and Monday
1	May Labour Day
8	May VE Day (France only)
May/Jun	Whit Sunday and Monday
June	Corpus Christi (Monaco only)
14 July	Bastille Day (France only)
15 Aug	Assumption
1 Nov	All Saints' Day
11 Nov	Remembrance Day (France only)
19 Nov	Monaco National Holiday (Monaco only)
9 Dec	Immaculate Conception (Monaco only)
25 Dec	Christmas Day

OPENING HOURS

○ Stores		● Post Offices	
● Offices		◐ Museums/Monuments	
● Banks		◐ Pharmacies	

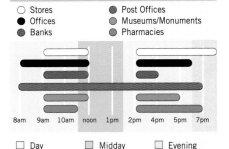

8am 9am 10am noon 1pm 2pm 4pm 5pm 7pm

☐ Day   ☐ Midday   ☐ Evening

Shops Shops are open from 9am to 7pm. Most shops close on Sunday and many on Monday. Small food shops open from 7 and may open on Sunday morning. Large department stores do not close for lunch, and hypermarkets open 10am to 9 or 10pm, but may shut on Monday morning.
Banks Banks are closed on Sunday, some branches open on Saturday morning.
Museums Museums and monuments have extended summer hours. Many close one day a week; either Monday (municipal ones) or Tuesday (national ones).

TIME DIFFERENCES

GMT	France	Germany	USA West Coast	New York	Australia
12 noon	1pm	1pm	4am	7am	10pm

PERSONAL SAFETY

The *Police Municipale* (blue uniforms) carry out police duties in cities and towns. The Gendarmes (blue trousers, black jackets, white belts), the national police force, cover the countryside and smaller places. The CRS deal with emergencies and also look after safety on beaches. Monaco has its own police.

To avoid danger or theft:
■ Do not use unmanned roadside rest areas at night.
■ Cars, especially foreign cars, should be secured.
■ Beware of pickpockets.

Police assistance:
☎ **17** from any phone

TELEPHONES

phoning from outside the principality).
Most public phones use a phone card (*télécarte*), sold in units of 25, 50 or 120 at France Telecom shops, post offices, tobacconists, newsagents and at railway stations. Cheap call rates generally apply Mon–Fri 7pm–8am, Sat–Sun all day.

All telephone numbers in France comprise ten digits (eight in Monaco). There are no area codes except for Monaco (377 precedes number when

International Dialling Codes
Dial 00 followed by

UK:	44
USA / Canada:	1
Irish Republic:	353
Australia:	61
New Zealand:	64

POST OFFICES

The PTT (*Poste, Téléphone et Télécommunications*) deals with mail and telephone services. Outside main centres, post offices open shorter hours and may close 12–2. Letter boxes are yellow. Post offices usually have an ATM.

ELECTRICITY

The power supply in France is 220 volts. Sockets accept two-round-pin (or increasingly three-round-pin) plugs, so an adaptor is needed for most non-Continental appliances. A transformer is needed for appliances operating on 110–120 volts.

TIPS/GRATUITIES

Restaurant, café and hotel bills must by law include a service charge, so a tip is not expected, although many people do leave a few coins in restaurants.

Taxis	€0.50–€1.50
Tour guides	€0.50–€1.50
Porters	€0.50–€1.50
Usherettes	small change
Hairdressers	€0.50–€1.50
Lavatory attendants	small change

POLICE 17

FIRE 18

AMBULANCE 15

HEALTH

 Citizens of EU countries receive reduced-cost emergency health care with relevant documentation (European Health Insurance Card), but private medical insurance is still advised, and essential for all other visitors.

 Dental Services As for general medical treatment (see above, Insurance), nationals of EU countries can obtain dental treatment at reduced cost. Around 70 per cent of standard dentists' fees are refunded, but private medical insurance is still advised for all.

 Weather July and August are likely to be sunny and very hot. When sightseeing, cover up, apply a good sunscreen, wear sunglasses and a hat, and drink plenty of fluids.

 Drugs Pharmacies – recognised by their green cross sign – possess highly qualified staff able to offer medical advice, provide first-aid and prescribe a wide range of drugs, although some are available by prescription (*ordonnance*) only.

Safe Water Tap water is safe to drink, and restaurants will often bring a carafe of water to the table, although you may prefer to buy bottled water. Never drink from a tap marked *eau non potable* (not drinking water).

CONCESSIONS

Students/Youths Holders of an International Student Identity Card (ISIC) are entitled to discounted admission to museums and sights, air and ferry tickets and meals in some student cafeterias. Holders of the International Youth Travel Card (or GO 25 Card) qualify for similar discounts as ISIC holders.

Senior Citizens If you are over 60 you can get discounts (up to 50 per cent) in museums, on public transport and in places of entertainment. You will need a *Carte Senior*, which can be purchased from the *Abonnement* office of any main railway station. You may get a discount if you show your passport.

TRAVELING WITH A DISABILITY

France has made great headway in providing access and facilities for visitors with disabilities. However, some tourist offices, museums and restaurants that are in historic, protected buildings are still not fully accessible. A telephone call before going to a restaurant is a good idea to arrange for an easily accessible table. The Association des Paralysés de France (17 boulevard Auguste Blanqui, 75013, Paris, tel: 01 40 78 69 00; www.apf.asso.fr) provides information on wheelchair access.

CHILDREN

Children are welcomed in most hotels and restaurants. Baby-changing facilities are excellent in newer museums and attractions, but limited elsewhere.

RESTROOMS

Modern unisex, self-cleaning, coin-operated toilets are found on the streets of most major cities. In smaller towns and villages, free public toilets can normally be found by the market square or near tourist offices. Cleanliness varies, and some older or more remote establishments may have a squat toilet. Café toilets are for the use of customers only.

CONSULATES

| UK 04 91 15 72 10 | US 04 91 54 92 00 04 93 88 89 55 | Germany 04 91 16 75 20 04 93 83 55 25 | Ireland 01 49 17 67 00 | Canada 04 93 92 93 22 |

Yes/no **Oui/non**
Hello **Bonjour/bonsoir**
Goodbye **Au revoir**
How are you? **Comment allez-vous?**
Please **S'il vous plaît**
Thank you **Merci**
Excuse me **Excusez-moi**
I'm sorry **Pardon**
You're welcome **De rien/avec plaisir**
Do you have...? **Avez-vous...?**
How much is this? **C'est combien?**
I'd like... **Je voudrais...**

DIRECTIONS

Is there a phone box around here?
**Y a-t-il une cabine téléphonique
dans le coin?**
Where is...? **Où se trouve...?**
...the nearest Métro **le Métro le plus
proche**
...the telephone **le téléphone**
...the bank **la banque**
...the toilet **les toilettes**
Turn left/right **tournez à gauche/droite**
Go straight on **allez tout droit**
The first/second (on the right)
le premier/le deuxième (à droite)
At the crossroads **au carrefour**

IF YOU NEED HELP

Could you help me, please?
Pouvez-vous m'aider?
Do you speak English? **Parlez-vous anglais?**
I don't understand **Je ne comprends pas**
Could you call a doctor quickly, please?
**Pouvez-vous appeler d'urgence un médecin,
s'il vous plaît?**

RESTAURANT

I'd like to book a table **Puis-je réserver
une table?**
A table for two please **Une table pour
deux personnes, s'il vous plaît**
Do you have a fixed price menu?
Vous avez un menu prix fixe?
Could we see the menu please?
Nous pouvons avoir la carte?
Could I have the bill please?
L'addition, s'il vous plaît
A bottle/glass of... **Une bouteille/un verre
de...**

MENU READER

apéritifs appetisers
boissons alcoolisées alcoholic beverages
boissons chaudes hot beverages
boissons froides cold beverages
carte des vins wine list
coquillages shellfish
fromage cheese
gibier game
hors d'oeuvres starters
légumes vegetables
plats chauds hot dishes
plats froids cold dishes
plat du jour dish of the day
pâtisserie pastry
plat principal main course
potages soups
service compris service included
service non compris
service not included
spécialités régionales
regional specialities
viandes meat courses
volaille poultry

NUMBERS

0 **zéro**	14 **quatorze**	40 **quarante**	500 **cinq cents**
1 **un**	15 **quinze**	50 **cinquante**	600 **six cents**
2 **deux**	16 **seize**	60 **soixante**	700 **sept cents**
3 **trois**	17 **dix-sept**	70 **soixante-dix**	800 **huit cents**
4 **quatre**	18 **dix-huit**	80 **quatre-vingts**	900 **neuf cents**
5 **cinq**	19 **dix-neuf**	90 **quatre-vingt-dix**	
6 **six**	20 **vingt**	100 **cent**	1,000 **mille**
7 **sept**		101 **cent un**	
8 **huit**	21 **vingt et un**		
9 **neuf**	22 **vingt-deux**	110 **cent dix**	
10 **dix**		120 **cent vingt**	
11 **onze**	30 **trente**	200 **deux cents**	
12 **douze**	31 **trente et un**	300 **trois cents**	
13 **treize**	32 **trente-deux**	400 **quatre cents**	

BRIEF A–Z

agneau lamb
ail garlic
ananas pineapple
anguille eel
banane banana
beurre butter
bifteck steak
**bière (bière
pression)** beer
(draught beer)
boeuf beef
boudin noir/blanc
black/white
pudding
brochet pike
cabillaud cod
calmar squid
canard duck
champignons
mushrooms
chou cabbage
choucroute
sauerkraut
chou-fleur
cauliflower
choux de Bruxelles
Brussels sprouts
citron lemon
civet de lièvre
jugged hare
concombre
cucumber
confiture jam
coquilles Saint-
Jacques scallops
cornichon gherkin
côte/côtelette chop
**côtelettes dans
l'échine** spare
ribs
couvert cutlery
crevettes grises
shrimps
crevettes roses
prawns
croque monsieur
toasted ham and
cheese sandwich
cru raw
crustacés seafood
**cuisses de
grenouilles**
frogs' legs
cuit (à l'eau)
boiled
**eau mineral
gazeuse/non
gazeuse**
sparkling/still
mineral water

ecrevisse crayfish
entrecôte
sirloin steak
entrées first course
épices spices
épinards spinach
épis de maïs
corn (on the cob)
escargots snails
farine flour
fenouil fennel
fèves broad beans
figues figs
filet de boeuf fillet
filet mignon
fillet steak
filet de porc
tenderloin
fines herbes herbs
foie gras
goose liver
fraises
strawberries
framboises
raspberries
frit fried
friture deep-fried
fruit de la passion
passion fruit
fruits de la saison
seasonal fruits
gaufres waffles
gigot d'agneau
leg of lamb
glace ice-cream
glaçons ice cubes
grillé grilled
groseilles
redcurrants
hareng herring
haricots blancs
haricot beans
haricots verts
french beans
homard lobster
huîtres oysters
**jambon blanc/
cru/fumé** ham
(cooked/Parma
style/smoked)
jus de citron
lemon juice
jus de fruits
fruit juice
jus d'orange
orange juice
**lait demi-écrémé/
entier** milk
semi-skimmed/
full-cream
langouste
crayfish

langoustine
scampi
langue tongue
lapin rabbit
lentilles lentils
lotte monkfish
loup de mer
sea bass
macaron
macaroon
maïs sweetcorn
marron chestnut
**menu du jour/à la
carte**
menu of the
day/à la carte
morilles morels
moules mussels
mousse au chocolat
chocolate mousse
moutarde mustard
myrtilles bilberries
noisette hazelnut
noix walnut
noix de veau
fillet of veal
**oeuf à la coque/
dur/au plat**
egg soft/hard-
boiled/fried
oignon onion
origan oregano
pain au chocolat
croissant with
chocolate centre
part portion
pêche peach
petite friture
fried fish
(whitebait or
similar)
**petits (biscuits)
salés** savoury
biscuits
petit pain roll
petits pois
green peas
pintade
guinea fowl
poire pear
pois chiches
chick peas
poisson fish
poivre pepper
poivron green/red
pepper
pomme apple
pommes de terre
potatoes
pommes frites chips
poulet (blanc)
chicken (breast)

prune plum
pruneaux prunes
queue de boeuf
oxtail
ragoût stew
ris de veau
sweetbread
riz rice
**rôti de boeuf
(rosbif)**
roast beef
rouget red mullet
saignant rare
salade verte
lettuce
salé/sucré
salted/sweet
saumon salmon
saucisses sausages
sel salt
soupe à l'oignon
onion soup
sucre sugar
thon tuna
thym thyme
tripes tripe
truffes truffles
truite trout
truite saumonée
salmon trout
vapeur (à la)
steamed
venaison venison
viande hachée
minced meat/
mince
vin blanc white
wine
vin rosé rosé wine
vin rouge red wine
vinaigre vinegar
xérès sherry

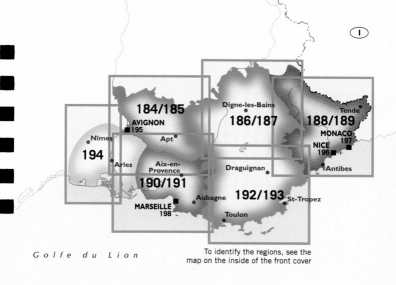

184/185
AVIGNON
195

Digne-les-Bains

186/187

Tende

188/189

MONACO
197

Nîmes

Apt

194

Aix-en-
Provence

Arles

Draguignan

NICE
196

Antibes

190/191

192/193

St-Tropez

MARSEILLE
198

Aubagne

Toulon

Golfe du Lion

To identify the regions, see the
map on the inside of the front cover

Regional Maps

- ━━━ Major route
- ═══ Motorway
- ═══ National road
- ═══ Regional road
- ──── Other road
- ·—·—· International boundary
- ·——· Regional boundary

- □ City
- ▫ Town/village
- ✈ Airport
- ▣ Featured place of interest

184 – 194 | 0 ——————————— 10 km
0 ——————————— 5 miles

Streetplans

- ═══ Main road/minor road
- ═══ Narrow road/path
- ━━━ Railway
- ∿∿∿ City wall
- ▨ Important building

- ▨ Park/garden
- ● Metro station
- ━●━ Tram line & stop
- ✝ Church
- ⓘ Tourist information

195 | 0 ——————— 200 metres
0 ——————— 200 yards

197 | 0 ——————— 300 metres
0 ——————— 300 yards

196 | 0 ——————— 400 metres
0 ——————— 400 yards

198 | 0 ——————— 400 metres
0 ——————— 400 yards

Atlas

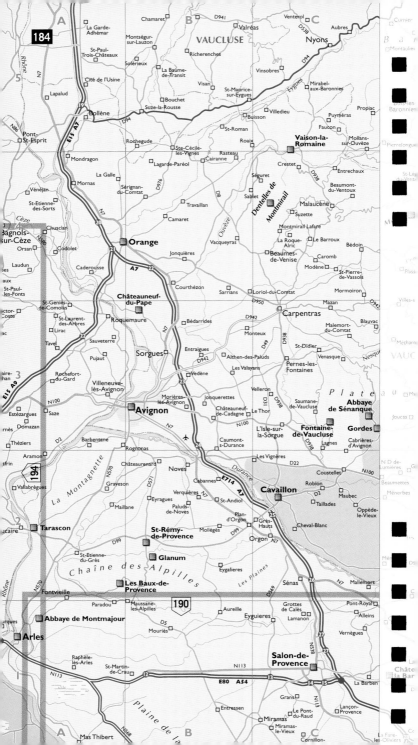

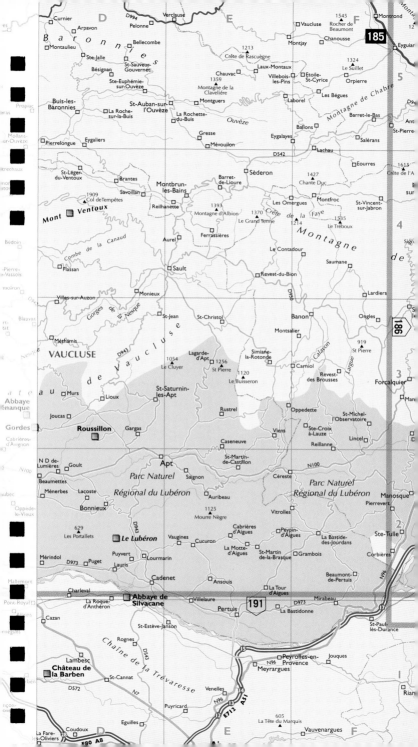

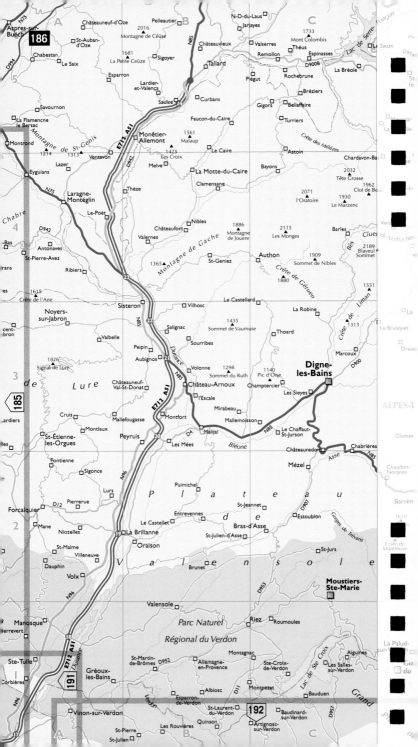

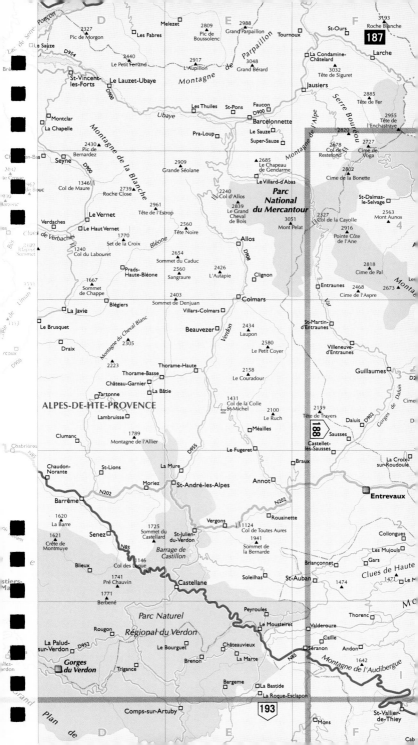

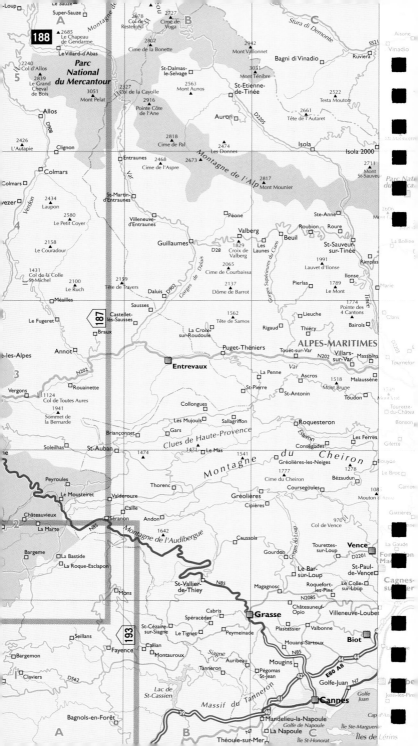

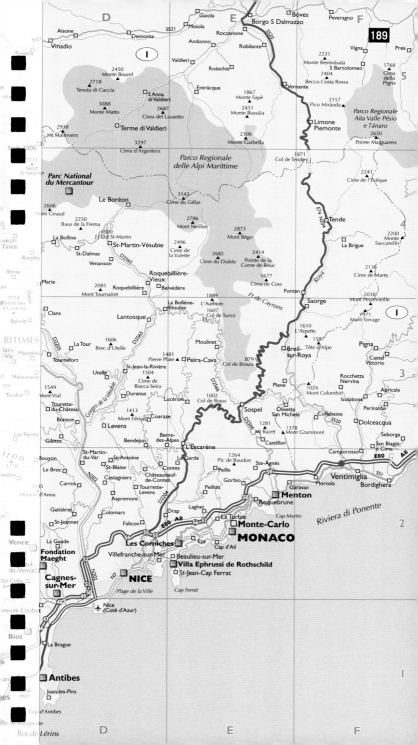

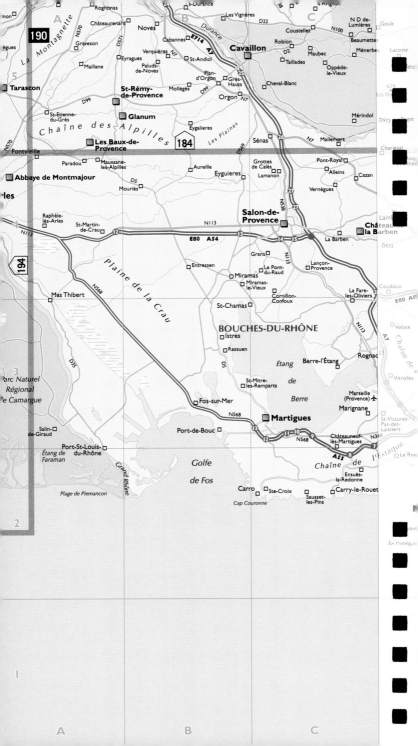

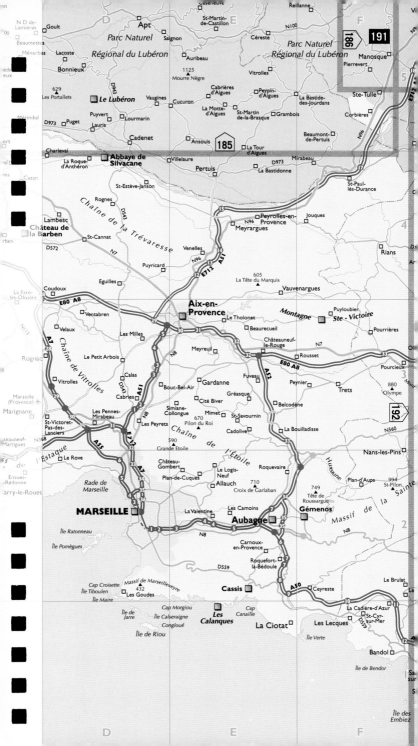

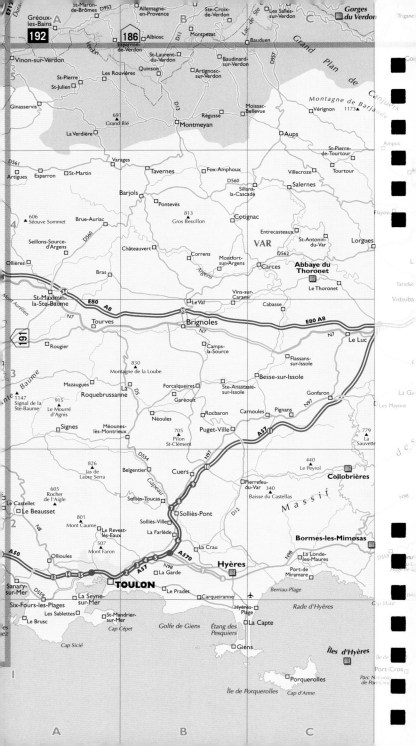

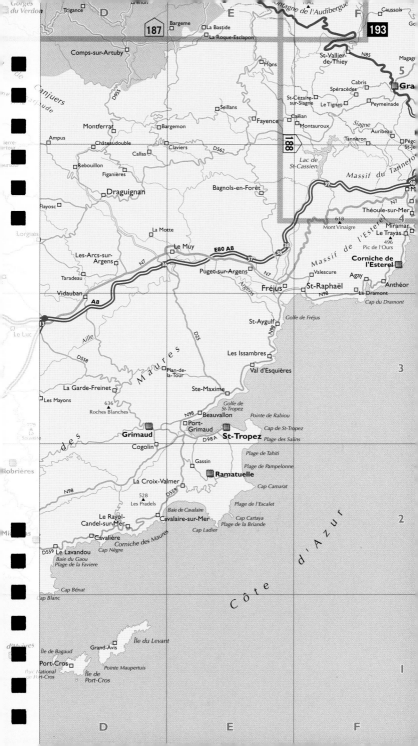

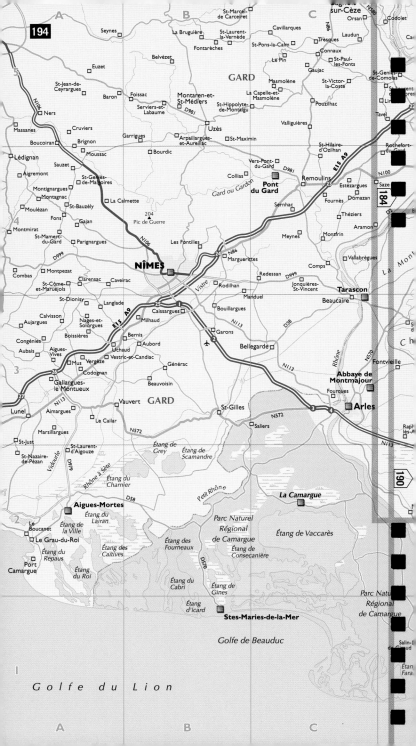

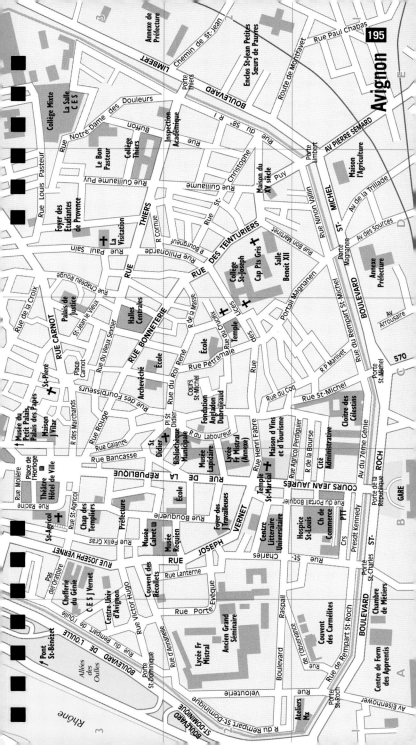

Avignon

Rhône

Allées des Oulles

Pont St-Bénézet

BOULEVARD DE L'OULLE

Porte St-Dominique

BOULEVARD ST-DOMINIQUE

Velouterie

Boulevard

Ateliers Mx

R du Rempart St-Dominique

Rue d'Annanelle

Lycée Fr Mistral

Ancien Grand Séminaire

Rue Raspail

Couvent des Carmélites

BOULEVARD St-Roch

Rue de Rempart St-Roch

Porte St-Roch

AV Eisenhower

Centre de Form des Apprentis

Chambre de Métiers

Rue de l'Observance

Rue Porte Evêque

Rue Victor Hugo

Rue du Rempart de l'Oulle

Pas de l'Oratoire

RUE JOSEPH VERNET

Chefferie du Génie

Centre Univ d'Avignon

C E S J Vernet

Couvent des Récollets

Rue Lanterne

RUE JOSEPH VERNET

St-Agricol

Place de l'Horloge

Théâtre Hôtel de Ville

Rue Molière

Rue Racine

Chap des Templiers

Préfecture

Rue St-Agricol

Rue Félix Gras

Musée Calvet

Musée Requien

VERNET

RUE

Foyer des Travailleuses

École

Rue Bouquerie

RUE DE LA RÉPUBLIQUE

St Didier

Bibliothèque Municipale

Musée Lapidaire

Rue Bancasse

Rue Galante

Rue Rouge

Pl St Didier

R du Laboureur

Fondation Angladon Dubrujeaud

Rue Henri Fabre

Lycée Fr Mistral (Annexe)

Temple St-Martial

Maison d Vins et d Tourisme

Rue Agricol Perdiguier

R de la Bourse

Cité Administrative

COURS JEAN JAURÈS

Centre Littéraire Universitaire

Hospice St-Louis

Ch de Commerce

PTT

Présdt Kennedy

Rue St-Charles

Porte de la République

Porte St-Charles

GARE

ST- ROCH

Cloître des Célestins

AV du 7ème Génie

Rue St-Michel

Porte St-Michel

Rue du Coq

BOULEVARD du Rempart St-Michel

570

Av Arrousaire

Porte St-Michel

Annexe Préfecture

Portail Magnanen

Porte Magnanen

Av des Sources

Av de la Trillade

ST- MICHEL

AV Pierre Semard

Maison l'Agriculture

Rue Ninon Vallin

Porte Limbert

Rue du Bon Martinet

Salle Benoit XII

Cap Pts Gris

Collège St-Joseph

RUE DES TEINTURIERS

Rue de la Masse

R Bourgneuf

R Cornue

Rue St-Christophe

Rue Guillaume

Maison du XV siècle

Puy

Rue du 58e

École

Temple

Rue du Crucifix

Rue Petramale

Rue du Roi René

Rue des Lices

École

RUE BONNETERIE

Halles Centrales

Rue des Fourbisseurs

Rue du Vieux Sextier

St-Jean le Vieux

Palais de Justice

RUE CARNOT

Place Carnot

St-Piere

Musée du Petit Palais, Palais des Papes

Maison J Vilar

R des Marchands

Rue Chapeau Rouge

Rue de la Croix

RUE THIERS

RUE CARNOT

Cours St-Michel

Archevêché

Rue Paul Sain

La Visitation

Rue Philonarde

Rue Paul Sain

RUE THIERS

Foyer des Étudiantes de Provence

Rue Guillaume Puy

Le Bon Pasteur

Collège Thiers

Inspection Académique

Rue Notre-Dame des Douleurs

Buffon

La Salle C E S

Collège Mixte

Rue Louis Pasteur

BOULEVARD LIMBERT

Porte Thiers

Chemin de St-Jean

Annexe de Préfecture

Enclos St-Jean Petites Seurs de Pauvres

Route de Montfavet

Rue Paul Chabas

570

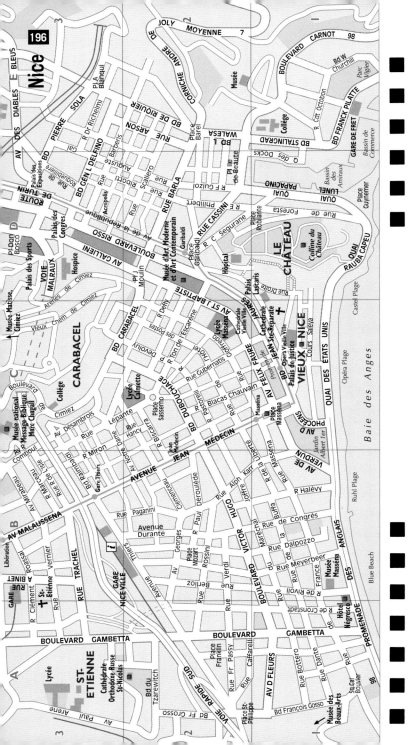

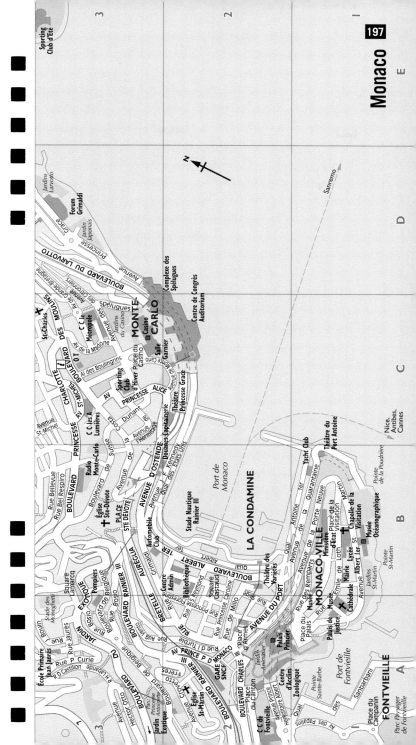

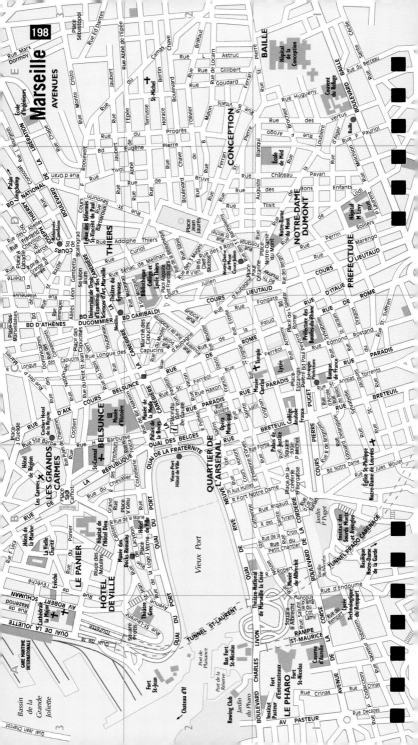

Nice

Credits

Picture Credits
The Automobile Association would like to thank the following photographers, companies and picture libraries for their assistance in the preparation of this book.

Abbreviations for the picture credits are as follows: (t) top; (b) bottom; (l) left; (r) right; (c) centre; (AA) AA World Travel Library.

2i AA/C Sawyer; **2ii** AA/J A Tims; **2iii** AA/J A Tims; **2iv** AA/R Moore; **2v** AA/C Sawyer; **3i** AA/B Smith; **3ii** AA/C Sawyer; **3iii** AA/P Bennett; **5l** AA/C Sawyer; **5c** AA/C Sawyer; **5r** AA/R Strange; **6** AA/A Baker; **7t** AA/A Baker; **7b** Bruno Morandi/Reportage/Getty Images; **8** Will Ragozzino/Stringer/Getty Images; **9t** AA/C Sawyer; **9c** AA/C Sawyer; **9b** AA/C Sawyer; **10/11** AA/A Baker; **12** AA/K Paterson; **13** The Night Cafe in Arles, 1888 (w/c on paper), Gogh, Vincent van (1853-90)/Professor Hans R. Hahnloser Collection, Bern, Switzerland/The Bridgeman Art Library; **14** AA/R Strange; **15** Sunflowers, 1888 (oil on canvas), Gogh, Vincent van (1853-90)/Neue Pinakothek, Munich, Germany/The Bridgeman Art Library; **17** AA/J A Tims; **19** AA/C Sawyer; **20/21** AA/C Sawyer; **21c** Dave M. Benett/Getty Images; **21b** AA/C Sawyer; **22** AA/C Sawyer; **23l** AA/J A Tims; **23c** AA/C Sawyer; **23r** AA/C Sawyer; **35l** AA/J A Tims; **35c** AA/J A Tims; **35r** AA/J A Tims; **36** AA/N Ray; **38** AA/C Sawyer; **39t** AA/C Sawyer; **39b** AA/C Sawyer; **40** AA/C Sawyer; **41t** AA/C Sawyer; **41b** AA/R Moore; **42t** AA/C Sawyer; **42b** AA/C Sawyer; **43t** AA/C Sawyer; **43b** AA/C Sawyer; **44** AA/A Baker; **45t** AA/R Strange; **45b** AA/R Strange; **46/47** AA/R Moore; **48** AA/C Sawyer; **49t** AA/C Sawyer; **49b** AA/A Baker; **50** AA/A Baker; **51** AA/C Sawyer; **52** AA/C Sawyer; **54** AA/R Strange; **55bl** AA/C Sawyer; **55br** AA/C Sawyer; **56/57** AA/C Sawyer; **63l** AA/R Moore; **63c** AA/C Sawyer; **63r** AA/C Sawyer; **64** AA/C Sawyer; **66** AA/T Oliver; **67t** AA/C Sawyer; **67b** AA/B Smith; **68** AA/C Sawyer; **69** AA/C Sawyer; **70/71** AA/C Sawyer; **71t** AA/R Strange; **71b** AA/C Sawyer; **72** AA/A Baker; **73** AA/A Baker; **74/75** AA/C Sawyer; **76** AA/R Strange; **77** AA/A Baker; **78** A/R Strange; **79** AA/C Sawyer; **80** AA/A Baker; **81t** AA/B Smith; **81b** AA/C Sawyer; **82/83** AA/B Smith; **83** AA/R Moore; **89l** AA/C Sawyer; **89c** AA/C Sawyer; **89r** AA/C Sawyer; **90** AA/C Sawyer; **92** AA/C Sawyer; **93t** AA/C Sawyer; **93b** AA/C Sawyer; **94** AA/C Sawyer; **95t** AA/C Sawyer; **95b** AA/C Sawyer; **96** AA/C Sawyer; **97** AA/C Sawyer; **98/99** AA/C Sawyer; **99** Mont Sainte-Victoire, 1904-05 (oil on canvas), Cezanne, Paul (1839-1906)/Pushkin Museum, Moscow, Russia, Giraudon/The Bridgeman Art Library; **100/101** AA/C Sawyer; **100** AA/C Sawyer; **101** AA/T Souter; **102t** AA/A Baker; **102b** AA/R Strange; **103** AA/A Baker; **104** AA/C Sawyer; **104/105** AA/B Smith; **105** AA/C Sawyer; **111l** AA/B Smith; **111c** AA/C Sawyer; **111r** AA/C Sawyer; **112** AA/C Sawyer; **113** AA/C Sawyer; **114t** AA/A Baker; **114b** AA/C Sawyer; **115t** AA/R Strange; **115b** AA/C Sawyer; **116/117** AA/R Strange; **117** AA/C Sawyer; **118t** AA/C Sawyer; **118b** AA/C Sawyer; **119** AA/R Strange; **120t** AA/A Baker; **120b** AA/R Strange; **121** AA/C Sawyer; **122/123** AA/B Smith; **124/125** AA/R Moore; **125** AA/A Baker; **127t** AA/R Moore; **127c** AA/A Baker; **128t** AA/R Strange; **128/129** AA/R Strange; **135l** AA/C Sawyer; **135c** AA/C Sawyer; **135r** AA/R Strange; **136** AA/C Sawyer; **138** AA/A Baker; **139t** AA/R Strange; **139c** AA/A Baker; **140** A/R Strange; **141t** AA/A Baker; **141b** AA/C Sawyer; **142/143** AA/A Baker; **144** AA/C Sawyer; **145t** AA/A Baker; **145b** AA/A Baker; **146c** AA/C Sawyer; **146b** AA/C Sawyer; **147** AA/A Baker; **148** AA/A Baker; **149t** AA/C Sawyer; **149b** AA/T Oliver; **150** AA/A Baker; **151t** AA/A Baker; **151b** AA/C Sawyer; **152c** AA/R Strange; **152b** AA/R Strange; **153** AA/A Baker; **154t** AA/C Sawyer; **154c** AA/C Sawyer; **155** AA/A Baker; **156t** AA/A Baker; **156b** AA/R Strange; **157** AA/A Baker; **165l** AA/P Bennett; **165c** AA/C Sawyer; **165r** AA/P Bennett; **169** AA/C Sawyer; **170** AA/R Strange; **171** AA/R Strange; **174** AA/R Strange; **175l** AA/J A Tims; **175c** AA/J A Tims; **175r** AA/C Sawyer

Every effort has been made to trace the copyright holders, and we apologise in advance for any accidental errors. We would be happy to apply the corrections in the following edition of this publication.

SPIRALGUIDE
Questionnaire

Dear Traveller

Your comments, opinions and recommendations are very important to us. So please help us to improve our travel guides by taking a few minutes to complete this simple questionnaire.

You do not need a stamp (unless posted outside the UK). If you do not want to remove this page from your guide, then photocopy it or write your answers on a plain sheet of paper.

Send to: **The Editor, Spiral Guides, AA World Travel Guides, FREEPOST SCE 4598, Basingstoke RG21 4GY.**

Your recommendations...

We always encourage readers' recommendations for restaurants, night-life or shopping – if your recommendation is used in the next edition of the guide, we will send you a FREE AA Spiral Guide of your choice. Please state below the establishment name, location and your reasons for recommending it.

_____

_____

_____

_____

_____

Please send me AA Spiral _____

(see list of titles inside the back cover)

About this guide...

Which title did you buy?

_____ **AA Spiral**

Where did you buy it?_____

When? m m / y y

Why did you choose an AA Spiral Guide? _____

_____

_____

_____

_____

Did this guide meet your expectations?

Exceeded ☐   Met all ☐   Met most ☐   Fell below ☐

Please give your reasons _____

_____

_____

_____

_____

continued on next page...

Were there any aspects of this guide that you particularly liked?

_____

_____

_____

_____

_____

Is there anything we could have done better?

_____

_____

_____

_____

About you...

Name (Mr/Mrs/Ms) _____

Address _____

_____ **Postcode** _____

Daytime tel no _____ **email** _____

Please *only* give us your email address and mobile phone number if you wish to hear from us about other products and services from the AA and partners by email or text or mms.

Which age group are you in?

Under 25 ☐ 25–34 ☐ 35–44 ☐ 45–54 ☐ 55–64 ☐ 65+ ☐

How many trips do you make a year?

Less than one ☐ One ☐ Two ☐ Three or more ☐

Are you an AA member? Yes ☐ No ☐

About your trip...

When did you book? mm/ y y   **When did you travel?** mm/ y y

How long did you stay? _____

Was it for business or leisure? _____

Did you buy any other travel guides for your trip? ☐ Yes ☐ No

If yes, which ones? _____

_____

Thank you for taking the time to complete this questionnaire. Please send it to us as soon as possible, and remember, you do not need a stamp (unless posted outside the UK).